POST-TRAUMATIC STRESS DISORDERS:

A HANDBOOK FOR CLINICIANS

Tom Williams, Psy. D., *Editor*

Disabled American Veterans

Published in 1987
by the Disabled American Veterans
National Headquarters
P.O. Box 14301
Cincinnati, Ohio 45214

Printed in the United States of America.

Cover photo by Jerry Atchison.

Typesetting and layout by
Gourmet Type & Graphics, Alexandria, Virginia.
Times Modern was used for the text and Megaron for the headlines.

CONTENTS

FOREWORD

Much of the formative research on the diagnosis and treatment of post-traumatic stress disorder was based on work with Vietnam veterans. Recently, however, the professional literature, and treatment itself, have expanded to encompass other survivor groups—rape and assault victims, those who survived major natural and man-made disasters (earthquakes, plane crashes), and those who witnessed or were part of traumatic industrial or highway accidents. We are also beginning to recognize the importance of dealing with the psychological impacts of trauma for those whose work involves daily trauma—police and firefighters, rescue workers, and health care teams.

Indeed, my own work with police officers and with the victims of personal crime has reinforced my convictions that the situational context has singular importance in determining the nature of post-traumatic response. Those who have studied PTSD have acknowledged the effect of contextual variables in the event, but usually only as they apply to the direct trauma itself. Situational factors after the event have been less systematically considered—that is, the socio-environmental factors that follow the direct trauma. For example, we have learned that we must pay attention, in our clinical dealings, to the homecoming for the Vietnam soldiers, or to the type of interrogation and follow-up care a rape or crime victim received. The chapters by Agosta and McHugh and by Shovar in this book provide particular insight into the ways in which the socio-environmental situation after a trauma can protract or ameliorate the severity of the PTSD response itself. In my estimation, the emphasis on these stressors has been the exceptional contribution of those who have treated and studied the Vietnam veterans population. It has alerted the entire field to the critical importance of context, and, in many ways, has helped to demystify the nature of the therapeutic process.

Certainly different survivor groups require carefully tailored therapeutic techniques, but we increasingly find striking similarities across all groups. I am, therefore, especially glad to find that the first edition of this book—*Traumatic Stress Disorder among Vietnam Veterans*, published by the Disabled American Veterans in 1980—has been substantially expanded to consider other trauma victims as well. This enlarged second edition, written for clinicians and volunteers providing direct services to survivors, reflects a combination of mental health professionalism and "grass roots" experience in dealing with survivors.

The DAV, a nonprofit and nongovernmental organization, must be commended for their sponsorship of this volume. As with the earlier edition, they are making it available to practitioners at no cost. I sincerely appreciate their dedication to disseminating the knowledge that they have gained in working with Vietnam veterans, and thank them for allowing Tom Williams and his colleagues to share their experiences of working with other survivor groups.

Tom Williams, himself a Vietnam veteran, is now a member of the Board of Directors of the Society for Traumatic Stress Disorders and a consultant to the National Organization for Victim Assistance. The authors he has selected are frontline clinicians, not academicians, theoriticians, or administrators. These people, including Tom, deal with trauma victims on a daily basis, and their writing reflects their clinical experience. They talk about survivors from an experiential as well as theoretical base. They tell you what to do and how to do it.

This book is particularly timely now that society is beginning to recognize the effects of traumatic stresses on individuals. The victim advocacy movement and the mental health profession are giving serious attention to PTSD. International terrorism, workers' compensation decisions, and attention to stresses in protective services have all added to the growing interest in preventing the development of chronic PTSD and of effectively treating the disorder when it does appear.

Morton Bard, Ph.D.
Professor Emeritus of Psychology
The Graduate School
The City University of New York

INTRODUCTION

This book is written by and for mental health professionals who work with the psychologically traumatized on a daily basis. It is not easy to get clinicians to write about their work, as most of them are overburdened simply by the volume of their clinical practice. Yet, as the chapters to follow will attest, it is worth the effort.

This handbook had its origins in our earlier book, *Post-traumatic Stress Disorders of the Vietnam Veteran* (published by the Disabled American Veterans in 1980), which was taken off the shelf two years ago because of the tremendous growth in the professional literature on the diagnosis and treatment of this disorder. While most of the research and literature has focused on particular trauma groups, the inescapable conclusion among both academicians and clinicians is that traumatic stress creates symptoms of distress, and treatment issues are remarkably similar across trauma groups.

This book does not have any single theoretical perspective, nor does it espouse any particular approach to counseling, assessment, or treatment. It simply presents the insights of a group of clinicians with extensive experience in working with traumatized clients.

Post-traumatic stress disorder (PTSD) was only formally recognized as a mental disorder in 1980. The *Diagnostic and Statistical Manual, Third Edition*, is currently being revised. Where possible, we have included comments on the revision, and tentative guidelines proposed by the American Psychiatric Association are provided in Appendix A.

While the criteria for diagnosing PTSD remain essentially sound, clinicians are increasingly seeing clients who are "sub-clinical." These clients have many of the symptoms of PTSD, but may not officially meet the diagnosis. Treatment approaches with this sub-clinical population are similar in many respects to those that have been found to be effective with PTSD. Moreover, regardless of the type of survivor group you may work with, there are principles and strategies of other survivor groups that may be modified for your particular situation. Questions concerning issues brought up in this volume may be directed to me at the Post-Trauma Treatment Center. If we are unable to answer your questions, or you wish to communicate directly with an author, we will be glad to provide a referral.

The Disabled American Veterans and I are presenting this volume to you now as the state of the art of clinical practice in diagnosing and treating persons with stress disorders. And while research and practice will undoubtedly continue to change how we help those with traumatic stress, the chapters that follow will show that we have already come a long way.

The authors and I want to acknowledge the continued support of the DAV in making possible the preparation and distribution of this book. Our technical editor, Patti Lowery, was vital in making this a coherent volume. Our relationship with the National Organization for Victim Assistance has been extremely helpful in sensitizing us to the needs of various survivor groups. We want to thank the many people who helped with the production of the manuscript through several revisions and updates. Finally, I want to extend my very special appreciation to Phil Shovar for coordinating, telecommunicating, and keeping track of the manuscripts and the authors as we made this book.

Tom Williams
Post-Trauma Treatment Center
12361 East Cornell Avenue
Aurora, Colorado 80014

CHAPTER ONE

THE ETIOLOGY OF COMBAT-RELATED POST-TRAUMATIC STRESS DISORDERS

Jim Goodwin

INTRODUCTION

Below is a description of one Vietnam veteran's life more than ten years after the end of the war in Southeast Asia.

> My marriage is falling apart. We just don't talk any more. Hell, I guess we've never really talked about anything, ever. I spend most of my time at home alone in the basement. She's upstairs and I'm downstairs. Sure, we'll talk about the groceries and who will get gas for the car, but that's about it. She's tried to tell me she cares for me, but I get real uncomfortable talking about things like that, and I get up and leave. Sometimes I get real angry over the smallest thing. I used to hit her when this would happen, but lately I just punch a hole in the wall, or leave and go for a long drive. Sometimes I spend more time on the road just driving aimlessly than I do at home.
>
> I really don't have any friends and I'm pretty particular about who I want as a friend. The world is pretty much dog eat dog, and no one seems to care much for anyone else. As far as I'm concerned, I'm really not a part of this messed up society. What I'd really like to do is have a home in the mountains, somewhere far away.
>
> Night is the hardest for me. I go to sleep long after my wife has gone to bed. It seems like hours before I finally drop off. I think of so many of my Nam experiences at night. Sometimes my wife awakens me with a wild look in her eyes. I'm all sweaty and tense. Sometimes I grab for her neck before I realize where I am. Sometimes I remember the dream; sometimes it's Nam, other times it's just people after me, and I can't run anymore.
>
> I don't know, this has been going on for so long; it seems to be getting gradually worse. My wife is talking about leaving. I guess it's no big deal. But I'm lonely. I really don't have anyone else. Why am I the only one like this? What the hell is wrong with me? (Anonymous Vietnam veteran.)

Unfortunately, and contrary to the wisdom of the late 1960s and early 1970s,[1] this is not an unusual phenomenon. In 1979 and 1980, I worked with the Denver Office of the Disabled American Veterans (DAV) Vietnam Veterans Outreach Program. As chief of psychological screening and later as a referral professional (as a military psychologist on active duty), I interviewed more than 300 veterans of the Vietnam war. They were either attracted to our office by the DAV community-sponsored media campaign regarding the long-term effects of the war, or they responded to the word-of-mouth of family, friends, business associates, or mental health professionals who had contact with the program. My observations and experiences since then are similar to those I had with the DAV outreach. I have now seen veterans from other wars and military operations, such as Grenada, as well as victims of other traumas.

THE EVOLUTION OF POST-TRAUMATIC STRESS DISORDER (PTSD)

It was not until World War I that specific clinical syndromes came to be associated with combat duty. In earlier wars, it was assumed that such casualties were merely manifestations of poor discipline and cowardice. However, with the protracted artillery barrages commonplace during "The Great War," the concept evolved that the high air pressure of the exploding shells caused actual physiological damage, precipitating the numerous symptoms that were subsequently labeled "shell shock." By the end of the war, further evolution accounted for the syndrome's being labeled a "war neurosis" (Glass, 1969).

However, it was widely believed that predisposing factors were largely responsible for adverse reactions after the traumatic experiences of combat; this belief continued into World War II. Grinker and Spiegel (1945, p. 341) cite a case in which a 25-year-old gunner of a B-24 with 25 combat missions presented symptoms of depression, tiredness, paleness, anxiety, suicidal thoughts, homicidal ideation, and intense intolerance of his circumstances. He had been in the Army Air Corps for 27 months, experiencing two crashes in the United States and two combat-related crashes in Europe. In addition, he was once fired upon by a German battleship—shells screamed past his plane. On another occasion, while he was flying at 27,000 feet, the engines of his bomber failed, and the plane fell some 25,000 feet before they restarted. On his 23rd mission, his plane was hit and he was knocked out of his turret by the explosion; the copilot, bombardier, and radio man were all killed. Despite his traumatic military history, it was finally resolved that this veteran's presenting symptoms were primarily due to a problematic childhood and some severe feelings of hostility he had harbored for his mother, brother, and others representing authority. Ultimately, the veteran was forcibly discharged from the service with the diagnosis of psychopathic personality.

During the early years of World War II, psychiatric casualties had increased some 300 percent when compared with World War I, even though the preinduction psychiatric rejection rate was three to four times higher than in World War I (Figley, 1978a). At one point in the war, the number of men being discharged from the service for psychiatric reasons exceeded the total number of men being newly drafted (Tiffany & Allerton, 1967).

Needless to say, the military soon discovered that few would be immune if the assumption were that predisposing factors were the primary precipitant for psychological breakdown in combat. In fact, an Inspector General's report in 1944 concluded, "If screening is to weed out all those likely to develop a psychiatric disorder, all should be weeded out" (Anderson, 1966, p. 391). Thereafter, a much more pragmatic trend evolved toward observation and comparison of the various stresses of battle and their concomitant psychological casualty rates. The concept of the war neurosis, with its etiological basis in the preservice history of the combatant, had outlived its usefulness. Rather, various intrinsic qualities of the combat situation began to serve as the designated substrate for emotional decompensation. Recognizing the extreme physical stress of battle, the U.S. Army commander in Tunisia ordered all psychological casualties, regardless of the symptomatology, to be labeled as cases of exhaustion (Figley, 1978a).

During the Korean War, the approach to combat stress became even more pragmatic. As a result of the work of Albert Glass (1954), individual breakdowns in combat effectiveness were dealt with in a situation-specific manner: clinicians provided immediate on-site treatment to affected individuals, always with the expectation that the combatant would return to duty as soon as possible. The results were gratifying: during World War II, 23 percent of all evacuations had been for psychiatric reasons, but in Korea, psychiatric evacuations dropped to only 6 percent (Bourne, 1970). It finally became clear that the situational stresses of the combatants were the primary factors leading to a psychological casualty.

At about the same time, the original *Diagnostic and Statistical Manual I* (*DSM-I*) (American Psychiatric Association [APA], 1952) was published with a category of gross stress reaction that was characterized by an individual's being exposed to extreme emotional and physical stress, such as combat. The *DSM-II* (APA, 1968), on the other hand, deleted the category; combat-related stress was mentioned only in the context of adult adjustment reactions. The implication was that the stresses of combat could be more or less appropriately resolved.

Surprisingly, psychological battlefield casualties evolved in a new direction during the Vietnam war. What was expected from past war experiences—and what the military was prepared to manage—did not materialize. Battlefield psychological breakdown was at an all-time low: only 12 of every 1000 combatants (Bourne, 1970). It was decided that use of preventive measures learned in Korea and some added situational manipulation (which will be discussed later) had solved the age-old problem of psychological breakdown in combat. The media quickly noted what was thought to be progress in military psychology and psychiatry (see Notes). As the war continued for a number of years, some interesting additional trends were observed. Although some combatants' behavior undermined fighting efficiency, the symptoms presented rarely resembled the previous classical picture of combat fatigue. The effects, however, were the same, since any symptom of combat fatigue rendered the combatant unable to adhere to his role. Kormos (1978) made the logical step, therefore, of grouping all behaviors and syndromes that resulted in the combatants' refusal to fight under one central rubric: acute combat reaction.

Additionally, as the war progressed, a phenomenon emerged that had not been seen in Vietnam but that was well-documented during World War II. After the end of World War II, some men suffering from acute combat reaction, as well as some of their peers with no such symptoms at war's end, began to complain of common symptoms: intense anxiety, battle dreams, depression, explosive aggressive behavior, and problems with interpersonal relationships, to name but a few. These were found in a five-year follow-up (Futterman & Pumpian-Mindlin, 1951) and in a twenty-year follow-up (Archibald & Tuddenham, 1965).

This trend was observed in Vietnam veterans as the war wore on. Both those who experienced acute combat reaction and many who did not began to complain of the above symptoms long after their combat role had ended. What was so unusual was the large numbers of veterans being affected after Vietnam. The pattern of neuropsychiatric disorder for combatants of World War II and Korea was quite different than for Vietnam. For both World War II and the Korean War, the incidence of neuropsychiatric disorder among combatants increased as the wars intensified. As these wars wore down, there was a corresponding decrease in these disorders until the incidence closely resembled the particular prewar periods. The prolonged or delayed symptoms noticed during the postwar periods were poorly documented and occurred rarely; therefore, no great significance was attached to them.

However, the Vietnam experience proved different. As the war intensified, there was no corresponding rise in neuropsychiatric casualties among combatants. It was not until the early 1970s, when the war was winding down, that neuropsychiatric disorders were growing rapidly. With the end of direct American troop involvement in Vietnam in 1973, the number of veterans presenting neuropsychiatric disorders began to increase tremendously (President's Commission on Mental Health, 1978).

During the same period in the 1970s, many other people were experiencing traumatic episodes other than combat. There were large numbers of plane crashes, natural disasters, fires, acts of terrorism on civilian populations, and other catastrophic events. The picture presented to many mental health professionals helping these victims adjust after traumatic experiences was quite similar to the phenomenon of the troubled Vietnam veteran. Rape trauma, family violence, and sexual abuse of children began emerging in the professional literature; the behavioral symptoms of the victims were almost identical. Finally, after much research (Figley, 1978a) by various veterans' task forces and recommendations by those involved in treatment of civilian post-trauma clients, the *DSM-III* (APA, 1980) was published with a new category: post-traumatic stress disorder, acute, chronic and/or delayed. *DSM-III* (revised) is scheduled to be published with some minor revisions of the symptoms (see Appendix A).

VIETNAM'S PREDISPOSING EFFECTS FOR PTSD

When direct American troop involvement in Vietnam became a reality, military planners looked to previous war experiences to help alleviate psychological disorders in combat. By then, it was an understood fact that combatants with the most combat exposure suffered the highest incidence of breakdown. In Korea, this knowledge resulted in the limited use of a "point system": after accumulating so many points, an individual was rotated home, regardless of the progress of the war. This was further refined in Vietnam as the DEROS (date of expected return from overseas) system. Every man and woman serving in Vietnam, except general officers, knew before leaving the United States when he or she was scheduled to return. The tour lasted 12 months for everyone except the Marines who, known for their one-upmanship, did a 13-month tour. DEROS promised the combatant a way out of the war other than as a physical or psychological casualty (Kormos, 1978).

The advantages were clear: there would not be an unending period of protracted combat or of dealing with wounded men; the prospect of becoming a psychological casualty was no longer the only hope for return to the United States without wounds. Rather, if combatants or medical personnel could just hold together for the 12 or 13 months, they would be rotated to the United States. Once home, they could leave the war far behind.

The disadvantages to DEROS were not as clear, and some time elapsed before they were noticed. DEROS was a very personal thing; each individual was rotated on his or her own with a specific date of departure. This meant that tours in Vietnam were solitary, individual episodes. It was rare, after the first few years of the war, that whole units were sent to the war zone simultaneously. Bourne (1970) said it best: "The war becomes a highly individualized and encapsulated event for each man. His war begins the day he arrives in the country, and ends the day he leaves" (p. 12). Bourne further states, "He feels no continuity with those who precede or follow him. He even feels apart from those who are with him but rotating on a different schedule" (p. 42).

Because of this very individual aspect of the war, unit morale, unit cohesion, and unit identification suffered tremendously (Kormos, 1978). Many studies from past wars (Grinker & Spiegel, 1945) point out that unit integrity acts as a buffer for the individual against the overwhelming stresses of combat. Many of the veterans of World War II spent weeks or months with their units returning on ships from all over the world. During the long trip home, these men had the closeness and emotional support of one another to rework the especially traumatic episodes that they had experienced together. The epitaph for the Vietnam veterans, however, was a solitary plane ride home with complete strangers and a head full of grief, conflict, confusion, and joy.

For every Vietnam combatant, the DEROS date became a fantasy that on a specific day all problems would cease as he flew swiftly back to the United States. The combatants believed that neither they as individuals nor the United States as a society had changed. Hundreds of thousands of men lived this fantasy from day to day. The universal popularity of short-timer calendars is evidence of this. A short-timer was a GI who was finishing his tour overseas.

The calendars intricately marked off the days remaining of his overseas tour in all manner of designs with 365 spaces to fill in to complete the design and mark that final day. The GIs overtly displayed these calendars to one another. Those with the shortest time left in the country were praised by others and would lead their peers on a fantasy excursion of how wonderful and carefree life would be as soon as they returned home. For many, this became an almost daily ritual. For those who may have been struggling with a psychological breakdown engendered by the stresses of combat, the DEROS fantasy served as a major prophylactic to actual overt symptoms of acute combat reaction. These veterans fought hard to hold on until their time came due.

The vast majority of veterans did hold on, as evidenced by the low neuropsychiatric casualty rates during the war (President's Commission on Mental Health, 1978). Rates of acute combat reaction or acute PTSD were significantly lowered relative to the two previous wars. As a result, many combatants, who in previous wars might have become psychological statistics, held on, however tenuously, until the end of their tours in Vietnam.

The struggle for most was an uphill battle. Those motivators that kept the combatant fighting—unit *esprit de corps*, small group solidarity, and an ideological belief that this was the good fight (Moskos, 1975)—were not present in Vietnam. Unit *esprit* was effectively slashed by the DEROS system. Complete strangers, often GIs who were strangers even to a specific unit's specialty, were transferred into units whenever individual rotations were completed. Veterans who had finally reached a level of proficiency had also reached their DEROS date and were rotated. Green troops ("fucking new guys") with almost no skills were thrown into their places. These "new guys" were essentially avoided by the unit, at least until after a few months of experience; "short timers" did not want to get themselves killed by relying on inexperienced replacements. Needless to say, the unit culture or *esprit* was often lost in the lack of communication with the endless leavings and arrivals.

There were other unique aspects of group dynamics in Vietnam. Seasoned troops would stick together, often forming very close, small groups for short periods, a normal combat experience noted in previous wars (Grinker & Spiegel, 1945). However, as soon as a seasoned veteran got down to his last two months in Vietnam, he was struck by a strange malady: the "short-timer's syndrome." He would be withdrawn from the field and, if logistically possible, would be settled into a comparatively safe setting for the rest of his tour. His buddies would be left behind in the field without his skills, and he would be left with mixed feelings of joy and guilt. Interestingly, it was rare that a veteran ever wrote to his buddies still in Vietnam once he returned home (Howard, 1976). It has been an even rarer experience for two or more to get together after the war. This is a strong contrast to the endless reunions of World War II veterans. Guilt about leaving one's buddies to an unknown fate in Vietnam apparently proved so strong that many veterans were often too frightened to attempt to find out what happened to those left behind.

Another factor unique to the Vietnam war was that the ideological basis for the war was very difficult to grasp. In World War II, the United States was very clearly threatened by a uniformed and easily recognizable foe. Vietnam was quite the opposite: it appeared that the whole country was hostile to American forces. The enemy was rarely uniformed, and American troops were often forced to kill women and children combatants. There were no real lines of demarcation, and just about any area was subject to attack. Most American forces had been trained to fight in conventional warfare in which other human beings are confronted and a block of land is either acquired or lost in the fray.

However, in Vietnam, surprise firing devices (such as booby traps) accounted for a large number of casualties while the human foe was rarely sighted. A block of land might be secured but not held. A unit would pull out to another conflict in the vicinity, and, if it wished to return to the same block of land, it would once again have to fight to take that land. It was an endless war with invisible enemies and no ground gains—just a constant flow of troops in and out of the country. The only observable outcome was an interminable production of maimed, crippled bodies and countless corpses. Some were so disfigured it was hard to tell whether they were Vietnamese or American, but they were all dead.

The rage that such conditions generated was widespread among American troops. It manifested itself in violence and mistrust toward the Vietnamese (DeFazio, 1978), toward the authorities, and toward the society that sent these men to Vietnam but then would not support them. Rather than a war with a just ideological basis, Vietnam became a private war of survival for every American individual involved.

What was especially problematic was that this was America's first teenage war. The age of the average combatant was close to 20 (Wilson, 1979). According to Wilson (1978), this period for most adolescents involves a psychosocial moratorium (Erikson, 1968), during which the individual takes some time to establish a more stable and enduring personality structure and sense of self. This is an important step—identity versus role confusion—in Erikson's (1968) stages of psychosocial development. Unfortunately for the adolescents who fought the war, the role of combatant versus survivor, as well as the many ambiguous and conflicting values associated with these roles, led to a clear disruption of this moratorium and to the many subsequent problems that followed for the young veterans.

At this point, the reader is probably again wondering why there weren't more immediate psychological breakdowns among the troops in Vietnam. Again, it is important to stress the prophylactic aspects of the DEROS system. In addition, as it is for many contemporary people, when one is confronted with overwhelming stress, one reaches for the quickest cure: medication.

The administration of tranquilizing drugs and the phenothiazines on the combat front first occurred in Vietnam (Jones & Johnson, 1975). Thus, men who might have been evacuated in an earlier war were able to hang on until their normal rotation date.

By now, the use of illicit drugs in Vietnam has become legend. To aid the survival of her family, many a "mamasan" (GI slang for a Vietnamese woman with a child) with whom GIs made contact had her own supply of marijuana, opium, and heroin for sale. Bourne (1970), in fact, observed during his visit to Vietnam that there was widespread use of marijuana but that it had created almost no psychiatric problems. Quite to the contrary, it served its own medicinal purpose, muting the stresses of the Vietnam experience (Horowitz & Solomon, 1975), submerging and delaying symptoms.

Many veterans who consumed the more powerful opiates or copious amounts of alcohol came to the attention of their superiors because of side effects and aberrant behavior. The original reasons for their use of these buffers became secondary to the fact that they had become behavioral and medical problems for the services. Thus, many men who had used drugs to deal with the overwhelming stresses of combat or had developed other behavioral symptoms of similar stress-related etiology were not recognized as struggling with acute combat reaction or PTSD (acute subtype). Rather, their immediate behavior had proven to be problematic to the military, and they were offered an immediate resolution in the form of administrative discharges with diagnoses of character disorders (Kormos, 1978).

The administrative discharge proved to be another method to temporarily repress any further overt symptoms. It provided an end to the stress without the serviceman's becoming an actual physical or psychological casualty, and therefore lowered the actual incidence of psychological breakdown, as did the DEROS. Eventually, this widely used practice came to be questioned; it had been used as a convenient way to eliminate many individuals who had major psychological problems dating from their combat service (Kormos, 1978).

When the veteran finally returned home, his fantasy about his DEROS date was replaced by a rather harsh reality. In contrast to World War II vets who took weeks, sometimes months, to return home with their buddies, Vietnam vets returned home alone. Many made the transition from rice paddy to Southern California in less then 36 hours; most made it in less than a week. The civilian population of the World War II era had been treated to movies about the struggles of readjustment for veterans (i.e., "The Man in the Gray Flannel Suit," "The Best Years of Our Lives," "Pride of the Marines") that prepared them to help the veteran (DeFazio, 1978). The civilian population of the Vietnam era was treated to the horrors of the war on the six o'clock news. They were tired and numb to the whole experience. Some were even fighting mad, and many veterans were witness to this fact. World War II veterans came home to victory parades. Vietnam veterans returned in defeat and witnessed antiwar marches and protests. For World War II veterans, resort hotels were taken over and made into redistribution stations to which veterans could bring their wives and devote two weeks to the initial homecoming (Boros, 1973). For Vietnam veterans, there were screaming antiwar crowds and locked military bases where they were processed back into civilian life in two or three days.

The veterans may have made it *back*, but they quickly discovered the apparent truth of Thomas Wolfe's assertion that you can't go *home* again. They had drastically changed, and their world would never seem the same. Their fantasies were just that: fantasies. What they had experienced in Vietnam and on their return to their homes in the United States would leave an indelible mark that many may never erase.

THE CATALYSTS OF PTSD FOR VIETNAM COMBAT VETERANS

More than 8.5 million individuals served in the U.S. Armed Forces during the Vietnam era, 1964-1973. Approximately 2.8 million served in Southeast Asia. Of the latter number, almost one million saw active combat or were exposed to hostile, life-threatening situations (President's Commission on Mental Health, 1978). It is this writer's opinion that the vast majority of Vietnam-era veterans have had a much more problematic readjustment to civilian life than did their World War II and Korean War counterparts. This was due to the issues already discussed in this chapter, as well as to the state of the economy and the inadequacy of the GI Bill in the early 1970s. In addition, the combat veterans of Vietnam, many of whom immediately tried to become assimilated back into the peacetime culture, discovered that their outlook and feelings about their relationships and future life experiences had changed immensely. According to the fantasy, all was to be well again when they returned from Vietnam. The reality for many was quite different.

A number of studies point out that those veterans subjected to more extensive combat show more problematic symptoms during the period of readjustment (Figley, 1978b; Kormos, 1978; Shatan, 1978; Strayer & Ellenhorn, 1975; Wilson, 1978). The usual pattern has been that of a combat veteran in Vietnam who held on until his DEROS date. He was largely asymptomatic at the point of his rotation back to the U.S. for the reasons previously discussed; on his return home, the joy of surviving continued to suppress any problematic symptoms. However, after a year or more, the veteran would begin to notice some changes in his outlook (Shatan, 1978). But, because there was a time limit of one year after which the Veterans Administration would not recognize neuropsychiatric problems as service-connected, the veteran was unable to get service-connected disability compensation. Treatment from the VA was very difficult to obtain. The veteran began to feel depressed, mistrustful, cynical, and restless. He experienced problems with sleep and with his temper. Strangely, he became somewhat obsessed with his combat experiences in Vietnam. He would also begin to question why he survived when others did not.

For approximately 500,000 veterans (Wilson, 1978) of the combat in Southeast Asia, this problematic outlook has become a chronic lifestyle affecting not only the veterans but countless millions of persons who are in contact with them. The symptoms described below are experienced by all Vietnam combat veterans to varying degrees. However, for some with the most extensive combat histories and other variables that have yet to be enumerated, Vietnam-related problems have persisted in disrupting all areas of life experience. Furthermore, without any intervention, what was once a reaction to a traumatic episode may become for many an almost unchangeable personality characteristic.

THE SYMPTOMS OF PTSD— CHRONIC AND/OR DELAYED DEPRESSION

The vast majority of the Vietnam combat veterans I have interviewed are depressed. Many have been continually depressed since their experiences in Vietnam. They have the classic symptoms (APA, 1980) of sleep disturbance, psychomotor retardation, feelings of worthlessness, difficulty in concentrating, etc. Many own weapons, and they are no strangers to death. (In treatment, it is especially important to find out whether the veteran keeps a weapon in close proximity [see section on anxiety reactions]; the possibility of suicide is always present.)

When recalling various combat episodes during an interview, the veteran with PTSD almost invariably cries. He usually has had one or more episodes in which one of his buddies was killed. When asked how he handled these deaths when in Vietnam, he will often answer, "In the shortest amount of time possible" (Howard, 1976). Due to circumstances of war, extended grieving on the battlefield is very unproductive and could become a liability. Hence, grief was handled as quickly as posible, allowing little or no time for the grieving process. Many men reported feeling numb (see section on avoidance of feelings) when this happened. When asked how they are now dealing with the deaths of their buddies in Vietnam, they invariably answer that they are not. They feel depressed: "How can I tell my wife, she'd never understand?" they ask. "How can anyone who hasn't been there understand?" (Howard, 1976; see Hickman, this volume).

Accompanying the depression is a very well-developed sense of helplessness about one's condition. This feeling very closely resembles Seligman's (1967) construct of learned helplessness. Essentially, Vietnam-style combat held no final resolution of conflict for anyone. Regardless of how one might respond, the overall outcome seemed to be just an endless production of casualties with no perceivable goals attained. Regardless of how well one worked, sweated, bled, and even died, the outcome was the same. Our GIs gained no ground; they were constantly rocketed or mortared. They found little support from their "friends and neighbors" back home, the people in whose name so many were drafted into military service. They felt helpless. They returned to the United States, trying to put together some positive resolution of this episode in their lives, but the atmosphere at home was hopeless. They were still helpless. Why even bother anymore?

Many veterans report becoming extremely isolated when they are especially depressed. Substance abuse is often exaggerated during depressive periods. Self-medication, an easily learned coping response in Vietnam, remains an appealing choice.

Isolation

Combat veterans have few friends. Many veterans who witnessed traumatic experiences complain of feeling like old men in young men's bodies, isolated and distant from their peers. The veterans feel that most of their nonveteran peers would rather not hear what the combat experience was like; therefore, they feel rejected. Much of what many of these veterans had done during the war would seem like horrible crimes to their civilian friends. But, in the reality faced by Vietnam combatants, such actions were frequently the only means of survival. It was beyond understanding for a civilian.

Many veterans find it difficult to forget the lack of positive support they received from the American public during the war. This was especially brought home to them on the return from the combat zone to the United States. Many were met by screaming crowds and the media calling them "depraved fiends" and "psychopathic killers" (DeFazio, 1978). Many personally confronted hostility from friends as well as strangers. Once home, some veterans found that the only defense was to search for a safe place; they found themselves criss-crossing the continent always searching for that place where they might feel accepted. To this day, many veterans cling to the hope that they can move away from their problems. It is not unusual to interview a veteran who, either alone or with his family, has effectively isolated himself from others by repeatedly moving from one geographical location to another. The stress on his family is immense.

The fantasy of living the life of a hermit plays a central role in many veterans' daydreams. Many admit to extended periods of isolation in the mountains, on the road, or just behind a closed door in the city. Some of the veterans in the Denver area have actually taken a weapon and attempted to live off the land in isolated regions of the Rocky Mountains.

It is not rare to find a combat veteran who has not had a social contact with a woman for years—other than with a prostitute for carnal reasons, which is an accepted military procedure in the combat setting. If the veteran does marry, his wife will often complain about the isolation he imposes on the marital situation: he often stays in the house and avoids interactions with others, and resents any interactions that his wife may initiate.

Rage

The veterans' rage is frightening to them and to others around them. For no apparent reason, many will strike out at whoever is near, including their wives and children. This behavior leads many to question their sanity; they are horrified by their own behavior. However, regardless of their afterthoughts, the rage reactions occur with frightening frequency.

Often veterans will recount episodes in which they became inebriated and had fantasies that they were surrounded or confronted by enemy Vietnamese, a situation that is especially frightening when others attempt to confront the veteran forcibly. For many combat veterans, it is once again a life-and-death struggle, a fight for survival.

Some veterans have been able to sublimate their rage by breaking inanimate objects or putting their fists through walls; many display bruises and cuts on their hands. Often, when these veterans feel the rage emerging, they will immediately leave the scene before somebody or something gets hurt; subsequently, they drive about aimlessly, sometimes finding relief in verbal catharsis they achieve by hurling expletives at any other drivers who may wrong them.

There are many reasons for the rage. Military training equated the rage with masculine identity in the performance of military duty (Eisenhart, 1975). Whether one was in combat or not, the military experience stirred up more resentment and rage than most had ever felt (Egendorf, 1975). Finally, when combat in Vietnam was experienced, the combatants were often left with wild, violent impulses that had no outlet. The nature of guerrilla warfare—

with its use of such tactics as booby trap land mines and surprise ambushes with the enemy's quick retreat—left the combatants feeling like time bombs; the veterans wanted to fight back, but their antagonists had long since disappeared. Often they unleashed their rage indiscriminately for want of suitable targets (Shatan, 1978).

On return from Vietnam, the rage that had been tapped in combat was displaced against people in authority—those the veterans felt were responsible for getting them involved in the war in the first place—and those who would not support the veterans while they were in Vietnam or when they returned home (Howard, 1976). Fantasies of retaliation against political leaders, the military services, the Veterans Administration, and antiwar protesters were present in the minds of many of these Vietnam combat veterans. These fantasies are still alive and generalized to many in the present era.

Along with the specific rage at authority figures from the Vietnam era, many veterans now feel a generalized mistrust of anyone in authority and the current "system," with the unfortunate consequence that many combat veterans with stress disorders have a long history of constantly changing their jobs. It is not unusual to interview a veteran who has had 30 to 40 jobs during the past 10 years. One veteran I interviewed had had nearly 80 jobs in a 10-year span. The rationale quite often given by the veterans is that they became bored or the work was beneath them. However, after I had made some extended searches into their work backgrounds, it became apparent that they felt deep mistrust for their employers and co-workers; they felt used and exploited; at times, such was the case. Many have had some uncomfortable confrontations with their employers and job peers, and many have been fired or have resigned on their own.

Avoidance of Feelings: Alienation

The spouses of many of the veterans I have interviewed complain that the men are cold, uncaring individuals. Indeed, the veterans themselves will recount episodes in which they did not feel anything when they witnessed the death of a buddy in combat or the more recent death of a close family relative. They are often somewhat troubled by these responses to tragedy; but, on the whole, they would rather deal with tragedy in their own detached way. What becomes especially problematic for these veterans, however, is an inability to experience the joys of life. They often describe themselves as being emotionally dead (Shatan, 1973).

This emotional deadness began to evolve for Vietnam veterans when they first entered military boot camp (Shatan, 1973). There they learned that the Vietnamese were not to be labeled as people but as "gooks, dinks, slopes, zipperheads, and slants." When the veterans finally arrived in the battle zone, it was much easier to kill a "gook" or "dink" than another human being. This dehumanization gradually generalized to the whole Vietnam experience. The American combatants themselves became "grunts," the Viet Cong became "Victor Charlie," and both groups were either "KIA" (killed in action) or "WIA" (wounded in action). Often many "slopes" would get "zapped" (killed) by a "Cobra" (gunship), the "grunts" would retreat by "shithook" (evacuation by a Chinook helicopter), and the jungle would be sown by "Puff the Magic Dragon" (C-47 gunship with rapid-firing mini-gatling guns). The nicknames served to blunt the anguish and the horror of the reality of combat (DeFazio, 1978). In conjunction with this almost surreal aspect of the fighting, psychic numbing furthered the coping and survival ability of the combatants; feelings were simply anesthetized (Lifton, 1976). This defense mechanism of survivors of traumatic experiences dulls an individual's awareness of the death and destruction about him. It is a dynamic survival mechanism, helping one to pass through a period of trauma without becoming caught in its tendrils. Psychic numbing only becomes nonproductive when the period of trauma is passed and the individual is still numb to the affect around him.

Many veterans find it extremely uncomfortable to feel love and compassion for others. To do this, they would have to thaw their numb reactions to the death and horror that surrounded them in Vietnam. Some veterans I've interviewed actually believe that if they once again allow themselves to feel, they may never stop crying or may completely lose control of themselves; what they mean by this is unknown to them. Therefore, many of these veterans go through life with an impaired capacity to love and care for others. They have no feeling of direction or purpose in life. They are not sure why they even exist.

Survival Guilt

When some have died and others have not, the survivors often ask, "How is it that I survived when others more worthy than I did not?" (Lifton, 1973). Survival guilt provokes an enormous quantity of guilt, in part because it is not based on anything hypothetical but rather on the harshest of realities: the actual death of comrades and the struggle of the survivor to live. Often the survivor has had to compromise himself or the life of someone else to stay alive. The guilt that such an act elicits (or guilt over simply surviving) may eventually end in self-destructive behavior by the survivor (see T. Williams, this volume).

Many veterans who have survived when comrades were lost in surprise ambushes, protracted battles, or even normal battlefield attrition exhibit self-destructive behavior. It is common for them to recount the combat death of someone they held in esteem; and, invariably, the question comes up, "Why wasn't it me?" It is not unusual for these men to set themselves up for hopeless physical fights with insurmountable odds. "I don't know why, but I always pick the biggest guy," said the veteran in the transcript at the beginning of this chapter. Shatan (1973) notes that some of these men become involved in repeated single-car auto accidents. This writer interviewed one surviving veteran whose company suffered over 80 percent casualties in one ambush. The veteran had had three single-car accidents during the previous week, two the day before he came in for the interview. He was wondering if he were trying to kill himself.

I have also found that those veterans who suffer the most painful survival guilt are primarily those who served as corpsmen or medics. These unfortunate veterans were trained for a few months to render first aid on the actual field of battle. The services they individually performed were heroic. With a bare amount of medical knowledge and large amounts of courage and determination, they saved countless lives. However, many of the men they tried to save died. Many of these casualties were beyond all medical help, yet many corpsmen and medics suffer extremely painful memories to this day, blaming their "incompetence" for these deaths. Listening to these veterans describe their anguish and torment, seeing the heroin tracks up and down their arms, or the bones that have been broken in numerous barroom fights is, in itself, a very painful experience.

Another less destructive trend that I have noticed exists among a small number of Vietnam combat veterans who have become compulsive blood donors. One very isolated and alienated individual I interviewed actually drives some 80 miles round-trip once every other month to make his donation. His military history reveals that he was one of 13 men out of a 670-man platoon who survived the battle of Hue. He was the only survivor who was not wounded. This veteran and similar vets talk openly about their guilt, and they find some relief today in giving their blood that others may live.

Anxiety Reactions

Many Vietnam veterans describe themselves as very vigilant human beings; their autonomic senses are tuned to anything out of the ordinary. A loud discharge will startle many of them. A few will actually take such evasive action as falling to their knees or to the ground. Many veterans become very uncomfortable when people walk closely behind them. One veteran described his discomfort when people drive directly behind him. He would pull off the road and let others pass if they got within a few car lengths of him.

Some veterans are uncomfortable when standing out in the open. Many are uneasy when sitting with others behind them, often opting to sit up against something solid, such as a wall. The bigger the object is, the better. Many combat veterans are most comfortable when sitting in the corner in a room where they can see everyone about them. All of these behaviors are learned survival techniques, and if a veteran feels continuously threatened it is difficult for him to give them up.

Those veterans (and there are many) who own weapons are practicing another learned and comforting survival technique. Many still sleep with weapons in easy reach. The uneasy feeling of being caught asleep is apparently very difficult to abandon once having been in a combat zone. Audie Murphy, America's most decorated hero of World War II, kept a loaded German automatic pistol under his pillow up to the day he died (Shatan, 1978).

Sleep Disturbance and Nightmares

Few veterans struggling with PTSD disorders find the hours immediately before sleep very comfortable. In fact, many will stay awake as long as possible. They will often have a drink or smoke some marijuana to dull the uncomfortable thoughts that creep in just before sleep. Many report that they have nothing to occupy their minds at the end of the day's activities, and their thoughts wander. For many of them, it is a trip back to the battle zone. Very often they will watch TV late into the morning. A public service announcement for the DAV Vietnam Veterans Outreach Program in Denver was purposely broadcast during late-night programming for precisely this reason. A great number of the veterans I have interviewed mentioned the announcement, saying it seemed particularly relevant for them at these times, even though they had forgotten the content of the specific program they had been watching.

Finally, with sleep, many veterans report having dreams about being shot at or being pursued and left with an empty weapon, unable to run anymore. Recurrent dreams of specific traumatic episodes are frequently reported. It is not unusual for a veteran to re-experience, night after night, the death of a close friend or a death that he caused as a combatant. Dreams of everyday, common experiences in Vietnam are also frequently reported. For many, just the fear that they might actually be back in Vietnam is very disquieting.

Some veterans report being unable to remember their specific dreams, yet they feel dread about them. Wives and partners report that the men sleep fitfully, and some call out in agitation. A few actually grab their partners and attempt to do them harm before they have fully awakened. Finally, staying asleep has proven to be a problem for many of these veterans. They report waking up often during the night for no apparent reason. Many rise quite early in the morning, still feeling very tired.

Intrusive Thoughts

Traumatic memories of the battlefield and other less affect-laden combat experiences often play a role in the daytime thoughts of combat veterans. They frequently report replaying especially problematic combat experiences over and over again. Many search for possible alternative outcomes to what actually happened in Vietnam, and castigate themselves for what they might have done to change the situation. They then suffer feelings of guilt because they didn't act according to their new scripts when actually in combat. The vast majority report that these thoughts are very uncomfortable, yet they are unable to put them to rest.

Many of the obsessive episodes are triggered by common, everyday experiences that remind the veteran of the war zone: helicopters flying overhead, the smell of urine (corpses have no muscle tone, and the bladder evacuates at the moment of death), the smell of diesel fuel (the commodes and latrines contained diesel fuel and were burned when filled with human excrement), green tree lines (these were searched for any irregularities that often meant the presence of enemy movement), the sound of popcorn popping (the sound is very close to that of small arms gunfire in the distance), any loud discharge, a rainy day (it rains for months during the monsoons in Vietnam), and finally, the sight of Vietnamese refugees.

A few combat veterans find the memories invoked by some of these and other stimuli so uncomfortable that they will actually go out of their way to avoid them. When exposed to one of the above or similar stimuli, a very small number of combat veterans undergo a short period of time in a dissociative-like state in which they actually re-experience past events in Vietnam. These flashbacks can last anywhere from a few seconds to a few hours. One veteran described an episode to me in which he had seen some armed men and felt he was back in Vietnam. The armed men were police officers. Not having a weapon to protect himself and others, the veteran grabbed a passerby and forcefully sheltered this person in his home to protect him from what he felt were the "gooks." The passerby screamed, and the police stormed the house. The veteran was incoherent when they finally reached him, yelling about "the damn gooks." He was medicated and hospitalized for a week.

Such experiences among Vietnam veterans are rare, but not as uncommon as many may believe. For a surprisingly high number, the sound of a helicopter flying overhead is a cue to forget reality for a few seconds and remember Vietnam, re-experiencing feelings they had there. These intrusive thoughts are especially troublesome for those veterans who are still "numb" and specifically attempting to avoid these feelings. For others, it is just a constant reminder of their time in Vietnam, something they will never forget.

REFERRALS FOR THERAPY

Post-traumatic stress disorders present with widely varying degrees of impairment. When an unmarried veteran (whether bachelor or divorced) with the disorder requests therapy, I refer him to a group of other combat veterans. The reasons are twofold. First, the veteran is usually quite isolated and has lost many of his social skills. He has few contacts with other human beings. The group provides a microcosm in which he can again learn how to interact with other people. It also helps remove the fear, prevalent among these veterans, that each individual veteran is the only individual with these symptoms. In addition, many of the veterans form close support groups of their own outside the therapy session; they telephone each other and help each other through particularly problematic episodes. We support this extra-group contact as long as alcohol and drugs are not used.

Second, the most basic rationale for group treatment is that it finally provides the veteran with that "long boat ride home" with other veterans who have had similar experiences. It provides a forum in which veterans troubled by their combat experiences can work through their feelings with other veterans who have had similar conflicts. In addition, the current symptoms of the disorder are all quite similar, and there is more reinforcement in working through these symptoms with one's peers than in doing it alone.

The group situation is appropriate for most degrees of the symptoms presented. Especially isolated individuals will often be quite frightened of the initial group session. When reminded of the distress they were experiencing that brought them into counseling in the first place, however, they will usually respond by following through with the group. Those with severely homicidal or suicidal symptoms are best handled in a more crisis-oriented, one-to-one setting until the crisis is resolved. I refer these veterans to an appropriate emergency team, with the expectation directly shared with the veteran that he will join the group as soon as the crisis has abated.

Veterans who are married or living with a partner present a somewhat different picture. Their relationships with their partners are almost always problematic. Frequently, a violent, explosive episode at home created the crisis that brought the veteran in for counseling. When such is the case, or when there is a history of battering of the partner, it is extremely important to refer the veteran and his partner to a family disturbance counseling center. The consequences of this continued behavior are obvious. In addition, a referral for the veteran to a group with other combat veterans is appropriate. The veteran's partner may find some understanding of her plight, and additional support from a women's group created specifically for partners of Vietnam combat veterans (see C. Williams, "Women Partners," this volume).

Other veterans who are married or living with a partner will present with less serious problems, but the partners are often detached from one another; they just seem to live under the same roof. Referring the veteran to a combat veterans group and the partner to a partners of Vietnam veterans group is important.

Some veterans and their partners will jointly attend the screening session. Both are troubled by what has been happening and often want to enter marital therapy together immediately. In my experience, the veteran finds it extremely difficult in the beginning of therapy to deal with interactional aspects with his partner when other past interactions with traumatic overtones overshadow the present. When these traumatic experiences do surface, the partner is often unable to relate to them. Therefore, it is much more beneficial, in my opinion, to allow the veteran time with the combat veterans in a group. In the meantime, suggest a women's support group for partners of Vietnam veterans for the spouse. Here she would receive additional support as well as an understanding of PTSD. Sometime thereafter, marital therapy, couples group therapy, or family therapy may be appropriate.

Many veterans with PTSD, in addition to the symptoms already described, also have significant problems related to multiple substance abuse (see Jelinek and Williams, this volume). In my experience, those veterans who have habitually medicated themselves have compounded the problem. Not only do they experience many of the symptoms already described, but the additional symptoms of chronic multiple substance abuse and alcoholism may mask the underlying reasons for self-medication. Therefore, these chronic syndromes, which perpetuate themselves through addictive behavior, must be dealt with first. Then a more accurate picture of the underlying problem will result, and an appropriate referral can be made.

Here in Denver, the Veterans Administration (VA) system has been receptive to and effective in working with Vietnam veterans with substance problems. They have created a clinic away from the VA Medical Center; this avoids the conflict many Vietnam veterans have with the "system." The unobtrusive name, "Park Place," also de-emphasizes the "system" aspect. Not only is the VA working on the problem of multiple substance abuse with these veterans, but they have also acknowledged that many of these men are suffering from PTSD. Part of the treatment for many of these veterans is a Vietnam combat veterans group (see Jelinek, this volume).

Except for some help with an immediate crisis upon being first interviewed during the screening session, the combat veteran struggling with the symptoms of PTSD, chronic and/or delayed, benefits most from group interaction with his combat peers. Throughout this chapter, I have emphasized the individual, solitary aspect of the war for each veteran. The aftermath of the war has followed in kind. Now, with help from the community and the Vet Center program, a model for finally reintegrating the combat veteran of the Vietnam war with himself or herself and the rest of society has been established. Helping the community to recognize the problem and directing the veteran to the specialized services of the community have given the veteran struggling with this disorder a means of "coming home."

NOTES

"During World War II, US Army field commanders discovered one man in ten was knocked out of action by battle-induced mental disorder....Today in Vietnam the psychiatric casualty rate is down to one man in one hundred....Hot meals almost daily, swift evacuation of the wounded by helicopter, regular periods of R and R (rest and recreation)...steady troop rotation...have helped prevent mental wounds....In Korea... American soldiers...showed more stubborn loyalty to their military outfit than to their own moral values or even their country. In Vietnam, this knowledge is being applied by treating the battle shocked man not as an individual but as part of his unit....The Army is creating a new breed of lay therapist, from the battalion surgeon to the squad sergeant to the commanding officer....If they are taught to understand and deal with the factors that can cripple a fighting man without visibly injuring him, they can provide an effective, on-the-spot countermeasure against this elusive enemy. In Vietnam, the lessons are being learned." ("Dividend from Vietnam," 1969.)

REFERENCES

Anderson, R. S. (Ed.) (1966). *Neuropsychiatry in World War II*, (Vol. 1). Washington, DC: Office of the Surgeon General.

American Psychiatric Association. (1952). *Diagnostic and statistical manual of mental disorders, (I ed.).* Washington, DC: American Psychiatric Press.

American Psychiatric Association. (1968). *Diagnostic and statistical manual of mental disorders, (II ed.).* Washington, DC: American Psychiatric Press.

American Psychiatric Association. (1980). *Diagnostic and statistical manual of mental disorders, (III ed.).* Washington, DC: American Psychiatric Press.

Archibald, H. E., & Tuddenham, R. D. (1965). Persistent stress reaction after combat: A twenty-year follow-up. *Archives of General Psychiatry, 12*, 475-481.

Boros, J. F. (1973). Reentry: III. Facilitating healthy readjustment in Vietnam veterans. *Psychiatry, 36* (4), 428-439.

Bourne, P. G. (1970). *Men, stress and Vietnam.* Boston: Little, Brown.

Dancy, T. E. (1950). Treatment in the absence of pensioning for psychoneurotic veterans. *American Journal of Psychiatry, 107*, 347-349.

DeFazio, V. J. (1978). Dynamic perspectives on the nature and effects of combat stress. In C. R. Figley (Ed.), *Stress disorders among Vietnam veterans: theory, research and treatment.* New York: Brunner/Mazel.

Dividend from Vietnam. (1969, Oct. 10). *Time.* pp. 60-61

Egendorf, A. (1975). Vietnam veteran rap groups and themes of postwar life. In D. M. Mantell & M. Pilisuk (Eds.), *Journal of Social Issues: Soldiers In and After Vietnam, 31* (4) 111-124.

Eisenhart, R. W. (1975). You can't hack it little girl: A discussion of the covert psychological agenda of modern combat training. In D. M. Mantell & M. Pilisuk (Eds.), *Journal of Social Issues: Soldiers In and After Vietnam, 31* (4), 13-23.

Erikson, E. (1968). *Identity, youth and crisis.* New York: W. W. Norton.

Figley, C. R. (1978 a). Introduction. In C. R. Figley (Ed.), *Stress disorders among Vietnam veterans: theory, research and treatment.* New York: Brunner/Mazel.

Figley, C. R. (1978 b). Psychosocial adjustment among Vietnam veterans: An overview of the research. In C. R. Figley (Ed.), *Stress disorders among Vietnam veterans: theory, research and treatment* (pp 53-55). New York: Brunner/Mazel.

Futterman, S., & Pumpian-Mindlin, E. (1951). Traumatic war neuroses five years later. *American Journal of Psychiatry, 108* (6), 401-408.

Glass, A. J. (1954). Psychotherapy in the combat zone. *American Journal of Psychiatry, 110*, 725-731.

Glass, A. J. (1969). Introduction. In P. G. Bourne (Ed.), *The psychology and physiology of stress* (pp. XIV - XXX). New York: Academic Press.

Grinker, R. R., & Spiegel, J.P. (1945). *Men under stress.* Philadelphia: Blakiston.

Horowitz, M. J., & Solomon, G. F. (1975). A prediction of delayed stress response syndromes in Vietnam veterans. In D. M. Mantell & Pilisuk (Eds.), *Journal of Social Issues: Soldiers In and After Vietnam, 31* (4), 67-80.

Howard, S. (1976). The Vietnam warrior: His experience and implications for psychotherapy. *American Journal of Psychotherapy, 30* (1), 121-135.

Jones, F. D., & Johnson, A. W. (1975). Medical psychiatric treatment policy and practice in Vietnam. In D. M. Mantell & M. Pilisuk (Eds.), *Journal of Social Issues: Soldiers In and After Vietnam*, *31* (4), 49-65.

Kormos, H. R. (1978). The nature of combat stress. In C. R. Figley (Ed.), *Stress disorders among Vietnam veterans: theory, treatment and research.* New York: Brunner/Mazel.

Lifton, R. J. (1973). *Home from the war.* New York: Simon & Schuster.

Lifton, R. J. (1976). *The life of the self.* New York: Simon & Schuster.

Moskos, C. C. (1975). The American combat soldier in Vietnam. In D. M. Mantell & M. Pilisuk (Eds.), *Journal of Social Issues: Soldiers In and After Vietnam*, *31* (4), 25-37.

President's Commission on Mental Health (1978, February 15). Report of the special working group: Mental health problems of Vietnam era veterans. Washington, DC: Government Printing Office.

Seligman, M. E. P., & Maier, S. F. (1967). Failure to escape traumatic shock. *Journal of Experimental Psychology*, *74*, 1-9.

Shatan, C. F. (1973). The grief of soldiers: Vietnam combat veterans' self-help movement. *American Journal of Orthopsychiatry*, *43*(4), 640-653.

Shatan, C. F. (1978). Stress disorders among Vietnam veterans: The emotional content of combat continues. In C. R. Figley (Ed.), *Stress disorders among Vietnam veterans: theory, research and treatment.* New York: Brunner/Mazel.

Strayer, R., & Ellenhorn, L. (1975). Vietnam veterans: A study exploring adjustment patterns and attitudes. In D. M. Mantell & M. Pilisuk (Eds.), *Journal of Social Issues: Soldiers In and After Vietnam*, *31* (4), 81-93.

Tiffany, W. J., & Allerton, W. S. (1967). Army psychiatry in the mid-'60s. *American Journal of Psychiatry*, *123*, 810-821.

Wilson, J. P. (1978). Identity, ideology and crisis: The Vietnam veteran in transition. Part I. Identity, ideology and crisis: The Vietnam veteran in transition. Part II. Psychosocial attributes of the veteran beyond identity: Patterns of adjustment and future implications. *Forgotten Warrior Project.* Cleveland State University, 1978. (Reprinted by the Disabled American Veterans, Cincinnati, OH, 1979.)

CHAPTER TWO

DIFFERENTIAL DIAGNOSIS IN POST-TRAUMATIC STRESS DISORDER: IMPLICATIONS FOR TREATMENT

James Newman

INTRODUCTION

This chapter is intended as an overview of essential diagnostic issues in the treatment of post-traumatic stress disorder (PTSD). My experience with treating traumatic stress disorders has been mainly as a therapist at a Veterans Administration Vet Center. The Vet Centers are essentially outpatient mental health clinics for Vietnam-era veterans. Most of our clients are combat veterans (male and female) with a primary diagnosis of PTSD. However, we frequently see veterans with mixed diagnoses. While the great majority of these veterans evidence some symptoms of post-traumatic stress disorder, for many PTSD is not the primary diagnosis. Effective treatment interventions with this latter group can vary considerably from those known to be effective with veterans with a primary diagnosis of PTSD. Thus, differential diagnosis can be a key factor in focusing treatment on the issues relevant for a particular client.

My experience in treating PTSD has been largely confined to traumatic stress reactions in war veterans, but these clients, according to the literature, are not unique. The extensive research and clinical literature on post-traumatic stress disorder (for review, see Figley, 1985, and Van der Kolb, 1984) suggests that, despite widely differing circumstances and pre-existing personalities, persons who have been psychologically traumatized share some remarkably similar emotional reactions and psychological defenses. With this in mind, I will try to encompass, to the extent possible, diagnostic issues for traumatic stress disorders in nonveteran populations, a relatively easy task in regard to the more general and theoretical aspects of PTSD. However, in the latter portions of this chapter, which deal with specific clinical indications for differential diagnosis, I felt it necessary to stay largely with my experiences in treating veterans, limiting myself to occasional comments about diagnostic issues in other traumatized populations that I have picked up from the literature or other clinicians. (In that regard, I wish to especially thank Carolyn Agosta and Dr. Nancy Bowman for their valuable comments on the earlier drafts of this chapter.)

PTSD is classified in the *Diagnostic and Statistical Manual (DSM-III)*[1] of the American Psychiatric Association (APA, 1980) as an anxiety disorder, in which

> ...the essential feature is the development of characteristic symptoms following a psychologically traumatic event that is generally outside the range of usual human experience.
>
> The stressor producing this syndrome would evoke significant symptoms of distress in most people, and is generally outside the realm of such common experiences as simple bereavement, chronic illness, business losses, or marital conflict. The trauma may be experienced alone (rape or assault) or in the company of groups of people (military combat). Stressors producing this disorder include natural disasters (floods, earthquakes), accidental man-made disasters (car accidents with serious physical injury, airplane crashes, large fires), or deliberate man-made disasters (bombing, torture, death camps) ....The disorder is apparently more severe and longer lasting

when the stressor is of human design. (p. 236)

PTSD is unique among mental disorders in that the symptoms arise as the direct result of a psychologically traumatic event. While pre-existing psychopathology may increase the likelihood of an individual's developing this disorder, PTSD can and does occur in people who had healthy pre-trauma personalities. The diagnosis of PTSD in individuals without serious pre-trauma psychopathology is, in my experience, relatively easy once the traumatic stressor has been identified. Primary symptoms in such cases can then be traced back to the specific circumstances of the traumatic event.

Diagnostic dilemmas tend to arise when PTSD symptoms are embedded within a context of pre-existing psychopathology. The intent of this chapter, then, is to provide the clinician with an understanding of how PTSD symptoms present within the context of commonly encountered mental disorders as described in *DSM-III* (APA, 1980), an issue *DSM-III* itself fails to address. A model that has evolved from my own clinical experience, however, is presented below.

A CONTEXTUAL MODEL FOR THE DIFFERENTIAL DIAGNOSIS OF PTSD

In attempting to place PTSD within the context of pre-existing psychopathology, I have found it useful to think of mental disorders as existing on a continuum from severe pathology to relative psychological health. This continuum is demarcated by levels of psychological, or ego development. At the severe end of this continuum lie the psychoses, in which reality testing is grossly impaired and a coherent ego is largely absent. Nearest the healthy end of the continuum lie what have traditionally been referred to as the neuroses (Figure 1).

While *DSM-III* has omitted the diagnostic *class* of neuroses found in earlier DSMs, it has retained the diagnostic categories that formerly comprised the neuroses. Interestingly, PTSD has been placed within one of these categories, the anxiety disorders, along with phobic and anxiety neuroses. In the glossary of *DSM-III*, a "neurotic disorder" is defined as, "A mental disorder in which the predominant disturbance is a symptom or group of symptoms that is distressing to the individual and is recognized by him or her as unacceptable and alien (ego-dystonic); reality testing is grossly intact. Behavior does not actively violate gross social norms (though it may be quite disabling)." (APA, 1980, p. 364)

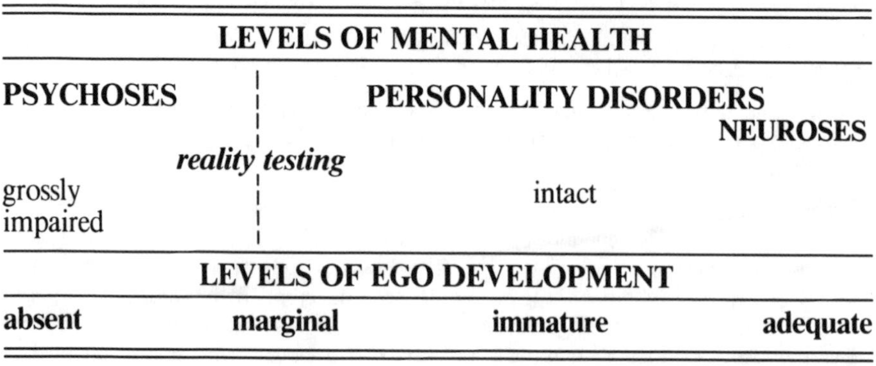

LEVELS OF MENTAL HEALTH			
PSYCHOSES	**PERSONALITY DISORDERS**		**NEUROSES**
reality testing			
grossly impaired	intact		
LEVELS OF EGO DEVELOPMENT			
absent	**marginal**	**immature**	**adequate**

Figure 1. Major classes of mental disorders *(DSM-III)* and their relationship to levels of ego development.

Falling somewhere on the continuum between the psychoses and the neuroses (according to the model) are what *DSM-III* calls the personality disorders (Figure 1). Personality disorders are discontinuous with psychotic disorders because reality testing is largely intact (with the possible exception of more severe borderline pathology). They overlap to some extent with the neuroses, but have certain distinguishing features. Social and occupational functioning tends to be more grossly impaired in individuals with personality disorders than in those with a neurotic level of ego development. Many (although not all) individuals with deeply ingrained, maladaptive personality traits do not experience their symptoms as ego-dystonic. While they may or may not be distressed by their behavior, their capacity for insight into the role they play in their problems tends to be limited. Social and self-awareness, in general, are significantly impaired in persons with characterological problems. Simply stated, these individuals are characterized by a level of ego development that I refer to as "immature" (Figure 1).

In contrast, the level of ego development found in individuals with neurotic disorders is generally "adequate" (Figure 1); these people share certain essential psychological capacities with more normal individuals. Social and self-awareness are adequately developed. Persons with neurotic disorders are capable of a sense of personal responsibility for their behavior, and a concern for the opinions and feelings of others. As a consequence, they generally experience guilt and shame about their symptoms and maladaptive behaviors. Finally, the neurotic employs essentially the same types of defenses as the normal individual, only in more chronic and symptomatic forms. In personality disorders, defenses tend to be more exaggerated and inflexible, and are more often associated with overt, maladaptive behaviors.

PTSD IN RELATION TO PRE-EXISTING PERSONALITY

Where does PTSD fit within the model of psychological development disorders described above? Let us look first at individuals with essentially normal pre-trauma personalities. Exposed to a "psychologically traumatic event outside the range of usual human experience ....most people" will develop PTSD (APA, 1980, p. 236). In its acute stage (up to 6 months), PTSD is a natural recovery process, a normal reaction to an abnormal event. Whether PTSD develops into a chronic disorder depends upon a complex interaction of factors, pre-existing psychopathology being only one of them. The University of Cincinnati Traumatic Stress Study Center has identified "factors on three planes—traumatic stressor, personality, and social and environmental support—[which] interplay in complex ways over time in the development of post-traumatic stress disorder" (Lindy, Grace & Green, 1984, p. 45).

In its chronic (and delayed) forms, PTSD has all of the hallmarks of a "neurotic process" (APA, 1980). Thus, in persons without any serious pre-existing mental disorders, PTSD can be thought of as a "reactive neurosis" arising out of an actual traumatic event itself rather than childhood (unless, of course, the trauma occurred in childhood). Clearly, then, in cases where a traumatized person's pre-existing personality structure was normal or only mildly neurotic, the primary diagnosis will be PTSD. By "primary diagnosis" I simply mean the mental disorder that should be the primary focus of treatment. The importance of this distinction will become clearer in subsequent sections. The point I wish to make here is that individuals with a primary diagnosis of PTSD can have unresolved developmental issues, but the primary source of their symptoms, and their distress, is the painful recollection of the traumatic event.

My experience has been that individuals with significant pre-existing neurotic conflicts also display classic PTSD symptoms, but ones that take on added meanings in relation to their pre-trauma conflicts. These conflicts are usually exacerbated by the PTSD, and frequently remain unresolved, even after the PTSD symptoms have been successfully treated. For such cases, traditional psychotherapeutic treatment is often indicated. Because these individuals are functioning at the neurotic level, however, they are appropriate candidates for treatment for their PTSD as well.

The critical dividing line, in terms of differential diagnosis, comes with cases in which the pre-existing personality of the individual lies somewhere on the continuum between the psychoses and the severe neuroses (which are almost indistinguishable from personality disorders). While almost anyone exposed to a traumatic stressor will develop "significant symptoms of distress," the dynamics of the resulting disturbances are likely to be significantly different in individuals who have not attained at least a neurotic level of ego development. In such cases, PTSD may or may not constitute the primary diagnosis. In any event, the therapist should expect these individuals to pose significant treatment problems over and above the PTSD symptomatology. This is particularly likely because, as Scurfield (1985) points out, PTSD commonly exacerbates pre-existing, maladaptive personality traits.

PTSD AS A PRIMARY DIAGNOSIS

In individuals with a primary diagnosis of PTSD, the dynamics of the disorder can be understood in terms of two main factors: the intrusion of painful, unacceptable recollections of the actual events of the trauma, and the characteristic defenses that the person develops to ward off these recollections. Recollections can take a number of forms; the most common are: (1) intrusive thoughts, during which the person involuntarily re-experiences the traumatic event, or thoughts related to it, and (2) nightmares, in which the events of the trauma are re-experienced, often in vivid detail. The pattern of nightmares tends to be episodic, showing a sharp increase during times of stress or the approaching anniversary of the traumatic event. A characteristic pattern of sleep disturbance nearly always follows psychological traumatization, even if the individual does not report having nightmares. The pattern manifests as a difficulty in going to sleep initially, and remaining asleep thereafter. It is not unusual for the individual to use alcohol or drugs as a means of "self-medicating" for the sleep disturbance. This is dangerous, since there is frequently a "rebound effect" in which nightmares become even more intense.

Intrusive recollections are less predictable than nightmares, partly because environmental stimuli are as likely to trigger them as are internal states of mind. Intrusive recollections are generally of brief duration, and in most cases the person remains in touch with reality. More prolonged dissociative states, commonly referred to as "flashbacks," are generally symptomatic of more severe forms of traumatization (e.g., physical brutalization, torture, incest), and the likelihood of flashbacks is greater in cases where substance abuse is present. Regardless of the particular circumstances, dissociative flashbacks should be considered as symptomatic of a serious PTSD-related condition.

Intrusive symptoms can also manifest behaviorally. Trauma victims inevitably experience waves of powerful emotions when remembering or dreaming about the event. To cope with their anxiety around re-experiencing the trauma, these individuals often become "counter-phobic" in an effort to avoid any situations that might remind them of the traumatic event. In individuals with chronic PTSD, such counter-phobic behaviors develop into a generalized withdrawal from, and diminished responsiveness to their environment (APA, 1980). Conversely, the person may actively seek out situations similar to that which led to the trauma. We frequently see this pattern in Vietnam veterans: an ex-infantryman will join a

SWAT team; a nurse will take a job in the emergency room of a busy inner-city hospital. While there is some element of conscious choice in these behaviors, in individuals with PTSD there is generally a strong unconscious component maintained by the person's need to defend against anxieties or guilt feelings associated with the traumatic event.

The symptoms highlighted above are connected with what Horowitz (1979) calls the "intrusive/repetitive phase" of PTSD. These symptoms may or may not be apparent in the initial assessment. Most acutely traumatized persons have a strong need to talk about the traumatic event. The emotions expressed at such times, however, vary considerably from individual to individual, as well as over time. Burgess and Holmstrom (1974), for example, interviewed 146 women immediately following rape, and reported that:

> The women may experience an extremely wide range of emotions. The impact of the rape may be so severe that feelings of shock or disbelief are expressed. When interviewed within a few hours of the rape, the women in this study mainly showed two emotional styles: the expressed style, in which feelings of fear, anger, and anxiety were shown through such behaviors as crying, sobbing, smiling, restlessness, and tenseness; and the controlled style, in which feelings were masked or hidden and a calm, composed, or subdued affect was seen. A fairly equal number of women showed each style. (p. 982)

The Burgess and Holmstom (1974) study also found that a significant proportion of the women had not told anyone about the incident up to that point. In interviewing these nonrevealing women, the authors found that a number of them "had been raped or molested at a previous time, often when they were children or adolescents" (p. 985). This finding points to the importance of asking about previous history of traumatization when interviewing individuals suspected of having PTSD.

In more chronic or compounded cases of PTSD, it is not unusual for the individuals to present with only the defensive symptoms characteristic of the "avoidance/denial phase" (Horowitz, 1979) of this disorder. Characteristically, they will deny or downplay any connection between the traumatic event and their present problems, sometimes in the face of obvious evidence (e.g., repeated avoidance of, or depressive or angry reactions to stimuli that remind them of the trauma). Even if they do admit to a connection, they may steadfastly maintain that "talking about it can't change anything." If the traumatic event is brought up, the person either talks in vague generalities or describes what happened with a complete absence of emotion. More often than not, the person will come in for treatment as a last resort, and only after considerable pressure has been brought by a family member or employer to seek help.

While denial, avoidance, and a general numbing of emotional responsiveness are characteristic symptoms of this disorder, the clinician must keep in mind that persons with a primary diagnosis of PTSD have a relatively healthy character structure. These individuals (in contrast to those with pre-existing characterological disorders) are capable of insight into their own maladaptive behavior. They generally accept responsibility for this behavior, and are genuinely distressed by it. Although they view their PTSD symptoms as irrational and ego-alien, they tend to blame themselves for being the way they are.

Guilt is a central issue for nearly all trauma victims with a primary PTSD diagnosis. It is strongly experienced by them precisely because of their acceptance of individual culpability and their pre-existing capacity for emotional bonding. Individuals with primary PTSD inevitably blame themselves to some degree for "allowing" the trauma to happen ("If only I'd...."). This irrational self-blame (which, unfortunately, is often reinforced by our cultural prejudices to see victims as somehow "tainted") can be particularly severe in PTSD victims who witnessed the death or disfigurement of others. It has been described extensively in the literature on Vietnam veterans, holocaust survivors, and other victims of mass traumatization as survivor guilt, or, "Why was I spared when others were not?" Such unresolved guilt feelings are frequently a factor in the depressive symptoms that are an associated feature of PTSD (see T. Williams, this volume).

A final symptom that is helpful in the differential diagnosis of PTSD is fear of loss of control. Most individuals with PTSD fear being overwhelmed by the powerful images, emotions, and impulses evoked by the traumatic event (even though they may not connect these fears with the trauma). Because individuals with a primary diagnosis of PTSD tend to view themselves as responsible for their thoughts and actions, they find these autonomous impulses and emotions (e.g., violent urges for revenge, returning feelings of helplessness as a victim, rage at the injustices of life) particularly disturbing. To ward off these unacceptable impulses and thoughts, these individuals frequently develop maladaptive, "over-controlled" patterns of behavior designed to "protect" themselves and others. In suppressing the urges and emotions connected with the trauma, the victim tends to suppress all forms of affect. Thus, when these powerful emotions finally are expressed, they tend to be explosive and out of character. Sadly, such "outbursts" (particularly if they persist beyond a few months) are frequently interpreted by the individuals themselves and those around them as evidence of deep-seated psychopathology. In fact, instances of such behavior in persons with a primary PTSD diagnosis are *generally infrequent* and when they do occur create intense feelings of guilt and shame. Moreover, such behaviors usually cease as soon as the underlying PTSD symptoms begin to be addressed. If they do not, then it is highly likely that complicating diagnostic issues exist.

Up to this point, this chapter has been concerned with how PTSD presents as a primary diagnosis. Diagnosis, for the clinician, is a useful tool only to the extent that it aids in deciding upon appropriate treatment interventions. By this criterion, a person with a primary diagnosis of PTSD is someone who needs treatment, first and foremost, for traumatic stress. Treating such a person for depression or a traditional neurosis avoids the central issues that the therapy should be addressing, and thus does little to relieve core symptoms.

PTSD, however, does not occur in a vacuum. Every traumatized individual has a "pre-trauma personality," whether healthy or otherwise. PTSD is frequently seen in otherwise normal individuals, but of course people with pre-existing mental disorders are at risk for traumatization as well, and their pre-trauma disorders can greatly complicate diagnosis and treatment. Thus, the issues of differential diagnosis, with which the remainder of this chapter will be concerned, are crucial in the treatment of PTSD.

PTSD AND SUBSTANCE ABUSE

Substance abuse is probably the single most common factor complicating the diagnosis of PTSD (see Jelinek and Williams, this volume). Drugs and alcohol are widely used in this society to seek relief from physical and psychological distress. Since levels of such distress are generally high in traumatized persons, substance abuse is commonly encountered in treating PTSD. Certain traumatized populations appear to be at high risk for substance abuse. Agosta (1985) has found this to be true in her clinical experience with incest victims. A high percentage of the Vietnam veterans seen at the Vet Center have some history of substance abuse.

Drugs and alcohol were readily available in Vietnam and were generally sanctioned as a means of coping with the boredom and terror experienced in war. Upon their return, significant numbers of veterans turned to drugs and alcohol as a way of dealing with the stresses of transition to civilian life, and to numb the feelings of low self-esteem and alienation brought on by a society that basically spurned them. Most of the veterans we see have stopped using hard drugs, of their own volition, before presenting at the Vet Center. Many, however, continue to use alcohol as a maladaptive way of dealing with their PTSD symptoms. In dealing with this group of veterans, we have found that it is absolutely crucial that an accurate differential diagnosis be made between individuals with a primary diagnosis of PTSD and those with a primary substance use disorder (APA, 1980). I expect that this diagnostic issue is important to the effective treatment of other classes of trauma victims as well.

Therapists who regularly deal with veterans with PTSD frequently refer to the tendency of these individuals to "self-medicate." To the clinician trained in the treatment of substance abuse, this term may appear as an ingenuous excuse for not dealing with the patient's real problem—and it can be just that. But wide clinical experience indicates that many veterans with PTSD, who also abuse alcohol, do not fit the diagnosis of substance use disorder (Jelinek and Williams, 1984). I expect that this statement applies to many veterans with drug abuse problems as well. Such cases present additional complications, however, and for this reason, the discussion that follows will be restricted to alcohol abuse.

It is not always easy to differentiate between self-medicating veterans and those with a primary substance use disorder, but there do appear to be certain distinctive diagnostic features. "Self-medicating" veterans are usually episodic rather than habitual drinkers. Their episodes of drinking tend to coincide with stressful periods when intrusive thoughts are more frequent and intense. They drink to "numb out," to forget, to get some relief from painful memories and sleepless nights. They seldom drink to have a good time or "let off steam." Indeed, they often report distressing intrusive imagery associated with their drinking, or a loss of their usual control over their trauma-related emotions and impulses. Unlike many alcoholics, they tend to prefer drinking by themselves (or only with another veteran). They are not "social drinkers."

During my initial session with a veteran, I always ask about substance use. If it is a problem, the PTSD veteran will generally acknowledge such. When I explain that the use of alcohol or drugs, while it may have brought some relief from PTSD symptoms in the beginning, is now just making things worse, the veteran usually agrees. When I point out that he/she uses alcohol to avoid dealing with the painful recollections of Vietnam, and make it clear that this pattern will have to stop if treatment is to be beneficial, the veteran usually indicates a willingness to "give it a try." The first time I employed this direct approach (suggested by a clinical supervisor), I was somewhat amazed at how readily the veteran accepted what I said. I have since come to realize that these veterans long ago acknowledged to themselves the futility of treating their PTSD with alcohol or drugs, but have persisted because no one had offered them a viable alternative. Agosta (1985) has noted very similar responses in rape victims and battered women who "self-medicate," and has observed that crime victims with a primary diagnosis of PTSD "are seeking relief from their pain, and want alternatives."

Individuals with a primary substance use disorder present an entirely different picture. They often come to the session intoxicated. Suggestions of an abuse problem are deflected or denied. Even if they agree that alcohol or drugs are a problem, they will maintain that they "can stop any time," and that their "real problems" are caused by others. In exploring their history of abuse, veterans with this diagnosis tend to report a pattern of heavy use of alcohol and/or drugs beginning shortly after their arrival in Vietnam. Some have a pre-service history of drinking problems, or one of their parents was an alcoholic. What one picks up in interviewing the veteran with a primary substance use disorder is a chronic pattern of excessive use of alcohol or drugs, not just to numb out Vietnam, but the general problems of life as well.

The treatment approach we use with the "self-medicator" is completely different from that employed with a veteran with a diagnoseable substance use disorder. If the primary diagnosis is PTSD, and substance abuse is secondary, then the veteran is treated for PTSD. After an initial two to three sessions to determine this and prepare the veteran for the next phase, he/she is encouraged to join a therapy group in which the primary focus is on PTSD. Our experience with this is similar to that reported by Jelinek and Williams (1984): "As PTSD symptomatology decreases in intensity and frequency, we have found that many combat veterans reduce or eliminate alcohol consumption" (p. 94). The therapist needs to monitor such persons for lapses, and if a continuing pattern of using alcohol to avoid painful issues persists, the veteran must be confronted with the need to become involved in an alcohol treatment program.

For veterans with a clear substance use disorder, and a secondary diagnosis of PTSD, the alcohol or drug problem *must* be addressed first. These veterans cannot benefit from a PTSD group, and assuming they do not drop out early on, are likely to seriously undermine the efforts of other group members to come to grips with their treatment issues. I explain to these veterans that we are willing to work with them on their PTSD issues, but only *after* they have become abstinent. I strongly encourage them to become involved in some kind of established treatment program (including Alcoholics or Narcotics Anonymous) and, if they accept my recommendation, aid them in finding a suitable program.

Once these veterans have come to grips with their abuse problem, treatment for PTSD becomes possible, although the therapist should keep in mind that these individuals, as "recovering abusers," will often be more difficult to treat than veterans with a single diagnosis of PTSD. Substance use disorders, while a separate diagnostic category in *DSM-III* (APA, 1980), share many similarities with personality disorders in which "inflexible and maladaptive personality traits" tend to be ingrained and difficult for the person to modify, "despite great effort" (APA, 1980). Substance use disorders, of course, are commonly encountered in combination with personality disorders.

PTSD AND PERSONALITY DISORDERS

Veterans with a primary diagnosis of PTSD are frequently misdiagnosed by inexperienced clinicians as having personality disorders. Since more than a decade has passed since the Vietnam veteran's traumatic period, both the veteran and the therapist often fail to see any connection between Vietnam and current problems. The irritability and guardedness common to veterans with this disorder also make it easy to overlook the underlying traumatic symptoms. Misdiagnosis precludes effective treatment, since the *central* issue does not lie in the veteran's early emotional development or in current maladaptive behaviors, but rather in the issues surrounding the traumatic event. Even in cases where a secondary diagnosis of personality disorder is justified, failure to address the veteran's PTSD issues is likely to lead to treatment failure. Agosta (1985) and Bowman (1985) have reported similar diagnostic issues with victims of child abuse who are often unconscious of or extremely reluctant to talk about the childhood trauma.

The lasting negative impact that traumatic experiences can have on almost anyone is only just beginning to be accepted by our profession. Much of the resistance to such acceptance stems from the traditional emphasis on the influence of early childhood development in the etiology of mental disorders. For those of us who work intensively with Vietnam veterans, however, a sort of "counter-bias" can develop. We have a strong desire to establish that Vietnam veterans who have chronic PTSD need not be "predisposed" to developing the disorder, and consequently sometimes lose sight of the fact that *every* veteran brings a "predisposing personality" into treatment. As Hedlin *et al.* (1981, 1983) point out, every traumatic event is interpreted within the personal context of the veteran's previous life experiences, whether these have been pathogenic or not. The authors give an excellent example of two veterans with PTSD, and nearly identical traumatic experiences, but markedly differing treatment issues. They note that one of the veterans "would probably not have developed serious problems as an adult had [he] not been in combat," while the second veteran "would likely have had difficulties...whether or not he went to Vietnam..." (Hedlin *et al.*, 1983, p. 531). The first veteran had a primary diagnosis of PTSD, the second, pre-service conflicts that interacted with the traumatic event in a pathological manner. Failure to recognize such complicating factors, particularly if they are serious enough to warrant a diagnosis of personality disorder (APA, 1980), is the single most common cause of treatment failure in the Vet Centers.

The differential diagnosis of personality disorders in veterans who have been exposed to combat is not easy, even for the experienced therapist. For one thing, the symptoms of PTSD and personality disorders are often both present in bewildering combinations. Since nearly every Vietnam veteran with PTSD has suffered from the disorder for 10 to 15 years, the chronic, maladaptive personality structures many of them present could reasonably be attributed to factors and experiences that occurred some time after the precipitating event (as opposed to events preceding the trauma or the trauma itself).

This diagnostic dilemma exists for nonveteran populations as well. In adults who were victims of child abuse, molestation, or incest, it is often difficult or impossible in the early stages of treatment to differentiate between PTSD-related symptoms and maladaptive personality traits. One reason for this, as Scurfield (1985) has noted, is that traumatization can result in the "aggravation" or significant deterioration "beyond natural progression" of pre-existing character problems. Another is the extreme guardedness and fear of "revealing the secret" that is seen in child abuse victims (Agosta, 1985; Bowman, 1985).

For Vietnam veterans, a thorough knowledge of the veteran's pre-service history is essential to making an accurate differential diagnosis. A history of severe family problems, repeated difficulties in school, and/or serious delinquent behaviors is probably the best single predictor of a pre-existing personality disorder. If a veteran reports serious or chronic disciplinary problems in the service, *before* any exposure to combat, this should be considered as indicative of pre-existing characterological problems. Be sure that you also ask about any traumatic experiences *predating* Vietnam. In a veteran with a pre-service history of sexual molestation or child abuse, the earlier trauma is often a more central treatment issue than what occurred in Vietnam (although this may only become apparent later in treatment). A clinical finding that has been confirmed for me again and again is that in individuals who have been previously traumatized, subsequent traumatization inevitably leads to the re-emergence of images and issues of the original trauma.

Veterans with clear characterological problems present themselves very differently from veterans with a primary diagnosis of PTSD. A subgroup of this first type of veteran, frequently encountered at Vet Centers, is described by Merback (1984). These veterans often actively seek treatment for their "PTSD." Unlike veterans with a primary diagnosis of PTSD, who generally blame themselves for their maladaptive behaviors, these veterans use their PTSD symptoms as a justification for acting as they do. They tend to seek advantage through their disorder. Typically, their angry feelings (shared by nearly all Vietnam veterans) are externalized and expressed with little concern for their effects on others. This subgroup does not manifest the "fear of loss of control" commonly seen in veterans with a primary diagnosis of PTSD. Angry and aggressive impulses tend to be experienced by them as ego-syntonic.

In more extreme cases, this lack of concern for others merits a primary diagnosis of antisocial personality (APA, 1980). This diagnosis should only be given, however, in cases where there is a clear history of antisocial behavior dating from before traumatization. Antisocial personalities do display such PTSD symptoms as nightmares and flashbacks. A distinguishing feature of such individuals is that the intrusive imagery is almost always associated with threats to themselves, rather than with concerns about others.

The subgroup of veterans described by Merback (1984) is the most typical, but hardly the only form of personality disorder seen at the Vet Centers. The classification of personality disorders presented in *DSM-III* includes a variety of diagnoses ranging from borderline to narcissistic, compulsive to histrionic, schizoid to paranoid. Any of these diagnoses may be encountered at a Vet Center. Scurfield (1985) notes a distinction that can be helpful (although not sufficient) in differentiating PTSD from borderline disorders: the veteran's needs for social interaction. PTSD veterans commonly show an aversion to social contacts while borderlines generally have a strong fear of being alone. This difference may stem from the fact that in Vietnam veterans with primary PTSD we are dealing with a "reactive neurosis of adult life," whereas in the borderline personality the etiology of the disorder lies in childhood.

Personality disorders are difficult to treat, and where there is no clear connection between the veteran's presenting problems and his or her Vietnam experiences, it is probably best to refer the individual to a practitioner with some expertise in treating the primary personality disorder. Even in those cases where PTSD is a secondary diagnosis, it is unlikely that veterans with serious personality disorders will gain any lasting benefit from therapy in which PTSD is the primary focus, and their behaviors can seriously undermine the progress of a PTSD group.

What I have said about personality disorders thus far is not meant to support the common prejudice that anyone with such a diagnosis is untreatable. At the Vet Center, we work with individuals with mixed PTSD and personality diagnoses all the time. They are found in every group we lead. They often benefit from being in treatment with veterans with healthier pre-service personalities; sometimes they do not. In rare instances, we ask them to leave a group because of their disruptive influence; more often, they drop out of their own accord. In cases where such veterans receive little or no benefit from group treatment, the therapist has frequently failed to realize that character pathology (or an earlier trauma), not Vietnam, is the primary issue.

The approach I have found to be most effective with veterans with personality traits like those described by Merback (1984) is a "reality-based therapy." Table 1 lists common interventions used with this approach: limit-setting, focusing on present-day problems, increasing the veteran's sense of responsibility for his actions, etc. In the left-hand column of the table is another list of interventions effective in treating veterans with a primary diagnosis of PTSD. Since many veterans need treatment for both PTSD and characterological problems, the therapist must be able to switch back and forth between treatment interventions as the circumstances dictate.

Table 1. Treatment Interventions: PTSD versus Personality Disorders.

PTSD	PERSONALITY DISORDERS
- educate veteran about nature of PTSD	- help vets see current self-defeating behaviors
- encourage expression of frozen emotions: anger, grief, caring, empathy	- establish limits around externalization of anger and acting-out behaviors
- help reduce irrational guilt around trauma	- help increase sense of responsibility for actions
- encourage discussion of broader context of Vietnam War	- emphasize impact of their behavior on others

(after Merback, 1984)

PTSD AND SEVERE PSYCHIATRIC DISORDERS

The severity of the symptoms of PTSD ranges across a broad continuum. For some, the symptoms are manifest only as occasional, painful remembrances in an otherwise normal life; for others, the trauma seems to have been a shattering experience from which they are likely never to recover. The considerable range of severity in traumatic events themselves partially explains this phenomenon. *DSM-III* notes that, "Some stessors frequently produce the disorder (e.g., torture) and others produce it only occasionally (e.g., car accidents)" (APA, 1980, p. 236). Yet the nature of the original trauma is only one factor among several in determining how severe the subsequent disorder will be. As Card (1983) summarizes in her review of earlier research (Kadushin, Boulanger & Martin, 1981; Laufer *et al.*, 1981) on the sociological context of readjustment problems in Vietnam veterans:

> Minority status, low educational attainment, low income, and irregular or unsatisfying employment were associated with higher levels of stress. These negative associations were reduced or eliminated (1) for those veterans who fought in the early (pre-1968) years of the war, before public support for the conflict disappeared, (2) for combat veterans who received positive social support from their spouse upon return from military service, (3) for combat veterans who came from stable families of origin, (4) for veterans in large cities who had many Vietnam veteran friends, and (5) for veterans in smaller cities and towns with friends who formed a community, each knowing one another. (p. 94)

Clearly, "levels of stress" in veterans with PTSD depend upon a complex interaction among pre- and post-trauma factors, and the trauma itself. Some of those factors relate to traditional indicators of psychopathology (e.g., family of origin), while others can only be described as sociological (e.g., public support). As a more concrete example of the latter, I have treated dozens of veterans for whom the "homecoming" they received from anti-war protestors upon their return from Vietnam was a major factor in their subsequent "reduced involvement with the external world" (APA, 1980, p. 237). Symonds (1980) has noted a similar phenomenon in victims of violent crime whose distress is made light of, or negatively interpreted, by a responding professional or family member; Symonds calls this the "second injury." In my experience, an unsupportive post-trauma environment is one of the most critical factors in exacerbating acute PTSD so that it becomes a chronic disorder (see Agosta and McHugh, "Sexual Assault," this volume).

Severe cases of PTSD nearly always involve a combination of unfavorable stress factors. Generally, the veterans we see with severe PTSD have a poor history of familial support (parents/siblings and/or spouse) both before and after their Vietnam service. Often, the traumatic events that trouble them the most involve excruciating moral dilemmas. For example, one of the most severe cases of PTSD I have seen involved a veteran who intentionally shot and killed a fellow soldier who abandoned his position during a firefight. This veteran had severe memory and concentration problems, and a history of self-destructive behavior, but despite his being flooded by anxiety and guilt around the traumatic event, he showed no symptoms of psychosis.

Vietnam veterans with primary psychotic disorders seldom present at the Vet Center, and if they do, are generally referred to a VA medical center or public mental health facility for treatment. More frequently, combat veterans who have been misdiagnosed as having a psychotic disorder (most commonly paranoid or paranoid schizophrenic) are referred to the Vet Center (Domash and Sparr, 1982). Many of these combat veterans are actually a mixed diagnosis of severe personality disorder and PTSD. Occasionally, we see veterans who would appear to have developed a reactive "psychosis-like" condition as a result of their experiences in Vietnam. In most of these cases, however, the precipitating factor appeared to be high levels of *chronic* life-threatening stress (e.g., four years of duty on the flight deck of an aircraft carrier) rather than a particular traumatic event.

POWs, who have nearly always been systematically abused or tortured, can be misdiagnosed as being psychotic while in the acute or delayed stages of PTSD. Prolonged and degrading traumatization can cause severe depressive episodes that look like a major depression (APA, 1980). POWs are also at risk for severe flashbacks that superficially resemble psychotic hallucinations. These flashbacks, however, are inevitably connected with the POW's incarceration. For example, I treated a Korean War POW whose delayed PTSD began with his hearing everyone at a meeting speaking in Korean. This disturbing experience happened some 30 years after he had been repatriated, and had lead to his steady withdrawal from what, up to then, had been a highly successful business career.

Our experience has been that individuals who develop classic schizophrenic symptoms following service in Vietnam most likely suffered from a significant pre-existing personality disorder (probably schizoid or paranoid). It is important, diagnostically, to differentiate between veterans with these reactive or latent psychoses and severe cases of PTSD (although the prospects for treatment are generally poor for both disorders). Severe PTSD can be every bit as debilitating as a psychosis, but the symptoms are distinctive. As would be expected, overwhelming anxiety is the most prominent feature of veterans with severe PTSD. The anxiety is often accompanied by equally overwhelming feelings of guilt about one or more traumatic incidents. Multiple somatic complaints are common (often related to actual war wounds). These veterans have few psychological defenses against intrusive images and emotions. They often have a history of multiple drug use, both prescription and nonprescription. Suicide attempts, self-destructive behavior, and/or serious accidents are common, and severe memory and concentration problems are frequently present. While it is likely that many of these veterans had adjustment problems pre-dating Vietnam, such problems pale in comparison with the irrefutable symptoms of PTSD.

As noted above in the example of the Korean War POW, dissociative states are common in veterans with severe PTSD. The Veteran often seems preoccupied with internal imagery or thoughts; some report hearing voices. These symptoms resemble those of classic schizophrenia, but differ in one very important respect: the disturbing intrusive images and thoughts are all connected with the traumatic event (or events—these individuals have frequently been multiply traumatized). As another example, I recently saw a veteran who reported hearing persecutory voices. When I asked whether he could identify any of the voices, he said that the main one belonged to a good friend who died in a fire-fight and was calling the veteran to "come join us." Severe PTSD differs from classic schizophrenia in other important respects. While memory and concentration problems are common, *the bizarre symbolic images and thought processes characteristic of schizophrenia are absent in PTSD veterans.* The schizophrenic often presents as a person who has taken refuge in a fantasy world of his or her own making. The veteran with severe PTSD acts more like the victim of an unrelenting nightmare.

Severe PTSD usually needs to be treated, at least initially, in an inpatient setting. Veterans with severe stress disorders are frequently impulsive, self-destructive, and/or addicted to one or more substances. After stabilization and detoxification, they may be prepared for one of the growing number of Veterans Administration inpatient treatment programs specifically for Vietnam veterans. The prognosis for these veterans is guarded; many make great progress while in the inpatient program, but rapidly deteriorate when they return to their previous maladaptive support system. Coordinated outpatient follow-up, preferably through a Vet Center (or a contract provider designated by the Vet Center) is vital if the veteran is to make a successful re-entry into the community. While many claims have been made for the short-term alleviation of PTSD symptoms in Vietnam veterans, our experience has been that PTSD is a *chronic* disorder; in all but the most favorable cases, it requires longer term treatment (a year or more). As I frequently say to a veteran in the initial interview, "It has taken ten years for things to get where they are, so you have to expect that it's going to take some time before things begin to get better."

DIAGNOSIS AND TREATMENT: SOME FINAL OBSERVATIONS

Having argued the importance of differential diagnosis in the treatment of PTSD for the past several pages, I need to make a few comments about the limitations of this approach. Diagnosis in psychiatry is a very imperfect science with a very limited range of usefulness. Like a powerful drug, it is best used sparingly and only when it clearly benefits the patient. Diagnosis does not lead to cure, and where improperly applied can actually interfere with the person's getting better. Initial diagnoses are frequently incorrect or incomplete, and, even when accurate, provide us with little more than a first approximation, a rough guide, to treatment decisions. A diagnosis should not be thought of as an answer to a problem, but rather as an *hypothesis* to be tested and revised where indicated. It should assume increasingly less importance in therapy as the work proceeds. In our profession, we treat fellow human beings, not symptoms.

NOTE

1. In a memo dated September 12, 1986, members of the American Psychiatric Association's Advisory Committee on Post-traumatic Stress Disorder were asked to review the final proposed criteria for PTSD as they will appear in the revised *DSM-III*. These criteria are reprinted in fully in Appendix A to this book.

REFERENCES

Agosta, C. (1985, November). Personal correspondence.

American Psychiatric Association. (1980). *Diagnostic and statistical manual of mental disorders* (3rd ed.). Washington, DC: American Psychiatric Press.

Burgess, Ann W. and Holmstrom, Linda Lytle. (1974). Rape trauma syndrome. *American Journal of Psychiatry, 131* (9).

Card, J. J. (1983). *Lives after Vietnam: The personal impact of military service.* Lexington, MA: Lexington Books.

Domash, M.D., & Sparr, L.F. (1982, September). Post-traumatic stress disorder masquerading as paranoid schizophrenia: A case report. *Military Medicine, 147.*

Figley, C. R. (1985). *Trauma and its wake.* New York: Brunner/Mazel.

Hedlin, H., Pollinger Haas, A., Singer, P., & Ulman, R. (1981). Meanings of combat and the development of post-traumatic stress disorder. *American Journal of Psychiatry, 138,* 1490-1493.

Horowitz, M. J. (1979). Psychological response to serious life events. In V. Hamilton & D. Warburton (Eds.), *Human stress and cognition: An information processing approach.* New York: Wiley and Sons.

Jelinek J. M., & Williams, T. (1984). Post-traumatic stress disorder and substance abuse in Vietnam combat veterans: Treatment problems, strategies and recommendations. *Journal of Substance Abuse Treatment, 1,* 87-97.

Kadushin, C., Boulanger, G., & Martin, J. (1981). *Long-term stress reactions: Some causes, consequences and naturally occurring support systems.* Vol. 4 of *Legacies of Vietnam: Comparative adjustment of veterans and their peers.* Washington, DC: Government Printing Office.

Laufer, R. S., Yager, T., Frey-Wouters, E., Donnellan, J., Gallops, M., & Stenbeck, J. (1981). *Post-war trauma: Social and psychological problems of Vietnam veterans in the aftermath of the Vietnam war.* Vol. 3 of *Legacies of Vietnam: Comparative adjustment of veterans and their peers.* Washington, D.C.: Government Printing Office.

Lindy, Jacob D., Grace, Mary C., and Green, Bonnie L. (1984). Building a conceptual bridge between civilian trauma and war trauma: Preliminary findings from a clinical sample of Vietnam veterans. In Van Der Kolk, Bessel A. (Ed.), *Post-traumatic stress disorder: Psychological and Biological Sequelae.* Washington, D.C.: American Psychiatric Press.

Merback, K. (1984, August). A vet center dilemma: Post-traumatic stress disorder and personality disorders. *Vet Center Voice Newsletter,* p. 7.

Scurfield, R. M. (1985). Post-trauma stress assessment and treatment: Overview and formulations. In C. R. Figley (Ed.), *Trauma and its wake.* New York: Brunner/Mazel.

Symonds, M. (1980). The second injury to victims of violent crime. *Evaluation and change.*

Trigos, G. (1983, November/December). The influence of precombat personality on post-traumatic stress disorder. *Comprehensive Psychiatry, 24,* 530-534.

Van Der Kolk, Bessel A. (Ed.) (1984). *Post-traumatic stress disorder: Psychological and Biological Sequelae.* Washington, D.C.: American Psychiatric Press.

CHAPTER THREE

POST-TRAUMATIC STRESS DISORDER IN FORMER POWS

Ron Langer

INTRODUCTION

In the summer of 1983, while working in the psychiatric emergency room and the outpatient psychiatry clinic of the VA Medical Center in Denver, I began to notice a significant number of World War II combat veterans who were manifesting symptoms of post-traumatic stress disorder (PTSD). Some of these veterans had been chronically symptomatic. Others had displayed brief periods of symptoms shortly after the war, but began developing symptoms again in their late 50s and early 60s. I hypothesized that the exacerbation of PTSD symptoms was due to the various losses these veterans were currently experiencing: e.g., retirement, deterioration of physical health, deaths of contemporaries, and loss of previous physical and sometimes mental abilities.

Aware of the success of group treatment of Vietnam veterans with PTSD, I began talking with other psychiatric staff about a therapy group for World War II combat veterans with PTSD. Another therapist at the clinic, Cynthia Ochs, expressed interest in being co-therapist for such a group. When I mentioned the group to Steve Oboler, who wrote another chapter in this book, he described to me the exPOW protocol evaluation program he was coordinating and noted that he was identifying many exPOWs not currently in psychiatric treatment who could benefit from the program. Dr. Ochs and I then decided to do a therapy group exclusively for World War II exPOWs.

In December 1983, we began a weekly, one-hour psychotherapy group with five exPOWs from both the European and the Pacific Theaters. The group has now been in existence for over two years. During this time, we have added six members, and one of the original members has discontinued. During this two-year period, I have evaluated perhaps a dozen other exPOWs who were either not interested in or not appropriate for the group. I see approximately half of these in individual psychotherapy at frequencies ranging from once a week to once every few months. We have also run a time-limited (six months) support group for wives of exPOWs, with the primary purposes of education and helping the women develop a mutual support system (see C. Williams, "Women Partners," this volume).

COMMON FEATURES OF PTSD AMONG FORMER POWS

I have come to understand the PTSD syndrome among exPOWs as a result of the traumas they experienced and their attempt to adapt to and/or master these catastrophic experiences. This section will review some of the more prominent features I have noted among exPOWs, and will attempt to clarify my belief that these symptoms are the result of the POW experience and are an effort to adapt to and overcome the traumas.

How many of these exPOWs actually have PTSD? From Oboler's figures (this volume), we see that only 28 percent of Pacific Theater and 11 percent of European Theater exPOWs were diagnosed with PTSD on their exPOW protocol examinations; 82 percent of the former, and 60 percent of the latter received some psychiatric diagnoses. It is my impression, however, that the number of exPOWs with PTSD is far greater than this, and that some of these exPOWs who received other psychiatric diagnoses actually have PTSD. Whether this is true or not may be a question of semantics. What is undeniable, though, is the great frequency with which features of PTSD occur among this population.

PTSD is a diagnosis that is difficult to make, and one that is often missed. It is a new diagnosis (officially recognized in 1980), and its existence is controversial, especially among older clinicians. It is often confused with character disorders, on which it is sometimes an overlay. It is difficult to differentiate from dysthymic disorder and various anxiety disorders. In some cases, it is only after a significant period of evaluation and/or treatment that PTSD can be differentiated from character disorders, affective disorders, and other anxiety disorders. When PTSD has psychotic features, it is often confused with other psychotic disorders, including schizophrenia.

We have found the following symptoms among the World War II and Korean exPOWs whom we have evaluated and treated. Of course, not all symptoms are present in all patients (cf. Jacob, Goodwin, and Newman, this volume):

- Anger and irritability
- Depression
- Fear of loss of control
- Guilt
- Overstimulation
- Nightmares
- Acute psychoses
- Anxiety
- Interpersonal distancing
- Feeling misunderstood by—and distrustful of—nonPOWs
- Disorders of self-esteem (both inappropriately low and inappropriately high).

Anger and Irritability

Perhaps the most common presenting symptom, and the symptom most often described by exPOWs and their families, is excessive anger and irritability. These veterans are often involved in conflicts with the VA and other large systems. Anger at strangers for real or perceived slights, anger at Orientals, even anger at Japanese automobiles and their drivers, is common. One group member, Mr. A., frequently had to pull off to the side of the road when he felt he was being cut off by drivers in Japanese automobiles. He sometimes had thoughts of driving his vehicle into the offender. Another group member, Mr. B., was a frequent visitor to the Hospital Director's office to register complaints in an inappropriate—generally impatient—manner.

It is not difficult to understand why these people are angry. They have been subjected to deprivation, torture, humiliation, threats of death, and have seen their comrades die. Through all of this, they were unable to express the anger they felt. Therefore, massive amounts of anger still exist to be displaced on other authority figures.

Anger is a healthy, normal response to being abused, especially when one is helpless. On the other hand, it is difficult to be the object of anger. As a counselor, it is important that you be aware of your own emotional response to the anger of these patients, and not to allow them to push you away, as they have pushed away so many other people.

Anger is also functional. It is a good defense against depression, a symptom that is not far from the surface in many of these patients. Also, it serves to discharge psychic energy, thus avoiding overstimulation, a problem common among exPOWs, and one I will discuss in more detail later. Anger is also adaptive in keeping people away, and protecting the exPOW from the threat of intimacy. This must have been important in situations where death of comrades was frequent. This, too, will be treated in more detail at a later point.

Depression

Depression is very common, indeed almost universal, in exPOWs. However, it is often masked by anger, anxiety, and a variety of other defenses. Depression was not acceptable in the POW camps because it meant giving up and dying. "The testimony of survivors is practically unanimous that prisoners who became depressed or allowed themselves to become agitated by thoughts of home developed distaste for food and died" (Wolf & Ripley, 1947). Mr. C., a group member, describes being forced to eat by a friend shortly after his arrival in Manchuria from the Philippines: "I hated it then, but it saved my life."

In the exPOW therapy group, members often protect each other from sad feelings. When a group member cries, it is not uncommon for another member to attempt to change the subject, rather than stay with the feeling. It is important for the therapist to stay with the feeling and to empathize with it, modeling this behavior for the group members. It is also important to interpret the protectiveness of the group members as adaptive while they were POWs but as no longer adaptive. Depression no longer means death.

The most common service-connected diagnoses of exPOWs are "anxiety related disorders." (Veterans Administration [VA], 1980, p. 123; see also Oboler, this volume). It may well be that anxiety is a defense against the depression, and the depression is so well disguised that all that is seen on disability evaluations is the defense. Wolf and Ripley describe "the shallow optimism" or "a sort of dull euphoria" (1947, p. 191) after repatriation. This is probably a reaction formation, defending against depression. Nevertheless, there is a pervasive, chronic, generally low-grade depression found in most exPOWs that is apparent to anyone who has worked with them on a long-term basis. This depression is generally manifested in feelings of despair, defeat, and failure. This low-grade depression was itself adaptive in protecting the self against disappointment, which was so frequently felt. Indeed, even today these men are almost surprised when something good happens to them, and cannot believe it to be true.

Fear of Loss of Control

Early in the group, one member mentioned a fear of heights, and one after another group member acknowledged that they too had a fear of heights; all but one group member shared this fear. Acrophobia is symbolic of a more general fear of loss of control. Several members commented that they feared that they would slip or fall or even jump from a height. This is fear of loss of impulse control. Fear of loss of control is a key issue in the problems with interpersonal relationships faced by these veterans. Control issues were the problems most frequently cited by the wives in the wives group, as well. It is not surprising that these exPOWs fear loss of control since they had little or no control over their lives while prisoners. Furthermore, they had to "keep the lid on" their feelings and behavior. Humiliation was common, and displays of anger were severely punished, sometimes by death. Mr. C. recently had a dream, about which he felt "wonderful." In his dream, another therapy group member managed to leave a line of prisoners and steal some potatoes from under the noses of the Japanese. He was no longer under their control. POWs found many ways to maintain some feeling of control. They made up comical names for the Japanese guards, or managed to find a way for some infected stool to end up in the food of the Japanese officers.

In working with the control issue, it is best not to insistently confront or attack the defense—such assaults only strengthen the defensive response. If the therapist respects their needs for the defense, these veterans, in their own time, will slowly let go of their overly strong need for control.

Guilt and Shame

There is no exPOW who has not asked himself the question, "Why did I make it and others did not?" Mr. A. describes being placed on one "hell ship" and his six closest friends were placed on another. The ship carrying his friends was attacked and sunk, and they all died. There is, of course, no logical explanation for his survival and his friends' deaths, yet he has been trying to understand it for over forty years. When his own son suffocated to death about five years ago, nearly replicating his own almost fatal experience when his tank overturned in a river during the defense of Bataan, it brought back the old guilt and the old question, "Why not me?" Survival guilt (see T. Williams, this volume) is especially prominent with WW II Pacific Theater exPOWs and Korean exPOWs. This is due to two factors: first, there was an extremely high mortality rate among these two groups; second, because of the unbelievably harsh conditions to which they were subjected, these men sometimes did things of which they were later ashamed. Often this shame is unrealistic and out of proportion. For example, a Korean exPOW, Mr. D., feels guilty because he was not able to bring out every American captured in Korea. Others feel guilty over such things as eating while their comrades died of starvation.

Sometimes this guilt is so great that the individual cannot face other exPOWs. The clinician should be sensitive to this and gently explore it. When the guilt does not abate even after such exploration, the exPOW's wishes to be seen individually, rather than in group, should be respected. I have made the mistake of pushing such an individual into group therapy, and the result was counter-therapeutic.

In their article, Wolf and Ripley make an observation that is relevant here: "Among the survivors two personality types seem to dominate: (1) those with features of psychopathic personality, and (2) personalities of the highest order of adjustment" (1947, p.186). It is clear that these two personality types were the most adaptive in dealing with the POW experience, albeit in different ways. Notably, the findings of the "Morgan Board" regarding the factors that enabled some to survive while others died (Oboler, this volume) contain characteristics of both personality types.

Mr. E., for example, grew up on a ranch in Wyoming under conditions of severe deprivation. He had learned to take care of himself at a very young age, and had also learned to make do with very little in the way of food, shelter, and especially the emotional closeness of other human beings. He developed a somewhat sociopathic personality style, which served him in good stead throughout his more than 39 months of Japanese captivity as well as in his career as a senior "non-com" after the war.

In contrast, Mr. A., who was described above, was the son of a minister and had a successful professional career after the war. He survived his 39 months of Japanese captivity through close association with other prisoners and holding fast to the religious and moral values he grew up with. Mr. A.'s feelings might more properly be called "guilt" and Mr. E.'s "shame." Mr. E.'s feelings are more primitive, and he has poorer ability to tolerate them. Mr. A. is seen in group therapy; Mr. E. in individual therapy.

At times, the guilt is manifested in various self-destructive behaviors, ranging from mild to severe. Mr. D. compulsively involves himself in helping other exPOWs, even at his own emotional expense. His need to help other exPOWs has interfered with his marriage and with his own therapy. Another individual, Mr. F., convinced that he did not deserve to survive his POW experience, refused psychiatric treatment and hindered attempts to increase his service-connected compensation. He was recently diagnosed with pancreatic carcinoma, and may have delayed getting this condition diagnosed out of his unconscious need to punish himself. Still another individual, Mr. G, has found a way to almost literally repeat his POW experience by becoming involved in a relationship with a German woman from the town where he was held prisoner. She is pathologically jealous, perhaps to psychotic proportions, and prevents him from significant contact with other people—in effect, keeping him a prisoner.

This symptom—pathological guilt—is perhaps the most difficult to deal with because there is at times some reality to it. There is no satisfactory answer to the question "Why not me?", and POWs did behave in ways that they would not normally behave. What is most helpful is to assist the exPOW in recognizing the abnormal, psychotic nature of what he has been through, and to help him recognize that it is not shameful to do what one can to survive in such a situation, as well as recognize that *his behavior* did not kill his comrades. For those who are able to tolerate group therapy, the acceptance by their comrades in the group seems to be most effective in dealing with the guilt.

Overstimulation

We have encountered several exPOWs who are subject to overstimulation, which in this context may be defined as an inability to tolerate a normal degree of affect. These individuals look very agitated and extremely anxious, and at such times they often cannot speak intelligibly, need to leave the room and pace about, or engage in some other motor activity to dissipate the affect. A similar phenomenon has been noted among (nonPOW) combat veterans: "In my experience, motor activity as a defense against painful affects...is the rule with traumatized patients" (Schwartz, 1984, p. 54).

It seems that this symptom is often confused with anxiety, but it is qualitatively different from anxiety. It is more like the symptoms frequently observed in adult psychotherapy patients who were victims of physical or sexual abuse as children, who, like POWs, had to tolerate sensations they were not physically or emotionally able to discharge at the time.

This concept of overstimulation needs elucidation to help explain the prevalence of so-called anxiety disorders among exPOWs, their fear of loss of control, the often-observed anger and irritability, and possibly the vivid nightmares and flashback phenomena. It may be a later manifestation of the hysterical conversion reactions frequently observed by Wolf & Ripley (1947). In responding to symptoms of overstimulation, it is not helpful to try to impede the physical discharge unless such discharge would be dangerous. However, *at a later time*, helping the individual put his affect into words is an important treatment intervention.

Nightmares

At the time of their repatriation, exPOWs almost universally experienced nightmares. Themes were generally rather close to the individual's experience, either during captivity or when captured (Segal, 1974, p. 10; Wolf & Ripley, 1947, p. 86). With the passing of time, the prevalence of nightmares seems to have diminished among most exPOWs. However, during periods of stress, in response to current events like hostage situations, or at significant anniversaries (e.g., Pearl Harbor, V.E. or V.J. Day, the fall of Bataan, etc.), nightmares often reappear. The various losses being experienced by WW II exPOWs, now in their 60s, also seem to have contributed to an increased frequency of nightmares. Common nightmare themes center around being threatened and being helpless. For example, Mr. C., a survivor of the surrender of Corregidor, frequently dreams of being attacked by the Japanese, having one of his grandchildren with him, and running out of ammunition. Other dreams are less clearly understood. Mr. H., who was captured at the Battle of the Bulge, sometimes experiences strange, confusing, "science-fiction-type" dreams, which he cannot understand. He says he gets the same feeling of being lost and confused that he had as an infantryman lost in the fog at the time he was captured.

These dreams seem to be a way of discharging psychic energy, and can be very helpful, not only in their energy discharge function, but also as a means for understanding the internal conflicts of these veterans. In individual and group therapy, it is helpful to encourage these patients to talk about their dreams and nightmares so that they can come to understand them. As with the dreams of any psychotherapy patient, the level of interpretation should be appropriate to the needs and capabilities of the patient.

Acute Psychoses

In their 1947 article, Wolf and Ripley state: "Eight (of thirty-five) patients had psychoses. Three of these were classified as schizophrenia, one as manic depressive psychosis, manic type, and one as paranoid condition. One patient had a delirium associated with cerebral malaria and two were considered to be psychotic because of nutritional deficiency." (p. 185)

Although there is no way to be certain, I would speculate that at least some of these patients would now be more correctly diagnosed as having PTSD with psychotic features.

Some of the exPOWs I have met have described experiences in the early years after repatriation as very similar to "flashbacks" described by Vietnam veterans with PTSD. These sometimes occurred during hypnagogic or hypnopompic states, and at times were difficult to distinguish from nightmares.

Other exPOWs experienced psychotic symptoms of longer duration, but still not the more global deterioration that is characteristic of schizophrenia. Mr. I., a B-17 gunner taken prisoner in Germany in 1943, was hospitalized in 1948 for 2 years in a state hospital where he was treated with electroconvulsive therapy (ECT) after an incident of bizarre and uncharacteristic behavior. On admission, the examining psychiatrist noted that, "During the time [of the incident, Mr. I.]...felt as if he were watching a movie and that he was not doing it at all. Afterwards, he felt very guilty." (Clinical Record, 1948)

The psychiatrist wrote further that:

> At other times he noted that people were talking about him as he passed them on the street. He is sure that they were making derogatory remarks about him although he did not hear what they said. Although he has no idea what they were saying he

> thinks it may be about the way he was dressed. This is very similar to the experiences in prison camps when the guards would see him pass and make remarks about his appearance, etc. Also, when he became very tense, usually at night, he would smell rubber burning and blood. This compared to his experience in the burning plane and the sights he saw in prison camps. Vivid nightmares bothered him a good deal at first and he also heard his name being called; the voice was similar to that of a friend who called to him just after his landing in the bay and before his friend's parachute carried him under. The nightmares were a repeat performance of the experience in the Army (of seeing 1200 Jews killed). In addition to his irritability and nervousness, he has had several periods when he felt as if he were floating in air, light-headed, and describes a "funny feeling" all over. Also, several times he has just felt suddenly like getting away from things and wandered impulsively with no special goal in mind. He knows he should not, but seemingly cannot stop himself. (Clinical Record, 1948)

Mr. I. received a diagnosis of *dementia praecox*, or schizophrenia, at that time. He required only one other psychiatric hospitalization since: for one month, in 1969, when he suffered a "psychotic break" after seeing a war movie.

His disability examination in 1983 noted that: "It appears that he has suffered in the past from a post-traumatic stress disorder, however, although symptoms of this disorder remain, I would not currently diagnose him as suffering from such a disorder. It is my firm opinion, however, that his generalized anxiety disorder is a direct result of his POW experience." (Clinical Record, 1983)

Mr. I. was most likely *misdiagnosed* as schizophrenic, and consequently incorrectly treated with ECT. More likely, he had a PTSD with psychotic features of an hysterical, dissociative nature. This sort of misdiagnosis is, unfortunately, not uncommon:

> It seems that the florid symptoms of repetitive anxiety attacks, panic states, dissociative paranoid rage states, and other dissociative phenomena such as "flashbacks" often lead to the diagnosis of schizophrenia, rather than PTSD. Despite dissociative phenomena observed in these veterans, reality testing, and other ego functions known to be severely impaired in schizophrenic disturbances, remain intact. (Parron, 1984, p. 17)

Other exPOWs begin to show psychotic symptoms related to their POW experiences when an organic brain syndrome weakens their usual defensive structure. Mr. C., for example, who was described above as suffering from frequent nightmares, has become psychotic on two occasions, both immediately following major surgery. On both of these occasions, he believed he was—and behaved as if he were still—a captive of the Japanese. He attempted to physically assault hospital personnel and to escape from his hospital room, almost jumping from his second-story window. On both occasions, he needed to be restrained for several days.

Mr. J., a European Theater exPOW who developed a chronic organic brain syndrome in his mid-60s after a successful professional career, concurrently began ruminating about his POW experiences. He eventually became paranoid and began hallucinating that people were breaking into his home and believed he had to guard it. In the hospital, during an initial mental status exam, he reported that the current president was Roosevelt.

Whether such cases fully meet the criteria for PTSD is probably not very important. What is important, however, is that such symptoms are undoubtedly related to the patient's POW experiences. It is not unusual to see exPOWs with psychotic symptoms. Much of the time, the POW experience provides a better etiological explanation than does a diagnosis of schizophrenia. As noted above, however, this is not to deny the importance of predisposing personality factors.

Anxiety

Anxiety disorders are the most common type of service-connected disability. Anxiety is a normal response to the constant uncertainty with which POWs had to contend. As discussed above, it appears that anxiety is sometimes confused with overstimulation. Several of the patients we have seen have experienced panic attacks, which is also a kind of overstimulation.

As these veterans become involved in treatment, their general level of anxiety tends to decrease, and they become overstimulated less easily. However, at the Denver VAMC, anti-anxiety agents, such as benzodiazepines, and tricyclic antidepressants, have been used with good results with this population (see Yost, this volume).

Interpersonal Distancing

The need to keep a certain amount of distance from other people is a common symptom among exPOWs. It is often seen in marital and family relationships as well as in work relationships and friendships. We have sometimes noticed a peculiar combination of distancing and dependence. There is often a considerable amount of dependence on a spouse or interdependence between spouses, accompanied by an avoidance of any real intimacy. It is not unusual to find a chronic state of conflict, which keeps the spouses connected, yet maintains a certain amount of distance.

At times, there is a repetition of "prisoner-guard" patterns in POW marriages. In some of these marriages, one spouse will always take the prisoner role and the other the guard role; in others, there is an interchangeability of roles, but the basic pattern does not change. The combination of distancing and dependency may be understood in light of the POW experience. POWs needed each other desperately, yet they also needed to keep a certain distance because of the possibility (sometimes probability) of the death of their comrades.

The subject of POW marriages deserves much more treatment than is possible here (see C. Williams, "Women Partners," this volume). However, we have found it very helpful, especially in the wives' group, to explain the "prison-guard" dynamic and to use it to explain interactional patterns otherwise difficult to understand. It is helpful to note that this pattern was adaptive in the POW situation but is no longer necessary.

Distrust of NonPOWs

There is a chronic feeling of being misunderstood among exPOWs. The assumption that nonPOWs will not understand is in part realistic (cf., Hickman, this volume). The VA system has not always responded with understanding toward these veterans. Many were told after repatriation to "just forget" about their POW experiences. This we now know is an impossibility. Many were told by clinical staff, who themselves must have felt helpless and hopeless, that they had "K-Z syndrome" or "concentration camp syndrome" or "POW syndrome," and that nothing much could be done. The feeling of being misunderstood is also the result of the psychotic nature of the POW experience. What exPOWs have experienced is often so far beyond the range of normal experience that they cannot imagine that anyone would believe what they have to say. Indeed, they sometimes mistrust their own memories. And it is not uncommon for the clinician to disbelieve what these people tell them as a defense against fully comprehending the horror. I have found myself disbelieving something an exPOW has told me, only to realize at a later time that it was my own inability to tolerate the awful nature of what I was being told that created my disbelief.

The exPOW's belief that he will not be understood also serves a defensive purpose. First, if he will not be understood then there is no need to have to open up old wounds and talk with other people about his experiences. Second, if he does describe his experiences to others, and is not then understood, he will not be as disappointed. The corollary to the feeling that nonPOWs will not be able to understand them is the belief that other exPOWs already understand, and thus do not have to be told the awful details. When exPOWs talk among themselves, they frequently avoid dealing with their more troubling memories. They often focus on the humorous aspects or "high points" of their experience. Guilt, fear of overstimulation, and above all, protection of their comrades, leads them to avoid talking about the most unsettling experiences. If they already understand, there is no need to talk.

Low Self-Esteem

Disorders of self-esteem and chronic lack of self-confidence are common among this population. Often there is an overcompensation through a brittle, narcissistic personality structure that is very vulnerable to narcissistic injury. These men were prisoners during a period of their lives when self-esteem is developed and reinforced through success. They had few successes. Indeed, while POWs, they were subjected to almost continuous humiliation and defeat. There is a tradition of victory in the U.S. Armed Forces, and these men were not victors. Among Pacific Theater exPOWs, there is often a feeling that "we lost our war."

Successes after repatriation have remedied these traumas with some exPOWs. However, with many of these individuals the various physical and emotional disabilities they received as POWs have prevented further successes. In some cases, the intense shame and guilt have led to a sort of "vicious cycle." Mr. K., a European Theater exPOW, who was eventually forced by his intense guilt to drop out of the group and fail in treatment, attempted and failed in more than two dozen jobs.

> ...a crisis is to be expected once the rapture (of repatriation) recedes and the realities of life appear. Some physical disabilities take years to overcome, if, in fact, they are ever overcome. Being below par psychologically as well as physically, the former prisoner has little chance of holding his own, yet finds himself in daily competition with completely healthy people. He is almost programmed to lose and social decline often follows. There is a high divorce rate. The inability to feel belonging anywhere, or understanding by anyone, leads to increased alcohol and drug use. (Russell, 1984, p. 253)

Some exPOWs defend against their feelings of low self-esteem by refusing to acknowledge their POW status. For example, they avoid POW organizations, free or low-cost license plates often offered to exPOWs, and treatment for their physical and psychological wounds offered at VA medical centers. Some exPOWs present at first as self-centered, overbearing individuals. This is generally an attempt to compensate for feelings of low self-esteem, and—as with most defenses—is best not directly confronted. It will disappear when it is no longer needed.

For other exPOWs, the status of being an exPOW or a disabled veteran is their *primary source* of self-esteem. When they begin to feel better about themselves as whole people, they are able to see themselves as more than just exPOWs.

TREATMENT CONSIDERATIONS

In writing this chapter, I asked the exPOW group, after two years of treatment, what had been most helpful to them from the therapists and from other group members. From the therapists, what was cited most often was a willingness to listen and the ability to understand what was being related with interest and respect. In addition, a willingness to allow the group members to maintain their defenses as long as they needed them, or as one member put it, "To allow us to wander around in left field for a while," was noted as helpful. What was cited as most helpful from other group members was their interest and caring.

Counter-transference

The most difficult issue for therapists working with this population is counter-transference. It is essential not to push these people away, like others have, because the therapist cannot tolerate what he is hearing or feels helpless and frustrated. Rejection is a major fear, and exPOWs are sensitive to even very subtle signs. It is difficult to really listen to stories of death, illness, torture, and general inhumanity, to empathize with feelings of hopelessness, intense sadness, humiliation, lack of control, and mortal fear without such defensive reactions as disbelief, intellectualization or other pulling away, or subtly discouraging talk about these experiences.

When the group was starting, I usually warned group members against "telling war stories." I thought I had good reasons for this, having experienced combat veterans' using often-told stories of their combat experiences to avoid affect. However, what I didn't realize until later was that what I had said discouraged group members from talking about some of their most painful experiences. This was unconscious on my part, and I did not realize it until over a year later when several group members told me about the inhibitory effect of my initial statement.

During the first two months of the POW group, I found myself frequently experiencing nightmares of being a POW myself or of being a victim of similar experiences to those being described by the group members. Just hearing about these experiences had precipitated a kind of derivative traumatic neurosis in me, shorter in duration and less intense, but nevertheless very real to me; it went away as I was able to talk about it with my co-therapist and other colleagues. Any therapist working with this population must convey his willingness to listen to the exPOWs he is working with. Not every therapist can work with every population. If a therapist cannot listen empathically to material of this sort without undue injury to himself, it is best to avoid working with exPOWs. With this population, perhaps even more than with other psychotherapy patients, failures in empathy are far more significant than failures in techniques. A superb discussion of the counter-transference issues involved in treating concentration camp survivors, which is applicable as well to the treatment of exPOWs, may be found in De Wind (1984).

Initial Contact: Evaluation of Treatment Needs

In the setting in which I work, many of the exPOWs referred to me are not coming as a result of their request for psychiatric treatment. Many of them have been seen for exPOW protocol examinations, where it was suggested that they talk to me. They are generally not presenting with an acute condition, or even an acute exacerbation of a chronic condition. Nevertheless, the intensity with which they present often makes it *appear* that they have an acute condition. We believe this is due to the fact that POW issues are always just below the surface, and when these patients finally find someone whom they feel will listen to them, their presentations have great intensity. Almost without exception, exPOWs feel they have not been heard in the past, and when they finally feel they've found a listener, there is a sense of great relief.

A psychiatric evaluation or a psychiatric referral may be seen as a narcissistic injury, and the referring clinician as well as the evaluating mental health professional needs to be aware of this. Although the exPOW may have marital problems, difficulty controlling anger, problems with interpersonal relationships, depression, or other psychosocial difficulties, these problems are generally chronic, and he may have become used to them. He may have long ago given up hope of changing anything. I generally begin by explaining what I do, note some of the more common problems I have observed in exPOWs, and try to determine the individual's interest in my services. Knowing what sorts of psychosocial problems other exPOWs experience helps the veteran normalize his problem and soften the blow to his self-esteem. Knowing what services are available makes it easier to ask for help. I attempt to explain the connection between current symptoms and past experiences, and ask the exPOW if any of this fits him. I generally focus primarily on group therapy, because I strongly feel that in the great majority of cases it is the treatment of choice for this population (see Jelinek, this volume). However, I also explain and sometimes offer individual or couples treatment.

I usually expect some resistance to getting into a group. However, I have come to respect the *strongly stated* desire not to get into a group. Some exPOWs cannot tolerate group therapy because of overwhelming guilt or shame.They cannot face other exPOWs. Others do not have the ego strength to tolerate the affect generated by the content of these groups. Still others, because of character pathology, may be too disruptive of the group process.

Some exPOWs referred to me are not interested in treatment; they simply want help in dealing with the VA system. Providing such services may be all the individual wants or needs, or may be the first step to getting into treatment.

It is significant to note that for some exPOWs, especially those from the European Theater, the experience surrounding their capture was more traumatic than the POW experience itself. Mr. L., for example, a B-17 pilot, became significantly more anxious when describing bailing out of his plane, being followed down in his parachute by a German fighter, and then nearly being killed by the civilians who surrounded him when he reached the ground.

> After landing, I peeked over the small knoll that surrounded me to see if anyone was coming. There was about 25 or 30 of them, and armed with knives, guns, clubs, pitchforks, axes, and other forms of concealed weapons. I knew then that everything was finished and that I may as well quit. Consequently, I simply raised my hands and stood up. Immediately I was surrounded by about 20 persons, all of whom tried to talk to me at the same time. I'd heard German in school before, but this jabbering could have been Chinese, for all I know and cared. At first, they didn't dare come near me because they thought I had a gun. You see, the type of heated flying suit that I was wearing had a little brown, rectangular junction box on its right-hand side about the hip level. I had to tear it off to convince them that it wasn't a gun, or I probably would have been shot right there on the spot. When they closed in around me somebody gave me a rabbit punch from behind. I fell down. When I got up, somebody hit me on the shoulder with a club, knocking me down again. I had just got up again when a wheezing little old man stepped up in front of me and took a swing at me with a double-bitted woodman's axe, causing me to fall down again. That was a good thing because the axe swung about a foot away from me. While I

> laid there on the ground, he lifted his axe to take another swing when a little Frenchman hopped out of the crowd, stood over me and began to reason with the German. He must have put his point across because the little German backed away and the Frenchman helped me to my feet. By now I was having a great deal of trouble in standing erect due to my leg, but nevertheless, they forced me to start walking toward the village. In order that I wouldn't run away they made me drop all my flying clothes down around my legs, except for my shirt, which is the only thing they allowed me for coverage, and grabbing the loose arms, made me move on ahead of them. Just before entering the town a woman stuck a camera in my face and got, what later probably turned out to be a very embarrassing picture. (Unpublished diary)

Mr. M. still feels guilty about his decision to try and make it back to England in his crippled B-17, during which time two crew members were killed. Neither Mr. M. nor Mr. L. report being affected as much from their stays in POW camps, despite suffering significant hardships and deprivation there.

The fact that for some European exPOWs their capture was more traumatic than was their internment may help account for the observation that "there does not appear to be a specific minimum length of internment before anxiety neurosis really appears in former European Theater POWs; this disability occurs in a significant number of the POWs interned a few days just as certainly as it does in those interned several years." (VA, 1980, p. 84)

Group Psychotherapy

We believe strongly that group therapy is the treatment of choice for most exPOWs. The group experience is therapeutic for many reasons, but primarily because it is only in group that these veterans feel understood and accepted *both* by other exPOWs and by nonPOWs.

Group members and therapists differ in their *symbolic* function in the group. This is in addition to the different roles they play. Group members are symbolic of fellow POWs (see Rheault, this volume). Their understanding and acceptance is the understanding and acceptance of the other prisoners in the camp. The therapist (or therapists), on the other hand, is symbolic of all nonPOWs, of family, friends, and of the society at large. The therapist's understanding and acceptance are on a different level and have a different significance than that of other group members. Both are essential, but each is different.

Some observations about the development of the now two-year-old exPOW group at Denver VAMC may be helpful. This is a group of only WW II exPOWs. Approximately half the group is from the European Theater and half from the Pacific Theater. (Although difficulties combining members from both Theaters of War have been noted by other therapists, we encountered no problems in this area.) The group initially had six members and two therapists. It now has ten members and one therapist. One member has permanently terminated from the group, and one of the therapists left the group due to a job change. Nearly all group members attend the weekly one-hour sessions whenever they are in town. Three members spend winters in warmer climates than Denver, and several other members travel frequently and consequently miss sessions during their travels. However, average weekly attendance is about seven or eight members.

After the first few sessions, it was observed that the group was exhibiting unusually strong and fast bonding among the members. The group *became* a group, and developed into a *solid group*, more quickly than any other group with which I have been associated. Related to this phenomenon was the initial exclusion of the therapists because of the feeling that "they won't understand." The therapists were commonly ignored in group interaction during the early weeks and months of the group. There was also an unconscious attempt on the part of nearly all group members to protect each other from painful affect. Whenever one member would begin to talk about a painful experience or would begin to show any emotion, another member or members would either change the subject or direct questions of a factual nature toward him, to move him away from the feeling. This was interpreted time and time again, and even after two years, it still occurs.

We also noticed the development of a "pre-group group" and a "post-group group." Some of the members would meet in the canteen for coffee for an hour or so before the group, and would go to the canteen for coffee after the group. We wondered whether this was another way of excluding the therapists. We also speculated that it might be a defense, necessary for the modulation of affect, and necessary for the members to keep attending group. At some points, a kind of "prisoner-guard" role-play seemed to be occurring, with the therapists being seen as guards.

Because of exPOWs' exquisite sensitivity to affect and fear of loss of control, defenses against affect play an important part in the process of the group. It is the therapist's role to track the defenses and interpret them when appropriate. It is a difficult—yet essential—task to recognize when defenses are necessary, either for the group or for an individual, and when they can be interpreted and the affect tolerated. Some therapists working with this population in group therapy have noted that shifts from present material to past material is a defensive maneuver. It is my impression that *either* a shift from past to present *or* from present to past can be defensive, but that neither is necessarily so. It is important to track where the affect is at any given time. Descriptions of events from the past, especially when they are recently de-repressed or have not been shared with other people, can contain tremendous affect, just as some recent events may not be affect-laden. The therapist's empathy in allowing himself *to feel with* the group or one or more of its members is the key here. The goal, of course, is to enable the group members to experience and tolerate previously intolerable affect.

In our therapy group, the initial defensive angry stage began to break down after about three to six months, at which point sadness became the most prominent feeling. Simultaneously, members began to talk about the therapists' (and other nonPOWs') not understanding them. There was a shared group fantasy that the therapists must either be bored or overwhelmed. It was extremely helpful when the group could recognize and talk about this as its fear with *all* nonPOWs. At a later point, the expectation of being misunderstood was more clearly analyzed. *Nearly all* of the group members felt "disfigured on the inside," whereas only *some* bore physical disfigurement. There was an expectation that since others could not *see* their psychological scars, they could not understand their pain.

Another noteworthy observation is the group's response to the absence of its members. Whenever a group member or therapist was absent, there was a serious concern about where he was and whether he was "O.K." This was especially significant when the group member did not call in to explain his absence. When the one individual who terminated from the group did so under less than ideal circumstances, viz., during a period of depression, the group was extremely concerned about his well-being, and whether or not they had "chased him away." Some members had teased him in a rather mild way a few weeks before his termination, and they felt intensely guilty about doing this, blaming this incident for his leaving. It became clear that unexplained absences rekindled feelings from the POW experience when absence usually meant that the missing person was dead. The guilt generated by the premature termination of the group member had revived feelings of survivor guilt. The group was so concerned about this member that about six weeks after he had left they wrote him a card expressing their concern; unfortunately, the card was not answered.

Individual Psychotherapy

Some exPOWs are seen in individual psychotherapy, but only when group treatment is clearly contraindicated. Two exceptions to this are (1) using the individual treatment to help prepare the veteran for group treatment, and (2) the occasional individual session that may be necessary while the veteran is in group treatment to help him deal with some particularly difficult issue that he cannot *yet* talk about in group. Ideally, the goal is to reach a level of comfort where any issue can be dealt with in the group.

Individual treatment cannot accomplish one of the essential psychotherapeutic goals obtainable in the group, viz., understanding and acceptance by other exPOWs. Individuals with lesser ego strength or with overwhelming guilt or shame are most appropriately seen for individual, rather than group, psychotherapy, and for them, individual psychotherapy does serve this purpose.

A word about marital treatment may be appropriate here. I have seen several exPOW couples for marital treatment, and I have recommended it in several other cases. However, the marital dynamics are usually so influenced by the POW experiences that I recommend marital treatment only in addition to, not instead of, group therapy.

Wives' Groups

We are now completing a weekly, time-limited (six months) group for wives of exPOWs, which was done with a female co-therapist. The initial goals for this group were (1) to educate the wives about the basic dynamics of exPOWs in order to help them understand their husbands and their marital relationships better, and (2) to assist the wives in forming their own informal support network.

Five wives began the group; four are completing it. Initial results seem promising, with all members noting an improved understanding of their husbands, themselves, and their marital relationships, and two members noting distinct improvements in their marriages. One of these had been in individual and couples therapy for over two years before this group, but showed little improvement. Some of the women have also begun seeing each other and calling each other outside of the group for both social activities and support.

The decision to make the group time-limited was based on our intention not to foster unrealistic dependence on the VA system. A previous open-ended group for wives of veterans being treated at the mental hygiene clinic had encouraged but could not meet such dependency needs, and when the group was disbanded, some of the participants felt severe disappointment and anger. Setting this group up as time-limited avoided this problem, and does not seem to have had any adverse effects.

CONCLUSION

ExPOWs are a very special subgroup of the veteran population. They have been subjected to some of the harshest treatment of any of our veterans and as a group have probably been more misunderstood. This misunderstanding has exacerbated pre-existing feelings of guilt, shame, unworthiness, and anger.

Consequently, perhaps the greatest service we can provide for these veterans is to demonstrate enough empathy, patience, and willingness to listen so that they will feel more understood and accepted. This requires creating an environment where they can tell their stories to their comrades and to us—the American society that has never really listened, let alone full understood, the experiences and sacrifices of these extraordinary individuals.

REFERENCES

De Wind, E. (1984). Some implications of former massive traumatization upon the actual analytical process. *International Journal of Psychoanalysis, 65*, 273-281.

Parron, E. R. (1984).The reparation of the self: Clincial and theoretical dimensions in the treatment of Vietnam combat veterans. *Journal of Contemporary Psychotherapy, 14*, 4-56.

Russell, C. F. (1984). The captivity experience and its psychological consequences. *Psychiatric Annals, 14*, 250-254.

Schwartz, H. (1984). Unconscious guilt: Its origin, manifestations, and treatment in the combat veteran. In H. Schwartz (Ed.), *Psychotherapy of the Combat Veteran* (pp. 47-84). New York: Spectrum Publications.

Segal, J. (1974). *Long term psychological and physical effects of the POW experience: A review of the literature*. Springfield, VA: National Technical Information Service.

Veterans Administration. (1980). *POW: Study of former prisoners of war*. Washington, DC: Veterans Administration Office of Planning and Program Education.

Wolf, S., & Ripley, H. S. (1947). Reactions among allied prisoners of war subjected to three years of imprisonment and torture by the Japanese. *American Journal of Psychiatry, 104*, 180-193.

CHAPTER FOUR

A PASTORAL RESPONSE TO THE TROUBLED VIETNAM VETERAN

Melvin R. Jacob

INTRODUCTION

PTSD of the Vietnam Veteran was first published by the Disabled American Veterans (DAV) in 1980 (Williams, 1980). This book gave affirmation to Vietnam veterans, especially the ones experiencing adjustment problems. It gave insight and help for the health care provider working with the troubled Vietnam veteran. I benefited from this book, and was especially pleased to learn that the DAV was planning a sequel and was broadening its observations and recommendations for treatment of the veteran and his or her family.

Jim Goodwin, in his chapter on the etiology of combat-related PTSD, wrote of the life-sucking symptoms of this disorder:

> Many veterans find it extremely uncomfortable to feel love and compassion for others. To do this, they would have to thaw their numb reactions to the death and horror that surrounded them in Vietnam...; many of these veterans go through life with an impaired capacity to love and care for others. They have no feeling of direction or purpose in life. They are not sure why they even exist. (Goodwin, in Williams, 1980, p. 14)

Goodwin identified in this dilemma a symptom that psychological treatment alone has not addressed. Laufer (1985) described this issue quite clearly: "The problem can be seen as the difficulty in answering the question, 'Who am I' after learning more than one wants about the question, 'What am I capable of?'" (p. 51)

The existential dilemma challenges their reason and purpose for human existence. I assert it also points to the Vietnam veteran's need for spiritual, pastoral care, a need that has largely been avoided in the literature on the treatment of PTSD.[1] This article is an attempt to respond to this need. My purposes are fivefold: (1) to present pastoral problems with Vietnam veterans; (2) to reframe PTSD symptoms from a pastoral perspective; (3) to examine pastoral goals within the reality of PTSD symptoms; (4) to offer pastoral interventions for these goals; and (5) to theologically describe forms of positive change.

My response to the pastoral care needs of the Vietnam veteran has developed within my ministry over the past six years. During this period, I have worked extensively with veterans (on both an in- and outpatient basis) who have sought treatment at the Augusta, Georgia, VA Medical Center. They have taught me much. My response to them has been formulated from a Judeo-Christian philosophy that presupposes that life, as a creation of God, has direction and purpose and that recognizes a redemptive hope within human brokeness and pain. My response acknowledges renewal in the human spirit above and beyond human ability to effect change.

PASTORAL PROBLEMS

The reality of Vietnam ate away at the spirit of many of its soldiers. The constant inconsistencies and incongruities, the gut-wrenching absurdities, and the endless emptiness left their indelible marks on the hearts of American warriors. A 35-year-old veteran, diagnosed with PTSD, recently allowed me into the horror and fear inside him. He recalled a night his company was overrun by the Viet Cong. Graphically and painfully, he described the vigilance he maintained while picking up the pieces of a buddy "held together at his middle by a thin stretch of skin." This vigilance replaced grief, and fear was his constant companion. He walked in the valley of the shadow of death, but, unlike the psalmist, he concluded that, "God was not there on that hill."

A religious or spiritual vacuum was created by the Vietnam war. Many soldiers sought to theologize their experiences (that is, bring spiritual significance to them), but found it futile; emptiness engulfed their attempts for theological meaning, which, itself, was challenged with demonic interpretations. Many looked to the chaplain for meaning and strength. (Some veterans readily affirm the importance of the chaplain and the relationship he gave; meaning and strength were caringly incarnated in his presence.) Others recall negative memories of the chaplain.

Lifton (1978) describes an "ironic rage" directed at both chaplains and psychiatrists ("shrinks") by Vietnam veterans. This rage flowed from the soldiers' perceptions that the chaplains' battlefield work was incongruent. Lifton elaborates these incongruities: (1) the chaplains blessed the troops, mission, guns, and killing; (2) they endorsed "phoniness" in advocating confession of meaningless transgressions—for example, use of drugs—while holding back accountability to the ultimate transgression: killing; (3) they promoted "false witness" by not acknowledging loss (in the intrinsic and extrinsic experience of war), but affirming and legitimizing the death and destruction; and (4) they sanctioned an "unholy alliance" between themselves and the military in perpetuating the ironies and incongruities of Vietnam. Lifton concluded: "It was one thing to be ordered by command into a situation they came to perceive as both absurd and evil, but it was quite another to have that process rationalized and justified by ultimate authorities of the spirit and mind—that is, by chaplains and psychiatrists." (p. 220)

Other pastoral problems are present in the interventions with veterans diagnosed as having PTSD. These problems are summarized in the negative transference that accrued to the chaplain. The chaplain is often seen as God's representative. If God was viewed as not present in Vietnam, then the chaplain's legitimacy, his reason for existence, was in question. The chaplain is seen as the embodiment of what was felt as God's betrayal, and his post-war interventions may receive the brunt of the rage felt toward his role in Vietnam. The veteran is often unable to distinguish between the chaplain who was perceived as sanctioning the incongruities of Vietnam and the one who now offers purpose, hope, and renewal in the brokenness and pain of PTSD symptomatology.

Arnold (1985) presents basic principles in the treatment of Vietnam veterans with PTSD, and lists an assortment of therapy interventions. He identifies "religious counseling" as one intervention, thus giving some legitimacy to the clergy's role in treatment (although he does not define what is meant by religious counseling). He warns against certain theological emphases and highlights possibilities with others:

> Religious or spiritual counseling has been very helpful to some veterans, but great sensitivity is required to arrange it. The clergy have an acknowledged legitimacy in the area of morality, but if the tenets of faith of a particular clergyman stress sin and punishment or portray expected human nature as being incredibly pure, veterans

> having serious problems with self-acceptance may reject the counseling which is offered. On the other hand, nonjudgemental guidance in dealing with combat experiences in moral terms may lead to the formulation of a new personal moral position which enhances productive living. (p. 253)

The possibilities for ameliorative pastoral work with troubled Vietnam veterans necessitate a look at how this intervention takes place. I believe the first step in this process is to consider the troubled veteran from a pastoral perspective.

PASTORAL PERSPECTIVE

Much has been written on the veteran and PTSD. The American Psychiatric Association's (APA) *Diagnostic and Statistical Manual III* (APA, 1980) provided the psychiatric diagnostic criteria. It describes the symptoms of this disorder as developing after a psychologically traumatic event that is outside the range of usual human experience. I seek to examine the behaviors and feelings from which this psychiatric diagnosis is derived. But, instead of using a psychological perspective, I will use a pastoral one that involves analyzing events, behaviors, and emotions from a theological or spiritual point of view and that embraces a wholistic view of the person.

The pastoral perspective recognizes the complexity and interrelationships existing among the components of the whole person—the emotional, social, mental, physical, and spiritual aspects of the person. The spiritual component provides a unique perspective from which to examine events, behavior, and emotions. Like the psychological perspective, the pastoral view has its own terminology to explain the observations. I use some of this terminology, rooted in Judeo-Christian thought, to describe the adjustment difficulties and internal struggles of the troubled Vietnam veteran.

A veteran in his late thirties requested some private time with me. He had been hospitalized for two or three months, and I knew him very well, but his initiative for an appointment surprised me. In our meeting, he described that on a recent trip home he found something he thought he had lost. Pulling a bent and worn Bible from his pocket, he said, "Chaplain, this Bible was with me all the time I was in Vietnam...I survived and it was in my pocket." He described his attachment to it, although he never spoke of actually opening or reading from it. He continued, "I am struggling now...this Bible helped me before. I would like for you to bless it the way it was blessed in Vietnam so it can help me now." I observed his fear; there was uncertainty in his eyes and hesitancy in his voice. His request seemed to involve more than "getting all the help you can get"—it appeared consistent with the teaching of his faith tradition about the Bible. He shared doubt and vulnerability. I listened to him and recalled how Thomas, in the New Testament, following the awesome mystery of Jesus' resurrection, was filled with fear and doubt. Thomas, like this veteran, asked for visible reassurance. He wanted to feel something tangible in his uncertainty. Jesus' response to Thomas spoke to his deepest fear and doubt.

This illustration exemplifies the use of a pastoral perspective. In my work with Vietnam veterans, I have discovered seven categories that illustrate PTSD symptoms from a pastoral perspective. These are (1) distrust and fear, (2) rejection and betrayal, (3) futility, (4) alienation and estrangement, (5) loss and grief, (6) guilt and shame, and (7) isolation and withdrawal. After discussing the use of Biblical analogies, an important part of pastoral work, I will explore each of these categories in detail.

Biblical Analogies

Biblical analogies provide an historical perspective to PTSD symptomatology. I have found them useful as didactic presentations on PTSD and religious faith. Like the illustration of Thomas associated with the discussion of distrust and fear (below), Biblical analogies are applicable to the remaining six categories of PTSD symptoms. The Biblical character Joseph illustrates the experience of rejection and betrayal. His brothers, selling him into slavery, rejected him; Pharoah's wife, lying about him, unjustly caused his imprisonment. The Old Testament book of Ecclesiastes describes the emotions of futility, darkly depicted in the injustices and frustrations of many Vietnam veterans. Reflecting on the contradictions of life, with its injustices and frustrations, the writer concludes, "All is vanity." Alienation and estrangement are seen in the person of Moses. Born a Hebrew, but raised an Egyptian, he struggled to find moorings, his real self. Loss and grief are clearly evident in the Biblical character of Job, who lost all his children and property and was afflicted with a repulsive disease. The Biblical analogy of the disciple Peter, who went out and wept bitterly after his denial of Jesus, gives us an example of guilt and shame. The experiences of isolation and withdrawal are vividly portrayed in Adam and Eve, who sought to hide after their transgression against God.

Distrust and Fear

The association of distrust and fear links the consequences of failed trust with the fear of death and annihilation. Fear, cultured in a petri dish of broken trust and confidence, breeds greater distrust that deepens the fear. The cycle feeds on itself, creating larger distances between oneself and a world perceived as cold, callous, and uncaring.

Vietnam is a saga of broken trust and confidence. Friend and foe looked much alike. Friendly villagers by day were Viet Cong sympathizers by night. A child's innocent smile made one cautious to the danger of the hidden explosive charge she carried. The children and elderly who responded warmly to the GIs likely were the offspring and parents of the enemy lurking nearby. Healthy distrust was learned, and fear was a bosom companion.

The soldiers distrusted the governments for whom they were fighting. The government of South Vietnam had a legacy of instability and fraud; the black market flourished; vice was as abundant as a natural resource. The environment of the Vietnam war was different and foreign to the values and standards most young soldiers had been taught, and this difference fostered distrust and made an easy target for personal fears.

The government that sent them to fight in such an environment over 6000 miles from home was also viewed with distrust and fear. The statements of U.S. political leaders simply did not mesh with the war's reality. Enemy body counts were valued over ground taken. Military tactics were compromised for political expediency. The soldier was caught in the middle, and catch-22 was the order of the day. Hearts could not absorb what eyes saw. War protests at home seemed to make no sense to the soldier in the field. Patriotism waned, and distrust gradually deepened. One veteran said to me: "If you can't trust your own government, who can you trust?"

Possibly the most frightening source of distrust and fear was inside each soldier himself. Many experienced their own potential for violence—for the first time. The real fight for survival unleashed emotions and actions that remain horrifying to recall. Many want to hide their destructive past, but find it flares up under the stresses of daily living: an inconsiderate motorist fails to use his turn signal; a child slams the back door; a boss vents anxiety. Such stresses may precipitate violent, destructive outbursts. Tremendous amounts of emotional energy are spent to control the urge to destroy again.

In one of my groups, a veteran yelled at me, "You don't know how close I came to knocking your head off!" I was surprised and threatened. He later was able to share his distrust of a particular facial expression that reminded him of someone he felt was untrustworthy.

I sense a constant readiness or state of alertness in many veterans—their necks and shoulders are tense, their movements are sudden and jerky, their eyes dart around warily. Some keep their bodies in a defensive posture, constantly sitting with their backs to the wall (see Williams on "Peacetime Combat," this volume); it often seems to me that time bombs are ticking away inside these veterans. Some refuse to handle guns lest they lose their ability to control their violent impulses.

The veterans frequently talk of the dehumanizing process in becoming a combat soldier. Basic training reinforces defensive action and erodes trust of caring emotions. A bright, articulate college graduate described this process to me. "They take who you are, or who you think you are. They knock you down and take you apart. Then they put you back together piece by piece...the way they want you to be. You are taught not to think but to react." Another veteran echoed these feelings: "You are taught to be an animal. Then you're expected suddenly to forget you're trained to function as an animal." A third veteran tearfully amplified this thought: "I know how to act like an animal. I don't know how to be human."

Many veterans distrust their capacity to enter into significant relationships without eventually finding themselves exploding violently. On the battlefield, this distrust was exacerbated. Relationships with buddies who offered understanding and affirmation were short-lived. Each soldier had his own DEROS (date of expected return from overseas); *esprit de corps* waned (see Goodwin, this volume). Combat took its toll with the wounded and killed.

New faces too easily filled the gaps left by old, familiar ones and, because combat soldiers distrust anyone whose actions affect their own life or well-being, establishing relationships was even more difficult—and these were tested literally by fire—gunfire. A mortar crew member told me that he once lay awake all night because there was a new man on the crew: "I nearly was killed once by a new crew member who didn't know what to do."

Only when the fear of death and survival are shared can real significance be given to a peer relationship. Until this mutual struggle for survival was shared, there could be little or no understanding, much less affirmation, given and received. Unit cohesiveness suffered; the structure of survival in Vietnam inhibited such understanding and affirmation. Trust diminished. With the endless leavings and arrivals, impermanence was inherent in every fighting unit.

This distrust and the accompanying fear still spill out to institutions and their representatives who seek to help the troubled Vietnam veteran. Leventman (1978) gave the following description: "Bureaucratic formalism and inefficiency, inept and ill-informed policy-making, political and military gamesmanship, all capped by revelations of high-level executive misconduct, produced an unprecedented crisis of faith and confidence in American institutions." (p. 293)

The Veterans Administration (VA) is often not distinguished from the government that sent men and women to war but failed to support them, so the VA as an institution is distrusted, too. Its employees are often not distinguished from the institution, and so they, too, are not trusted by the people they want to serve. One veteran said: "The VA is like Vietnam. It's a survival trip. I have to fight and struggle every step of the way." Some veterans even suspect secret alliances between the care givers in the VA and the government that fostered their troubles.

The institutionalized church has also been unfavorably regarded by veterans. Many accuse the church of hypocrisy; they believe the church has been phony and that it has no comprehension of the harsh realities they learned in war. And, as with the VA, these feelings have been transferred to individuals who represent the institution—ministers and chaplains. One veteran lashed out at me: "You are just a hypocrite...any chaplain is a hypocrite. You profess to be something you can't be." Such feelings present both an obstacle and a challenge to those who seek to alleviate this distrust and fear.

Finally, distrust and fear are associated with God. One veteran angrily demanded: "Where was God when I needed Him [in Vietnam]? Now that I don't need Him, why should I trust that He is here?" The presence of God and the conviction of faith are often viewed in direct relationship. As faith waxes and wanes, so does God's reality and the clarity that comes for questions of life. Ambiguity clouds God's presence and suffocates the conviction of faith; Vietnam was filled with ambiguity.

Battlefield pleas to God became confused with distrust of sacred institutions (government and church) and the contorted maladies of the war. The symbols of faith—like the corner church—have done little to alleviate the distrust. Many veterans put God and faith on hold until a happy marriage between the war's reality and the message of the church could be realized. Many refused or feared the process of integrating Vietnam's reality into renewed faith. If old understandings of God failed them in Vietnam, then "...to hell with Him; I know how to survive by myself." I have heard this phrase often.

Distrust and fear come in waves that burden a pastoral relationship. The negative transference creates an undertow that takes pastoral intervention out to sea; it eventually increases distrust and fear—and we see again the vicious cycle. To resist the undertow threatens conflict; to give in to it exacerbates the symptom. A veteran told me poignantly that if he did not distrust people he would have to trust them. "I'm just not ready to trust others."

The next symptoms in the pastoral perspective—fears of rejection and betrayal—are discussed now, as they follow from the more general fear and distrust.

Rejection and Betrayal

The experiences of rejection and betrayal are closely linked. Rejection means not being accepted, in spite of efforts by significant individuals or a significant group. Betrayal expresses a more deeply felt experience of injustice. Rightness has been by-passed and ignored. Often, reactions to such injustices funnel into strong negative responses, spilling out into rage toward the perceived perpetrators or turning inward toward depression.

Many Vietnam combat veterans have a litany of rejection experiences. This rejection arose on the battlefield when they were not allowed to advance against the enemy; they felt hands were tied by political powers who squelched their mission. They experienced rejection from the authority that sent them on a mission of war.

Other veterans contort in rage when they recall reports in *Army Times* about well-known public figures back home questioning their sacrifices or about blood drives for the enemy. They felt their sacrifices and deeds in a foreign country had been rejected. This thought was expressed by a veteran who said, "I didn't ask to go there. I was sent there! They [the American public] don't understand." Many feel their legitimacy and integrity have been disavowed.

The welcome home was experienced as rejection. Many veterans recall vividly a cold reception, highlighted with an attitude of "we need to hurry and forget Vietnam." The nation's collective difficulty with the war and its ambiguous termination were frequently internalized as an invalidation of their struggle. "We did our job and we did it well, but, nobody accepted it [us]," is an often-heard statement.

A sequel to the initial "welcome home" was the lingering adjustments to society again. Goodwin (1980) describes how the Vietnam experience differed from previous wars and subsequently predisposed the combatants to PTSD. These maladjustments to society raised the question of acceptability of the Vietnam veteran. "If so many of us are having problems with society either something is wrong with society or something is wrong with us," a veteran said to an adjustment group. A sense of rejection seemed to be the catalyst for his comment.

Rejection deepens into a sense of betrayal. Conventional notions of good soldiering in Vietnam were sacrificed to political expediency; soldiers felt betrayed even by battlefield tactics. A block of land might be secured, but the unit would withdraw and engage in other nearby conflicts, only to be ordered to return to the initial block of land and retake it, often with the only results being maimed and crippled bodies and corpses. A clear sense of mission was clouded by battlefield realities. In addition, enemy tactics of booby trapping the villages and villagers and the surprise ambushes with quick retreats created an elusive foe. Guerilla warfare conflicted with Western mindset, which raised questions about the validity of the war. The Vietnam veteran searches for purpose with cries of betrayal and injustice. "Our country sent us to war, but would not support us," a veteran concluded.

Rejection and betrayal accumulated and grew into a rage that many veterans still struggle to quell. Often closest family and friends are the recipients of this rage as the veteran breaks inanimate objects, puts his fists through walls, or even physically abuses another person. This rage breeds a new cycle of rejection and betrayal. Employers do not understand, are threatened, and unable to tolerate it, especially as it is frequently directed toward authority figures. Health caregivers are frightened by its lethal potential. All too often, the veteran is himself afraid and rejects others, lest they reject him first.

This rage is exacerbated by other emotional experiences of the war, one of which was the seeming futility of the fighting. This sense of futility is now discussed.

Futility

The Old Testament book of Ecclesiastes describes the emotions of many Vietnam veterans: life is filled with weariness; absurdity overcomes congruency. The wisdom writer of this book reflects deeply on how short and contradictory life is, with its seemingly endless injustices and frustrations. He concludes, "All is vanity. Life is useless." He could not understand the ways of God among life's contradictions and ambiguities.

The soldier in Vietnam encountered continuous contradictions and ambiguities. Wilson (1977) identified eight existentially absurd situations in Vietnam that conflicted with the role for which the soldier was trained. These were:

- The limited military operation
- The lack of positive commitment from the South Vietnamese
- The intricacies of guerrilla warfare
- The black market operations

- The limited tour of duty in a depersonalized war
- Difficulty and helplessness in distinguishing the enemy
- The seemingly meaningless death of friends
- Faulty reentry from the war.

Laufer (1985) advanced a conceptual approach to this war trauma, focusing on the disruptive formative experiences inflicted on the soldier:

> The young soldier, prior to his entry into war, can be described as a cauldron of emotions, ideas, and themes waiting to be forged. War is a force which turns the emotional and moral world young men grow up in on its head. For example, the archetypical foundation of civil society, the injunction "Thou shalt not kill," is waived in war. (p.46)

Death, destruction and survival were ironically intimate. Laufer (1985) called this "a premature encounter with mortality."

With the failure to integrate the stress of war, many Vietnam veterans experienced a profound shattering of basic concepts of humanity. The endless supply of emptiness led them to conclude with the Biblical writer that "everything leads to weariness—a weariness too great for words."[2]

Marching along with futility, the soldier experienced separation and detachment from life's meaning. As one confided in me, "It's like walking in a bad dream that you can't wake up from...." This sense of alienation and estrangement from self and others is the next symptom we will consider.

Alienation and Estrangement

The sources of identity were confused for the young Vietnam combatant, whose average age was 19.5 years. He was easily separated from a sense of self by the threatening, violent waves of war.

According to Erikson (1963), the average age of the American soldier in Vietnam corresponded to a crucial stage in psychological maturity, Erikson's fifth stage of personality development, identity versus role confusion. In this age period, a person requires a basic sense of harmony, and congruency for healthy psychological maturity to occur. But Vietnam offered discord and incongruity, inhibiting ego synthesis, and fostering negative identity and role confusion. It was easy to cope with the absurdities by becoming numb to their emotional impact and warped in integrating them to one's own time, space, and person. The eyes and ears had seen and heard too much; the heart became separated from feeling.

Erikson's conceptualization of personality development informs a pastoral understanding of alienation and estrangement. Alienation is a separation from groundedness, the loss of a sense of purpose. This separation fosters detachment from previous identity and community, and the person shifts from place to place and person to person, seemingly disintegrated and impermanent. "I feel so freakish," a veteran said to explain his peripatetic lifestyle. A gulf of estrangement lies between the individual and his sense of meaning and purpose—estrangement and alienation from self, others, and God. There is a strangeness that pervades interpersonal and intrapersonal activity, and no firm attachments to meaning to one course of action over another.

The alienation and estrangement toward others are often fed by the veteran's fear of closeness. Wartime experiences of closeness—and loss—are painfully remembered. Personal confusion and unsure identity leave him cautious lest more hurt and pain be encountered. This estrangement fuels a suspicious attitude, which is often felt by others who steer clear, exacerbating the veteran's freakish, unnatural feeling, and intensifying his separateness.

The veteran settles for less and for dullness. There is a tendency for continual lateral or backward movement—from job to job, school to school, drifting without progress toward goals or achieving significant closeness. A magic "cure," meaning removal of all symptoms, is sought to deal with interpersonal and intrapersonal problems. A "born-to-lose" attitude develops.

The wives of many veterans complain of their cold (see Williams, "Women Partners," this volume), emotionally detached husbands, who seem unable to experience the joys of life, although some create transient joy through alcohol and a wide variety of street drugs (see Jelinek and Williams, this volume). Estrangement builds.

Alienation and estrangement are exhibited in separation from God. A massive cavern of religious incongruity exists in the minds of many Vietnam veterans because the creations of God encountered in Vietnam so starkly contrasted with the presentation of God in churches and synagogues at home. Rites and rituals learned as a child appeared removed from the death, destruction, and survival in Vietnam. Limited and unstructured patterns of devotion and spiritual development have left the veteran open to the vicissitudes of thought and feeling remaining from the evils of war. The veteran tends to invent his own gods to fill his gaps of religious meaning.

The personal creations of God have a blend of fundamental theology, cultural practices, and interpersonal and intrapersonal needs. They tend not to stand the test of time. These self-made creations are replaced as new insights, cultural change, altered and personal dynamics are presented. The unredemptive, ever-changing results of the personal creations lead to increased alienation from God. With a face filled with rage, a veteran cried out to me, "Chaplain, I went to Vietnam expecting some grace, but I found only more hell! Tell me what I should think of God? I dare you to tell me!"

Out of a pastoral perspective, the chaplain observes alienation and estrangement as symptomatic of the troubled Vietnam veteran. Alienation and estrangement are often aligned with another symptom that is the focus of the next section—the reaction to loss and the consequent grief.

Loss and Grief

Loss occurs before grief. Loss is the behavioral or existential experience in which someone or something significant is taken away. Grief is the emotional response to the loss. The process of grief is the healing of the emotional hurt and pain that result with the loss. If the healing act is significantly hindered or blocked, the reaction to the loss may impair the life functioning of the person in grief.

Losses come constantly with war. The Vietnam war was no exception. Human relationships in Vietnam were lost in several ways: (1) a tour of duty ended, (2) a change of orders meant a change of location and often of friends, (3) a wounded friend left for extended treatment, and (4) death brought finality to many. With flat affect, a veteran detailed the horrible ambush that wiped out all but a few of his company. He survived in the river by breathing through a water reed. Another veteran stoically shared a traumatic loss. His arms tensed and eyes winced as he pictured picking up the pieces of a dead friend. It is not uncommon for me to hear veterans say, "I've never been able to cry," and reveal that the healing process of grief has never begun.

Other losses occurred in the Vietnam experience. The innocence lost will never be regained or even relived at a slower, more easily accepted pace. As one veteran powerfully put it: "I grew old too fast and too soon....Once you've killed, your life is forever changed." Constant fear and weariness were strange motivations to deadly, atrocious acts. No one can describe it all. The discovery of youth was lost in the horror of repeated deaths and the constant struggle for survival.

The loss of faith and ideals accompanied the loss of innocence. The valor, the wounds, and the deaths appeared meaningless in the struggle of conflicting forces, most of which were not on the battlefield. Confidence in government declined in direct relationship to unproductive, repetitious policy. The sense of duty, honor, and prestige were lost in the cyclical patterns of deadly action.

These losses inflicted pain and sorrow that could not be forgotten by many upon return home. Because crying on the battlefield had been an extreme liability and threat to survival, many never grieved. And, because survival instincts are so intense, some could not grieve at home. Feelings of loss are not alleviated just because one wants them to go away.

As the losses increased, so did the need to grieve. But grieving was impossible in battle, so the reactions to losses became bottled up, impacted. With some, the grief is enormous: "I am afraid that if I start [to grieve] I don't think I can quit....I will lose control and it [survival] will be all over."

The fear of loss of control is associated with how grief was frequently handled on the battlefield—namely, through violent, deadly acts that created destruction. Such behavior, which helped release bottled emotions on the battlefield, was completely unacceptable at home, and the veteran feared others' reactions to his real grief. On the one hand, people might be "grossed out" by the blood and destruction of more war stories; on the other hand, they might see expressions of grief as weakness or unbecoming of a good soldier. These fears were provoked by a population that wanted to forget the unpopular war.

The cliche "time heals all wounds" was wrongly thought to apply to the grief from Vietnam; veterans expended more and more energy to keep it inside. Alcohol and illegal drugs often became easy buffers for the pain. Escapes into the woods or away from responsibility did not leave the hurt behind, and created new, self-inflicted losses that increased the need for healthy grief.

Impacted grief may often be confused with another symptom of the troubled Vietnam veteran: guilt and shame.

Guilt and Shame

Guilt describes the emotional pain that results from behavior that is judged to be wrong. This judgement is internalized and is often supported by external forces. Breaking a commandment may not create guilt, even though the external commandment is broken. Guilt begins when the person realizes his wrong, feels accused, and seeks relief from the emotional discomfort. Guilt, when left unattended, leads to lethargy and decreased responsiveness to the spirit in life.

Shame takes the experience of guilt into a deeper level of emotional pain. Wrong behavior is exposed. A person feels as if fingers are accusingly and laughingly pointed at him.

Shame takes guilt out into the open and, thus, increases its pain.

The Vietnam veteran describes guilt and shame. His pain arises from passive and active behaviors, covert and overt transgressions. Like a heavy yoke carried on his shoulders, guilt burdens the veteran and diminishes creative energy and vitality.

A veteran in his mid-30s described a life-altering event that had occurred 15 years earlier. He was driving in a truck convoy in Vietnam. His sergeant ordered him to change positions with the driver behind him. Within minutes after the exchange, his original truck was hit by a mortar and the driver immediately killed. "I've asked myself a thousand times, why wasn't that me?...I can't seem to get it out of my mind." Another veteran told me, "What I did in Vietnam went against everything I had been taught. I've been told by well-meaning types that war is different and I should feel different about it....The bottom line is I killed and I got to where I enjoyed it...I don't like that about me." The guilt arose from his actual behavior and how he reacted to it. He is perplexed that he could become such a person.

Vietnam veterans describe different sources of their guilt. They note how they inflicted pain, suffering, and death not only to the enemy, but on those who were only thought to be the enemy, and this uncertainty brought on clear emotional pain and multiplied their guilt. A forward observer related to me the day he did his job perfectly and called for artillery on an enemy company. His successful operation destroyed the entire VC company and saved his own. "I know, chaplain, it makes no sense, but I feel guilty as hell. I know my action saved countless lives in my company. I know that I was following orders. But, something inside me tells me I did an abhorrent act." He later shared how he now has found community with a group that seeks to protect the dignity of all forms of life; but, "I still feel guilty," he concluded.

The guilt that springs from overt behavior is also associated with inhumane, animalistic acts outside the line of fire. Some describe horrible escapes into drugs and alcohol. Some describe the misery of selfishness where you religiously apply the "first-take-care-of-yourself" attitude. The inevitable result was that self-indulgence did not satisfy, but it did produce twinges of guilt or a desire to increase the indulgence to avoid honesty with oneself.

Guilt arose from other aspects of the Vietnam experience. When some die and others do not, the survivors often ask, "Why not me?" (see T. Williams, this volume). This painful emotion is called survivor guilt. Goodwin (1980) wrote: "It [survivor guilt] is not based on anything hypothetical. Rather, it is based on the harshest of realities, the actual death of comrades, and the struggle of the survivor to live. Often the survivor has had to compromise himself or the life of someone else in order to live." (p. 14)

Associated with survivor guilt is its cold, cruel companion—namely, helplessness. A sense of powerlessness is remembered as one recalls his inability to change a bad situation. Powerless and impotent to alter past events, the veteran may turn his guilt inward into self-destructive behavior. Suicide has taken its toll.

Many veterans vow never to be caught where they do not have a weapon with them. This emotion is carried by some into provoking antagonism from others and possibly losing their life to take their place beside fallen comrades. In contrast, other veterans react differently with survivor guilt: they remove all weapons from their homes. One recently told me, "I vowed never to hurt anybody again. I've done enough of that...there's no way you'll find a weapon around me!" This contrast was sharply noted when another man described the difference between him and his brother, both combat veterans. "My brother has weapons inside his house and in his truck." He continued, "He loves guns. He talks about guns and studies about them. Me, I don't want to have anything to do with them. If I never see another one, that would be okay."

A final sense of guilt from Vietnam is the feeling of not having done enough. This guilt may have diffuse origins. It may arise from a generalized self-blame for the lost war. It may arise from unrealistic beliefs of what one should have done when a friend was killed. It may arise from a clear failure to perform as trained in a traumatic fire-fight. A tormented, tensed veteran shared the horror of being overrun on a never-to-be-forgotten night. He told how a friend chose to go up a hill while he stayed below. His friend died. He said, "I should have made him stay with me."

The burden of guilt weighs heavily, and is intensified for veterans who have had the appropriateness of their guilty feeling verified by others. The label "baby killers" has evoked especially bitter reactions. A veteran who killed a child to protect his squad from the child's hidden explosives expressed his vulnerability to this label. "I have to live with the knowledge of what I did. To be reminded of it does not help me either." He then defended himself as a caring person caught between two evils.

The undeclared nature of the war and the low public support tended to increase the shame experienced by many of the Vietnam veterans. They sought validation of the pain, but experienced coldness, misunderstanding and accusation. For some, this shame became confused with anger at a society that would send them to war but not support them.

These feelings of guilt and shame were often ignored. A good soldier supposedly does not look back. They sought to avoid their real selves. What sadly occurred was that many made this venture of escape a life-style. They found that they maintained control of themselves, including their guilt and shame, by isolating themselves from others. They withdrew to paradoxically maintain contact with themselves and others. The subject of isolation and withdrawal is now discussed from a pastoral perspective.

Isolation and Withdrawal

Isolation and withdrawal are often concomitant behaviors to the emotions of guilt and shame, and are frequent companions of the Vietnam veteran with PTSD. A struggling veteran paradoxically said, "Loneliness is my true companion." A common litany within my outpatient group is, "Society does not understand me...so I isolate myself." This statement is often followed by: "This group of fellow Vietnam veterans are the only people I feel comfortable around."

The wounds of war escape the description of words. Some veterans feel that words cheapen the experience of combat and disgrace the sacrifices of battle. Only fellow combat veterans understand. There is a fraternity with closed initiation rites. The ritual of the fraternity includes the unspoken message, "You don't need to say a word. I understand." What often grows from this ritual is an increase in loneliness and isolation (see Hickman, this volume).

The fraternal ritual is esteemed and remains sacred. When someone begins to break out of the patterns of withdrawal, suspicion is often cast on him, or a subdued questioning begins about the authenticity of his combat experiences. The scars of traumatic experiences in combat run deep, often leaving rough calluses that are insensitive to individual desires to escape the rituals of isolating behavior.

The terms of isolation and withdrawal are viewed here as uncreative behaviors. They are seen as means of avoidance and escape, rather than creative behaviors of joining and aligning. Isolation is living with the self to avoid contact with others. Withdrawal is the action of fleeing contact with others.

The experience of combat redefined closeness for many veterans. Closeness that is based on intimacy and that embraces vulnerabilities is often feared. To share oneself is perceived as sharing the wounds of war that are, themselves, too frightening and painful for the veteran himself. Some veterans say that their attempts to share vulnerabilities from the war were met with abuse and mocking laughter. With such receptions, some veterans develop defenses patterned after combat training; they know how to survive alone: create a safe place and do not expose yourself. Many veterans describe special havens of isolation along a parkway or in the mountains. A veteran spoke succinctly of the benefits of his isolation: "No one bugs me. I'm doing what I do well—surviving alone."

Agoraphobic behavior and the fear of intimacy remove veterans from others, yet many cite discomfort with their lonely life styles. They want to change, but are afraid. Some truly see themselves as strangers in their native land. They search for a home, a place that offers embrace. Countless veterans describe innumerable moves, validating their inability to find this place. "The woods" become a symbol of this nomadic, lonely life style.

Isolation and withdrawal are more than just physical behaviors. They are also manifestations of emotional detachment. Intimacy, although desired, is seldom described. The mask of symptoms covers a real person, capable of giving and responding creatively to closeness and caring. Inevitably the mask (the symptoms) has become so much a part of the person that the veteran stays behind it. Intimacy is yearned for and avoided.

Wives report detachment. Flashbacks, violent outbursts, and avoidant behavior create great stress on the marriage relationship. Families adjust by avoiding the father who is withdrawn and unpredictable. Wives feel bound to a person in a struggle they cannot fully comprehend. Children experience anger toward and resentment of a daddy they cannot talk to.

Triangulation occurs with the family unit (see Williams, "Women Partners," this volume). There is the husband (father) behind the mask, and there is the husband (father) with PTSD symptoms. There is often the husband relating to veterans or the VA. There is the husband's (father's) allegiance to fellow veterans and ties to the VA. Many family members separate from the veteran who is permanently alienated from the person and his mask of symptoms. Other family members struggle with the burden of continued attachment; some are able to protect themselves and detach the symptoms from the person.

A pastoral perspective looks for the person behind the symptoms. A pastoral perspective seeks to distinguish the "sins" from the "sinner." The symptoms are often interrelated and enmeshed in the life style and relationships of the veteran. These symptoms tend to wax and wane in intensity. Some may be more burdened with loss and grief, for instance, and less burdened with alienation and estrangement. The intensity and frequency of each symptom combine to define the set of symptoms (mask) that is unique to each veteran. A pastoral perspective seeks to gain entrance behind the mask of symptoms and offer healing and wholeness to the person. The next section describes the veteran's need for healing and wholeness from a pastoral perspective.

PASTORAL POSSIBILITIES

These seven distinct symptoms describe maladies of the human spirit. The chaplain offers good news—the pastoral possibilities for increased healing and wholeness, beginning with a deep understanding of the troubles and a commitment to care. (The term "pastoral possibilities" describes the goals of the chaplain's caring.)

A Pastoral Response

Fowler (1981) provided insight into how faith is affected by psychological stress. He noted that psychosocial influences are incorporated in the dynamics of faith. These influences may be beneficial or detrimental to growth in "faith stages." He wrote:

> Seeing [the] optimal correlations [of faith stages] with psychosocial eras gives a sense of how time, experience, challenge and nurture are required for growth in faith....Remedial or therapeutic nurture is called for when the anachronism of a lagging faith stage fails to keep pace with psychosocial growth. (p. 114)

Fowler's insight speaks to the Vietnam veteran struggling in the adjustment and meaning for life. I think Fowler's application of faith to life gives the chaplain a handle on what happens when a young soldier faces the trauma of war and the realities of readjustment. Fowler wrote: "Whenever we properly speak of faith it involves people's shaping or testing their lives, defining directions and relationships with others in accordance with coordinates of value and power recognized as ultimate." (p. 93)

For so many Vietnam veterans, the "ultimate" was clearly survival, taking care of self and then your buddy. Once allegiance to survival was maintained and achieved, life was frequently left with little meaning. A veteran shared this thought with me: "I had my biggest high (was it a religious experience?!) on the battlefield in Vietnam. Nothing has been able to match it!"

The realities of the seven symptoms inform a pastoral perspective with the troubled Vietnam veteran. These realities state that the Ultimate, survival, proved a false god. After Vietnam, new coordinates of value and power influenced the soldier at home. A search for a new Ultimate has led many down assorted, and often destructive paths, exacerbating the maladies in their troubled lives.

A multidisciplinary approach to treatment is continually advocated. A few have recognized the significance of the chaplain in providing therapeutic competence for the spiritual aspect of a person in treatment. But some have raised cautions about the chaplain's intervention—for example, Arnold (1985) warns against a legalistic or pietistic approach with the Vietnam veteran.

Part of the challenge that exists in proclaiming the pastoral possibilities for the troubled veteran is educating and illustrating to the interdisciplinary staff that the chaplain's intervention is beneficial to treatment. This education is accomplished by working with the staff, learning the staff's terminology and treatment methodology, and sharing their disappointments and celebrations. The chaplain integrates his unique message with those of the other members of the team. The chaplain also speaks for the dignity of the veteran by representing ethical dimensions in health care. This integration is most effective when the product of the chaplain's work and his example can easily be observed by the other staff. The chaplain's response to the troubled veteran recognizes the fine line between quality health care and patient misuse.

Health care ethics extend to the treatment of Vietnam veterans. Misuse arises when the veteran is viewed just as an object of research or when the veteran's health care needs are continually supplanted by bureaucratic expediency. Misuse surfaces when the potential of the human spirit is allowed to drown in the sea of diagnostic procedures and treatment methodologies. The chaplain uniquely questions such misuses while proclaiming the worth and dignity of God's children.

He also realistically assesses the brokenness of the human spirit, which is clearly seen through the seven symptoms. Tillich (1963) offered a strategy for interpretation and intervention within human brokenness. This strategy reads the brokenness and looks at its underside.

It confronts the ambiguities inherent in the veteran's struggles. It advocates courage. It sees the negative symptoms as having opposite polarities that illustrate positive pastoral goals with the Vietnam veteran. Trust is in opposition to the malady of distrust and fear. Similarly, acceptance counters rejection and betrayal; hope challenges futility; mending opposes alienation; mourning and new life offset loss and grief; forgiveness strikes at guilt and shame; and a sense of community battles isolation and withdrawal.

These goals illustrate the opposite polarities of the pastoral perspective toward PTSD symptoms. They are not mutually exclusive, but interweave to form a pattern of alleviated stress and improved adjustment. This pattern portrays a healing of the spirit.

These pastoral possibilities balance the maladies of the troubled veteran. They provide terminology to specifically describe the observations of a pastoral perspective. Certain maladies are evident in the chaplain's congregation of troubled veterans. Many of these have been forged in the crucible of war. Opposite traits on the seven theological continuums, the space between the poles, indicate positive change to these maladies. The chaplain's goal is to provide appropriate pastoral care and counseling that facilitate the movement of the individual from maladies of brokenness to possibilities of healing and wholeness.

Evidence of increased trust occurs as the veterans increasingly make attachments of lasting worth; a therapeutic relationship in a counseling context, a lengthy membership in a church community, or reports of a satisfying marriage or job situation all are noteworthy. When the veteran begins to reframe God's relationship to the ambiguity of Vietnam, we see positive therapeutic signs; God's providence is viewed as taking the ashes of defeat and the dry bones of distrust and constructing new life, secured in trust. As one veteran said: "I realize God never left me there [Vietnam] or here [now]...I do blur His presence, though."

Many Vietnam veterans are able to receive affirmation from recent public attention and recognition given to their sacrifice. A veteran commented, "I'm glad I lived long enough to see us being remembered...it could be more, but the recognition means some acceptance." Such statements are indicative of positive movements on the continuum from rejection toward acceptance.

Hope counterbalances futility. The writer of Ecclesiastes noted that life passages offered hopeful change; amidst futility, he noted, "For everything there is a season...a time for healing...a time for building...." (Ecclesiastes 3). A veteran heard a small group describe their bleak, futile view of the future. One in the group said, "There is no hope. I've flat given up." The listening veteran refocused his perception of this thought in the context of life passages. He said: "I've had 80 jobs; I've been hospitalized; I've had people tell me I'm crazy; I've hurt my family. But I've still got my family; I can learn. Something is there for me. It's going to take me a while to find it but something's there. I haven't given up...I don't know what my hope is yet, but it's there. I'm hanging in there...." This veteran appeared to grasp the thought of Ecclesiastes: he gave evidence of hope over futility.

Mending opposes alienation and estrangement. Moses fled from alienation and estrangement. But he returned, strengthened and empowered from his wrenching experience, to lead the Hebrews and offer mending for their enslaved lives; he refocused his alienation and estrangement toward a helpful purpose. I think of veterans who have shared such Moses-like refocusing with me. As examples, there is the near middle-aged veteran who is working on his degree. "Maybe I can help my brothers [Vietnam veterans]," he said. There is another veteran who took a job that his buddies claimed was too menial: "It's something I can do and it's got dignity in it," he responded. There is the veteran with young children: "I want to stay away, but I know they need me. I force myself to be with them as much as I can." These attitudes illustrate mending of the human spirit, positive behaviors away from alienation and estrangement.

Healthy grief in loss brings new life. Although losses in Vietnam may truly never be forgotten (nor should they be), their debilitating effects may be lightened through appropriate mourning. Regrieving may enable the reliving and revisiting of the loss to bring therapeutic change. The renewal of healthy grief offers the possibility of positive change on this continuum. A veteran confided in me, "It hurts so much [to grieve about Vietnam losses], but it hurts even more not to...."

Forgiveness counters guilt and shame. Forgiveness is the release of the shackles that have burdened an individual with bad feelings about past misdeeds, mistakes, or failures (real or perceived). Forgiveness is liberating; it frees energy toward beneficial productive behavior. A chaplain's reassurance of God's forgiveness, understood in the context of specific guilt, offers power and redemptive hope. A veteran told me of his insight about forgiveness: "I know the key is my ability to forgive myself...some days I do better with it than others." Receiving forgiveness is evidenced through reduced preoccupation with the paralyzing yoke of past misdeeds, mistakes, and failures. Even little signs of this ability to forgive and to be accountable to oneself may be indicators of this positive change.

Finally, a sense of community contrasts with isolation and withdrawal. This community counters individual isolation; it says "we're in this together" (see Rheault, this volume). It is ameliorative: it strengthens those who identify with its reasons for existence. Examples include church/synagogue, service organizations, or volunteer groups. Previously isolated veterans have found some identity in local organizations of Vietnam veterans. Others have maintained relationships with their church/synagogue. One veteran witnessed to his church's support: "I go to church. People care and say hello, even when I try to avoid them." Such examples are visible clues of positive recreative change away from isolation and withdrawal.

In seeking to realize these pastoral possibilities, we must not lose sight of the fact that the enormity of the brokenness is real, and the harsh realities of Vietnam and post-war adjustments may tempt the chaplain to search for a more tangibly rewarding congregation. The fruits of the labors appear most often swallowed in the ravenous mouths of brokenness and despair. Yet, the Judeo-Christian ethic calls for the possibilities of hope and renewal amidst brokenness, and for a more lasting "ultimate" than just survival. This Ultimate, received in faith, encourages the chaplain's persistence.

Fleming (1985) has emphasized that treatment of the Vietnam veteran must involve "concrete, not abstract thinking." This emphasis also applies to the chaplain's intervention. The chaplain's statements involving newness of the spirit must be specific to the realities of the veteran and his symptoms; clarity and specificity are vital. The final section deals with placing the pastoral possibilities into practice, that is, into specific pastoral interventions.

PASTORAL INTERVENTION

Pastoral intervention refers to the work by a designated representative—for example, a chaplain—of a faith group. This work integrates the chaplain's training and skill, the faith tradition and, one hopes, compassion for people. Pastoral intervention with the Vietnam veteran involves working with individuals of assorted faith backgrounds. This diversity challenges the chaplain to creatively develop vehicles on which to carry his message of healing and wholeness. Such a message arises within God's creative, redemptive, and sanctifying acts.

My work with the Vietnam veteran has taught me that traditional models of ministry—for example, organized Bible study—are rejected. I have also learned that these veterans do not want me to be their medical doctor, psychologist, or social worker. My unique contribution lies in my offering a faith perspective to their health care. My contribution offers spiritual, or theological, significance to the intervention, which listens to their deepest hurts, doubts, and yearnings. I look for blessings within the veterans struggles and am reminded of the story of Jacob's struggle. Jacob (Genesis 32:26) wrestled long and hard with an unknown assailant before a blessing emerged out of his struggle. It is also within the veteran's own perserverence against PTSD symptomology (assailants) that blessings emerge.

My work with Vietnam veterans has taught me to redefine what a blessing is. I have learned to look for renewal of the spirit in small measures that, however small, are still significant and worthy of the struggle to persevere. This struggle would be easy to forsake. I look for the change in behaviors illustrating increased trust, acceptance, and hope. I look for mending within the brokenness. My pastoral intervention interfaces a faith perspective, a spiritual dynamic, to the struggle and hurt of the troubled veteran. This interface occurs in five areas of pastoral intervention: (1) pastoral visitation, (2) group process, (3) pastoral counseling, (4) worship and prayer activity, and (5) interdisciplinary treatment plan development.

Pastoral Visitation

Pastoral visitation involves a regular routine of availability in which I am identified as chaplain. This availability communicates an interest in the veteran and his treatment and welfare. I do not seek to structure the content of visitation; I do structure a routine for availability—for example, one morning and two afternoons a week. I am open to hear the fears and yearnings, joys and accomplishments that are presented. It is not infrequent for a veteran to say, "Chaplain, I just want to tell you...[a struggle, a success, etc.]." As the presence of Jesus graced the region of Galilee, the chaplain may communicate care and availability through his/her presence.

Group Process

Group process refers to inter- and intrapersonal dynamics that result in the leadership of therapeutic groups with selected Vietnam veterans. I have co-lead two weekly groups (an inpatient and outpatient group) with two psychologists. The inpatient group is called "redirection group," and the outpatient group is called "readjustment group." The inpatient group is time-limited with three months as the maximum length of participation. The outpatient group is on-going and has no time limit. Each group is limited to eight to ten participants. Members of the outpatient group remain active in the group with regular attendance. New members are added as old ones drop out. These groups are not structured in content except for occasional didactic sessions pertaining to PTSD and faith perspectives. (I have a three-hour didactic presentation of "PTSD and Religious Faith.") There is an emphasis on the here-and-now, away from system or compensation issues, and toward interpersonal and intrapersonal issues. I utilize the pastoral perspectives of PTSD to offer clarity for the troubled veteran. I am often asked, "So, what do I do now?" Such questions indicate trust and a readiness to hear of the pastoral possibilities within PTSD.

Pastoral Counseling

Pastoral counseling refers to the process in which I utilize insights and principles derived from theology and the behavioral sciences to work with Vietnam veterans, couples, or families toward the achievement of healing and wholeness. Veterans request this intensive, in-depth pastoral intervention or they are referred by a psychiatrist or the interdisciplinary team. In my pastoral counseling, I seek to establish a deep relationship involving the therapeutic utilization of transference and countertransference issues. Pastoral counseling generally occurs once a week and lasts for forty-five to fifty minutes. The number of sessions varies according to the person, his treatment needs, and outpatient availability. The dynamics of pastoral counseling unfold deeply held maladies in the human spirit and allow for the reexperiencing of those maladies to foster healing and wholeness. Early childhood and developmental issues frequently are enmeshed in the PTSD symptomatology. Dynamic exploration of those issues offers potential holistic healing for the veteran's deepest hurts and conflicts (Wallace, 1983).

Worship and Prayer

In the specific acts of worship and prayer, I, as chaplain, provide religious leadership. This leadership may be prescribed (as in a public worship service or an invocation), or it may be extemporaneous (as in response to a prayer request). An appropriate liturgical format is taken for groups whose backgrounds are interdenominational.

Worship and prayer provide a distinctive opportunity for the spoken proclamation of faith—i.e., the sharing of the Gospel. This opportunity often comes only after a relationship is formed and trust is built. I have experienced that the spoken proclamation for the troubled veteran is best communicated in simple, down-to-earth fashion. Concrete images, illustrations, and stories with direct application to the veteran's struggle are most helpful. The symbols and rites of faith are best received when presented with sincerity without fanfare and adornment. The moments of worship and prayer are precious, deserving of clear, concise expressions of how the purpose and goals of faith fit into the maladies of troubled lives.

Interdisciplinary Team

The interdisciplinary team formulates the treatment plan of an individual veteran. This plan is devised to meet the needs of each veteran. My input is a chaplain's perspective on diagnosis and treatment.[3] Updates of the veteran's treatment involve notes of the chaplain's intervention and any revised assessments. I speak for the dignity of the person and humanity of treatment and assert there is a direct correlation between the success of treatment and the level of teamwork among the interdisciplinary staff. I have been fortunate to work with professionals who have been accepting of me and my place in the team.

FORMS OF CHANGE

From these areas of pastoral intervention, I have observed three unique forms of change that occur, and that have both theological and psychological significance. I categorize these changes as (1) rebuilding, (2) turning around, and (3) renewal. These categories are now described.

Rebuilding (Creative Action)

The biblical story of Joseph illustrates rebuilding. Joseph, who experienced betrayal, alienation, and loss, positively rebuilt his life over a period of time. He exhibited his worth and value as a person in spite of the hardship and injustices he had experienced. He maintained his honesty and integrity. He was valued, and he used this recognition to benefit others.

Tom experienced heavy combat duty in his 12 months in Vietnam. He was barely 19 at the time. He married shortly after his return and had two children. He drank heavily and lost jobs. Within a few years, he was divorced. During the succeeding years, he continued to lose jobs, as many as three in one year. He withdrew from his family and became hypervigilant and agoraphobic. At the request of his family, he sought help.

In his treatment, and for the first time, he exposed the deep fears and shared painful losses. He discovered mistakes of his own making. He claimed he felt a sense of acceptance as he exposed the brokenness and errors of his past. He began to examine the directions he took that were destructive to him. He benefited from examining his mistakes, analyzing what went wrong, and formulating alternate actions to rectify his mistakes. He took what was salvageable. The remaining pieces were seen as having creative potential. He developed plans to implement the resalvaging of his life: he reestablished contact with his ex-wife, and began a new relationship with her; his perception of God moved from a judging, vindictive view to an accepting, caring one. He saw God as blessing the salvageable pieces in his life.

This type of pastoral intervention had specific ingredients. A rational approach was taken to enable the veteran to clearly identify and formulate the destructive elements in his life. Problem-solving techniques enabled him to examine the alternatives he had. Like Joseph, Tom did not give up on what was left from the injustice and failure. He began a slow, arduous process of recreation. He found initiative and strength that had been dormant, and he used them to build new alternatives.

Recalling Tillich's polarities, we note that Tom moved from distrust with his ex-wife to increased trust. He experienced acceptance and stated "it felt good." He attached hope to the rebuilding of salvageable pieces and reestablished contact with his church. He reported mending within significant relationships. He shared losses and uncovered grief for buddies who were horribly killed. He described a relief of guilt, a sense of absolution. (Haley [1978] described the need for absolution in the treatment of PTSD. She wrote: "Absolution is necessary, but must evolve over time and within the protective shield and containment of the therapeutic alliance" [p. 266].) His contact with significant others increased, alleviating a strong sense of isolation.

The pastoral intervention modeled recreative possibilities for Tom. This intervention utilized a trusting relationship, developed slowly and carefully over time. It found opportunities that occurred through visitation, group process, and pastoral counseling to enable Tom to reframe the perception of his brokenness and despair, and centered on a view of a nonpunitive God who accepted him within his failures. Tom exposed the hurt and pain that lay beneath the mask of brokenness and failure as he began to rebuild his life. Creative action occurred.

Turning Around (Redemptive Action)

Certain dynamics appear in the turning around experience. A person acknowledges personal responsibility for his life. He seeks to learn from his emotional pain. This pain may arise from personal failures or errors of judgement but, in any case, pain affects attitudes toward oneself and others; a sense of purpose in life declines, and the spirit for life and vitality ebbs. There is a temptation to blame others for our failures and pain, and there is the tendency to expect others to extricate us from our misery.

The turning around experience brings fundamental changes in perception and attitude; the individual views the source of his pain as an issue he can control. He admits his failure and receives redemption for his misdeeds. Relief of conscience frees energy and refocuses his attention. New purpose arises with more energy released to find productive activity.

An example of this redemptive action is taken from a group experience. The chaplain's role illustrates specific actions taken to enable the redemptive experience.

Members in a weekly therapeutic group developed a sense of community with one another. They claimed their attachments and closeness and stated the value and trustworthiness of the group. One of the group members suddenly died, apparently of natural causes. He was a leader in the group.

The group was shocked by his unexpected death. Some wanted to attach blame for his early death on Vietnam. Some wanted to focus attention on the VA's response (or lack of it) to his death. The pain of loss was collectively avoided. The group members wanted to use this death as further evidence of the evils of Vietnam and reasons for their distrust, alienation, and withdrawal from others outside the group. The member who died was seen as another victim who faced the inevitable fate of external forces arising from Vietnam to inflict death and destruction.

In my pastoral intervention, I saw in his death an opportunity for a redemptive experience in the group. I believed our attachments had to be claimed and our loss needed to be grieved. Attention was focused on how his loss felt. The realities of his death and loss from the group were not avoided. Feelings of loss gradually oozed out, and some emotional ventilation occurred. Some shared personal vulnerabilities and pain. The realities of his death and burial were experienced, but they did not bring added death to the group. Some even spoke of losses from Vietnam for which they had never grieved. The death became the catalyst for a redemptive experience.

This redemptive experience was evidenced with our own memorial service. I worked with the group to develop a format, based on Scriptural sources, for an appropriate service in our group setting. Dislikes and fears toward formal religious activity were aired. Expressions of faith and hope came out. In their service, an opportunity was given for the group members to state their attachments. Selected Scripture readings presented the finality and hope of death and life. The Christian message of resurrection was affirmed. Hope was verbalized. We figuratively buried our friend. His death brought a new beginning for the group to face fear and loss within themselves. "I am sure glad we did this...he wasn't just forgotten," typified the group's reaction. Some made linkages to losses and unresolved grief from Vietnam. "I never did this [openly recognize loss] over there."

Renewal (Sanctifying Action)

The New Testament example of Paul gives a vivid portrayal of renewal in a person's life. Paul, known as Saul, was consumed with a passion to destroy that overwhelmed his outlook on life. He later expressed how the passion blinded him, creating alienation and despair in his life. His conversion experience created change; it renewed his perception of life. His passion to destroy changed. His eyes were opened to new meaning and reasons for existence, and what he was enabled to see brought him forgiveness, mending, and hope.

His attitudes and purposes were renewed. Within his faith, he made positive change in his life.

In the renewal experience, a person receives a gift external to his control. This gift has benefit to him. It is internalized to make ameliorative change. The gift gives credence and value for brokenness and pain in life. The person believes in the power of this spiritual experience. He has faith. Fowler (1981) explained faith as a response to transcendent value and power through cumulative tradition; it is the alignment of a person's heart or will with this transcendent value and power. Its effect is on the whole person. It is the substance of the things not seen, yet hoped for. Behavior is affected. Healing results.

Renewal for Vietnam veterans varies with faith traditions. Sacramental faith groups believe such renewing power comes through such events as Baptism and Holy Communion. These rites provide a person with external power to engender change in and for life. The rite of confession and absolution offer to unlock the mystery of renewed life. Another tradition may attribute the public profession of faith with renewal powers. This public action brings with it the support of the community of faith.

Horowitz and Solomon (1978) recorded specific suggestions for renewal with the issue of guilt. They identified in the Vietnam veteran "a realistic shame and guilt that cannot be relieved simply by clear expression and rational working-through" (p. 279). Horowitz and Solomon identified the therapeutic power of a renewal process to deal with the issue of guilt. Their recommendations involve a three-step process:

- Clarification of the guilt—for example, through the use of usual psychotherapeutic maneuvers for clear expression;
- Atonement and penance, called "the classical maneuvers"—for example, rites in the Roman Catholic Church—for the reduction of guilt. "The maneuvers are classical because they work comparatively well" (p. 280). This concept includes confession, a period of emotional pain, self-accusation, and possibly self-destructive behavior (job loss and object loss). Clarification with the veteran of how much harm he must continue to inflict is important; and
- Symbolic restitution, which involves actions that heal people or the environment and provide a route away from self-destructive patterns and towards life-affirming strategies.

Faith traditions utilize sacred rites and rituals—for example, the Seder and Holy Communion—that empower participants to regenerate and renew themselves. Chaplains have these powerful resources to enable renewal. In my experience, veterans do not report cures, or elimination of symptoms from their renewal experiences, but they do report added purpose and resolve to positively live with these symptoms and courageously continue their struggles. Within the Spirit's gift of faith and pursuing power, the veteran confronts his struggle with the certainty that comes for a loved, sanctified child of God.

CONCLUSION

I recently viewed the Vietnam Veterans' Memorial in Washington, D.C. I had heard various reports of how the black wall with so many names affected the veterans of that war. My reactions to this memorial provide some closure to this chapter on the care of troubled Vietnam veterans.

I observed mourning. Visitors were hushed, respectful, and appeared lost for words. I observed pain on faces in their recall of Vietnam's legacy. I observed ownership as people took time to find and touch the names of family members or acquaintances on the wall. I observed hope in the resolve that the sacrifices represented by those names were not in vain. (I claim my own feelings informed these observations.)

The symbolism of the wall evokes strong reactions in its observers. It is stark and powerful, in a quiet, sunken place by itself, but in historical context as it points toward the Washington Monument and Lincoln Memorial. The length of the list of names is awesome. The reactions are reminders of the war's realistic and continual effect on its veterans whose symptoms evoke powerful responses, as does the wall. A pastoral perspective of this response is vital to alleviate the enormity of these symptoms. A pastoral response takes its place among the interventions of other health-care givers.

This pastoral perspective is realistic about the brokenness that is encountered. The chaplain's presence may precipitate strong negative reactions from the veteran. It is important for the chaplain to understand the symptoms—distrust and fear, rejection and betrayal, futility, alienation and estrangement, loss and grief, guilt and shame, and isolation and withdrawal. In the development of a healing relationship with the veteran, the chaplain offers intervention to mend the brokenness and reduce the symptoms. This intervention may be recreative, redemptive, and renewing. These positive results are not exclusive, but overlap each other. They illustrate a hope that exists in the pastoral response with the troubled Vietnam veteran.

NOTES

1. New treatment approaches for PTSD have solicited a holistic intervention to the symptoms of the disorder. Fleming (1985) wrote, "To adequately understand the Vietnam veteran, a more holistic, interdisciplinary approach is needed" (p. 123). Fleming defines holistic to only include the social, political, historical, economic, and philosophical aspects of the person. Scrigner (1984) argues for a multidisciplinary approach to best meet the needs of the chronic PTSD patient. He stated, "A comprehensive, multidisciplinary approach should continue during all phases of treatment...." (p. 182). Scrigner's compilation of assorted disciplines affecting such an approach numbers two dozen, but fails to include a chaplain or anyone addressing the spiritual dimensions of the person. Indeed, there is a great gap in the literature on the chaplain's role in dealing with PTSD in the troubled Vietnam veteran.

2. There was a shattering of faith in the capacity for remaking into good that which was bad. Hurt and pain increased; cynicism and suspicion blossomed; and brokenness of mind, body, and spirit seemed to be the order of the day. A sense of futility deepened.

3. In conjunction with Medical Records and the Chief of Chaplain Service, I have developed a Chaplain's Assessment Form. This form contains basic information on the veteran's religious history, an assessment of the veteran's malady, and specific recommendations for the chaplain's intervention. These recommendations are approved interventions—i.e., groups or pastoral counseling. This Assessment Form becomes a part of the veteran's chart and permanent record.

REFERENCES

American Psychiatric Association. (1980). *Diagnostic and statistical manual of mental disorders* (3rd ed.). Washington, D.C: American Psychiatric Press.

Arnold, A. L. (1985). Inpatient treatment of Vietnam veterans with PTSD. In S. M. Sonnenburg, A. S. Blank, & J. A. Talbott (Eds.), *The trauma of war: Stress and recovery in Vietnam veterans.* Washington, D.C.: American Psychiatric Press.

Erikson, E. H. (1963). *Childhood and society* (2nd rev. ed.). New York: W. W. Norton.

Fleming, R. H. (1985, May). Post Vietnam syndrome: Neurosis or sociosis? *Psychiatry, 48*, 122-139.

Fowler, J. W. (1981). *Stages of faith: The psychology of human development and the quest for meaning.* San Francisco: Harper and Row.

Goodwin, J. (1980). The etiology of combat-related post-traumatic stress disorders. In T. Williams (Ed.), *Post-traumatic stress disorders of the Vietnam veteran and his family* (pp. 1-24). Cincinnati, OH: Disabled American Veterans.

Haley, S. A. (1978). Treatment implications of post-combat stress response syndromes for mental health professionals. In C. R. Figley (Ed.), *Stress disorders among Vietnam veterans* (pp. 254-267). New York: Brunner/Mazel.

Horowitz, M. J., & Solomon, G. F. (1978). Delayed stress syndromes in Vietnam veterans. In C. R. Figley (Ed.), *Stress disorders among Vietnam veterans* (pp. 268-280). New York: Brunner/Mazel.

Ingram, T. L., Hurley, E. C., & Riley, M. T. (1985, March). Grief resolution therapy in a pastoral context. *The Journal of Pastoral Care, 39*, 69-72.

Laufer, R. S. (1985). War trauma and human development: The Vietnam experience. In S. M. Sonnenburg, A. S. Blank, & J. A. Talbott (Eds.), *The trauma of war: Stress and recovery in Vietnam veterans.* Washington, D.C.: American Psychiatric Press.

Leventman, S. (1978). Epilogue: Social and historical perspectives on the Vietnam veteran. In C. R. Figley (Ed.), *Stress disorders among Vietnam veterans* (pp. 291-295). New York: Brunner/Mazel.

Lifton, R. J. (1978). Advocacy and corruption in the healing profession. In C. R. Figley (Ed.), *Stress disorders among Vietnam veterans.* New York: Brunner/Mazel.

Scrigner, C.B. (1984). *Post-traumatic stress disorder: Diagnosis, treatment, and legal issues.* New York: Prager Special Studies.

Tillich, P. (1963). *Systematic theology* (Vol 3). Chicago: University of Chicago Press.

Wilson, J. P. (1977). *Forgotten Warrior Project.* Washington, D.C: Disabled American Veterans.

CHAPTER FIVE
DIAGNOSIS AND TREATMENT OF SURVIVOR GUILT—THE BAD PENNY

Tom Williams

After seeing over two thousand trauma victims, it appears to me that the ones who do not improve in treatment are those who have not resolved their survivor guilt. At the Post-Trauma Treatment Center, we call this the "bad penny syndrome," because these clients tend to return to treatment periodically and do not seem to resolve their traumatic experience. Many clinicians working with trauma groups report that some form of survivor guilt is indeed a major concern for both diagnosis and treatment of trauma survivors.

THEORETICAL MODELS FOR UNDERSTANDING ACUTE AND CHRONIC PTSD

In looking to theory to try to understand what seems to perpetuate symptoms of post-traumatic stress disorder (PTSD) over time, two particular models appear to be important in understanding this phenomenon. We developed the acute trauma model, in Figure 1, after two years of experience in treating armed robbery and assault victims, police officers, war veterans, and exPOWs suffering acute trauma. We have treated some 350 people utilizing the trauma team concept, which includes intervention as quickly as possible after the trauma, preferably minutes but certainly no more than hours later. The model delineates three distinct phases of acute post-trauma reactions: the shock phase, the impact phase, and the recovery phase.

Two distinct emotional responses normally characterize the shock phase: (1) immobilization, confusion and disorganization, and (2) denial. However, people who are overtrained, such as military, police, or emergency medical workers, may by-pass these reactions, although residual elements of them are often evident. In the immobalization phase, the typical response is one of confusion, disorganization, and an inability to perform such simple routine tasks as opening a cash register for a robber. In the denial phase, the person does not believe that the trauma is actually happening. Some victims report perceptual changes in which time is altered and events seem to be happening in slow motion. Visual perceptions may be modified so that people sometimes have a derealized "out-of-body" experience or at least feel that they are simply observing rather than participating in the trauma. Another frequent perceptual alteration is a hysterical-like tunnel vision that focuses on the trauma scene itself to the exclusion of the rest of the environment. For instance, a robbery victim focuses on a weapon directed at him or her and doesn't recollect what the robber looked like, what was happening, or who was standing next to the robber.

The impact phase starts with a period of anger and/or extreme anxiety that is manifest as trembling, or crying, or subjective feelings of tension, anxiety, outrage, or anger. Initially, this anger may be displaced, as in the case of a store employee who gets angry with the store's owners for allowing themselves to be robbed instead of with the armed robber. War veterans have a difficult time blaming the enemy for the chaos of combat and the death and destruction, and instead may blame themselves or their government, or to be angry at inappropriate targets.

The next step in the impact phase we call the "what-if-and-maybe" phase, or stated simply, the process of self-doubt. This is a form of survivor guilt in which the survivor questions his or her behavior during the trauma. To try to change history and avoid facing the reality of

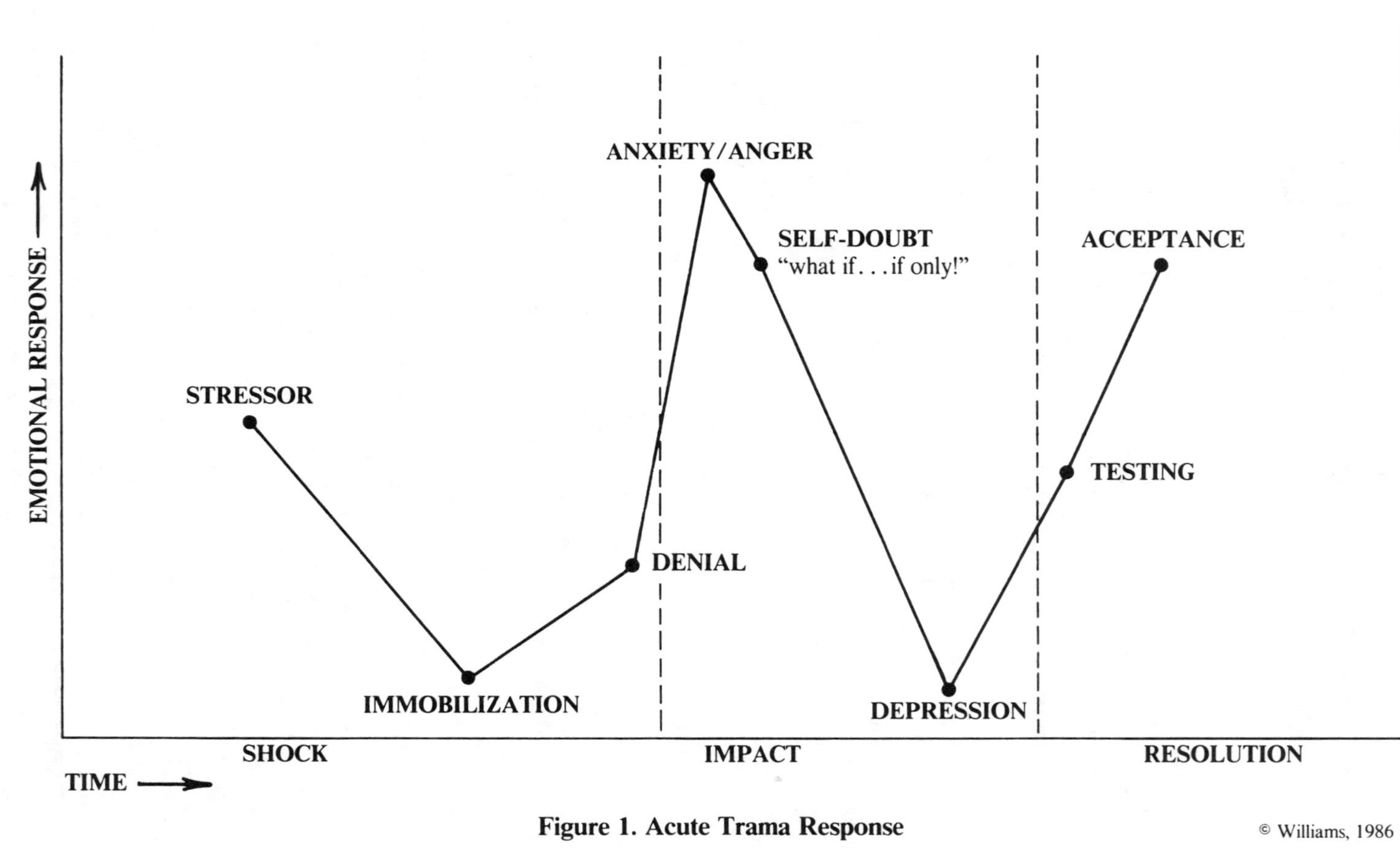

Figure 1. Acute Trama Response

the trauma situation, a woman whose child was killed in an automobile accident may say things to herself such as, "If I hadn't been going down the road at that time; if I had not had him in the car; if only I had been on the road ten minutes earlier, the drunk driver wouldn't have hit me." Trauma victims will go to great lengths to invent different scenarios that ignore the actual fact and outcome of the trauma. Thus, we often see self-blame in rape or robbery victims, or self-doubt in war veterans or police officers who have been involved in shootings. This survivor guilt is a way the trauma victim avoids the facts of the trauma, and may last indefinitely as the victim embroiders more and more elaborate "if-only" stories (Bard, 1986).

The final part of the impact phase is depression in its classical sense. The trauma victim generally shows the rather typical vegetative signs and is irritable, isolated, and feels misunderstood and hopeless and helpless about the future. If the self-doubt is not resolved in the impact phase, the trauma victim will continue to alternate between anger/anxiety and depression. Hence, the victim cannot progress to the recovery phase and attempt to reclaim a normal life. Over the last several years of treating trauma victims, it has become apparent to us that surviving a trauma and dealing with it does not make a person less susceptible to additional traumas. On the contrary, we find surviviors are more sensitized and more susceptible to new traumas. If the traumas are not dealt with, understood, and put into perspective, additional stresses accumulate more easily.

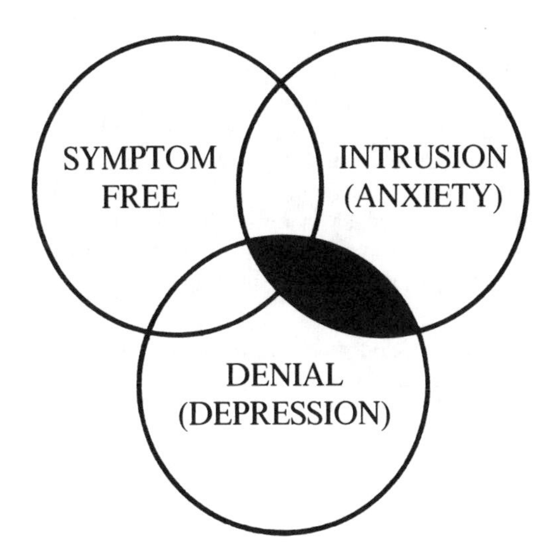

Figure 2. Chronic Post-traumatic Stress Disorder (after Horowitz, 1976, modified by Williams).

Survivor Guilt

In Horowitz' (1976) model of chronic stress, there is a period in which a person appears to be free of symptoms, but upon close investigation and careful discussion and observation, one notes that a trauma victim is never completely symptom free. The victim usually has difficulties in relationships, sleeping, and authority relationships, and has a general feeling of being misunderstood and lives a life perpectually altered by the traumatic event. I have modified this model (Figure 2) to show our actual clinical experiences with real-life trauma victims rather than theoretical models, because the latter lack the overlapping phases we have seen with actual practice.

Normally, the next phase is that of intrusive imagery. We call it the *anxiety phase* since the predominant mood as displayed is one of tension and anxiety. The unconscious thoughts as well as conscious memories of the trauma intrude on the mind in the form of daydreams, flashbacks, nightmares, or daytime intrusive imagery. They appear to be anxious and their physiological arousal state is higher than normal, leading to hypervigilance, exaggerated startle response, trouble in concentrating, sweaty palms, advanced heart rate, and traditional signs of autonomic nervous system response. Further, they complain of sleep disorders, especially intiation of sleep and, in the most severe cases, middle sleep disturbance—being awakened by nightmares—although some victims do sleep through the dream state. This phase is particularly distressing because of the psychic pain from being in a chronic anxious state.

The next phase is the denial phase, which we call the *depressive phase*. The subjective mood is one of depression. Victims have poor quality of sleep regardless of the amount of sleep, lose interest in normal activities, and are irritable with others. They tend to be extremely isolated, psychologically distant from others, uncommunicative, and nasty. Life simply has lost its flavor for a person in this phase. Persons in this denial phase often use antidepressant type drugs (including alcohol), or routinely have high-risk vocations or hobbies that generate excitement to counter the depressive symptoms.

In our work, we have found the most difficult part of this disorder occurs when the anxiety and depressive phase overlap to create a mixture of anxiety and depression. For example, individuals may have difficulty getting up in the morning in spite of early morning awakenings, will get through the day somehow in a depressed and grumpy mood, and then become tense and anxious in the evening. Following this, they may start to daydream about the trauma, becoming hypervigilant, which in turn interferes with their sleep, during which nightmares may occur. This phase is generally the one that brings people into treatment. They fear they are going crazy, since they are suffering from mood swings associated with the traumatic event.

In the acute trauma model, self-doubt or survivor guilt keeps a person cycling between anxiety and depression. In the chronic model, people who are stuck in the mixed anxiety and depression mode maintain this position of cyclical alternation because they are unable to resolve their survivor guilt. This is, of course, an exceptionally self-punitive way of coping with what happened.

If a person is able to resolve the survivor guilt and return to a relatively symptom-free mode of functioning, he or she may remain there for some time. However, we do find that a new trauma, or a reminder of the original one, tends to cause the victim to become symptomatic again. Similarly, an accumulation of stressors of daily life—marital or financial problems, employment difficulties, ill-health, or relationship tensions—may also cause the trauma survivor to become symptomatic and revert to a pattern of cyclical alternation. With effective treatment, survivors can learn to control many of the symptoms of anxiety and depression and function more adaptively. However, persons who are subject to constant high-level stress, such as emergency response workers, seem unable to remain in a symptom-free mode and experience much intrusive imagery because of constant immersion in trauma. As noted above, people experiencing intrusion and anxiety tend to self-medicate and alcohol and drugs can become a severe problem. A less obvious form of self-medication is sensation-seeking to generate a high arousal state and to get symptom relief through an adrenaline rush and the creation of dramatic distractions (Wilson, 1983). People suffering PTSD and who work in high-risk occupations frequently have interests in high-risk activities such as sports, parachuting, motorcycle driving, rock climbing, car racing, or they constantly seek excitement through numerous sexual encounters.

Survivor guilt shows itself in many ways: the officer in a police shooting may be consumed with self-doubts; the rape victim may feel shame; or the emergency medical person feels responsible for the death of a patient; the one who survived while others died is consumed with grief; the soldier is ashamed of his particpation in battlefield atrocities. We often see these people vibrate between anger/anxiety and depression, unable to continue the natural stress recovery process and acheive some sort of peace and understanding of their involvement in the trauma.

IDENTIFICATION OF SURVIVOR GUILT

Existential survivor guilt was first identified by Cobb and Linderman (1947) in their study of survivors of the Coconut Grove fire in New York in 1942. Such guilt is characterized by the survivor's confusion over his or her having lived and the meaning of this survival: "Why did I live when other people died?" With war veterans and holocaust victims, we sometimes see variations on this theme: the survivor wished to change places with the person who died, and the guilt is expressed as, "I should have died, and they should have lived." Often, their own lives have been chaotic since the stressor; they feel that the person who died would have had a better life, and more to live for. War veterans frequently say that the ones who were killed in war were the lucky ones—their pain and suffering are over and their names are on a monument. After hearing about the trauma in an interview, I frequently ask, "How come you lived through that?" Often I get the response, "I don't know, I ask myself that question all the time," or "perhaps there is some purpose for my life after facing the probabilities of my own death."

Content guilt, as contrasted with existential survivor guilt, is a result of a person's having done something to ensure his or her survival. This might have been to avoid responding to others in need, to have made a decision that resulted in other's deaths, or to have sought refuge for oneself when others remained threatened or suffering. This is a much easier form of survivor guilt to treat because the avoidant nature of this form implies a conscious effort to survive, or operate effectively in the traumatic environment.

Because survivor guilt has both emotional and intellectual components, a major treatment goal is to separate out the affective and cognitive elements. The survivor must learn that it is okay to feel sad about someone's having died in a traumatic situation, but it is not rational or appropriate to feel total responsibility for that person's death. A war veteran, failing to comprehend that, will blame himself for the death of a friend, failing to realize that the enemy was the killer. The war should be blamed, not those who lived through it.

ABREACTION

The course of treatment I prescribe is individual therapy initially, followed by group or marital therapy, depending on the individual and the presenting problems. I have found that it is essential to get the story before putting a person in a group. While much of the real healing takes place in group, its precursors are in individual treatment. Putting a person into a survivor's group without knowing the story is like an attorney's examining a witness on the stand without knowing in advance what the witness would say. Not all survivors are appropriate for all groups, and most groups are homogeneous and trauma-specific (i.e., combat veterans, special operations operatives, rape victims, medical personnel).

Getting the Story of the Traumatic Event

As noted earlier, trauma victims tend to remember the actual event in a slow-motion time warp, and often have tunnel vision—they forget many of the environmental factors in the trauma situation. The longer the trauma has been in the past, the less they remember of the environmental situation.

For a therapeutic intervention to be successful, one must get the story of the trauma in precise detail. For example, it is helpful to know the details about environmental conditions, particularly smells, articles of clothing, and other situational cues. It is important for them to tell you about the trauma scene as clearly and vividly as possible. It may be important for them to bring in memorabilia, such as newspaper clippings, photographs, letters written home, or perhaps audiotapes. Sometimes it is important to remind them that people do not die from crying, and that once they start crying they will stop. The more they tell the story, and the more successful you are with them in resolving the guilt issues, the less intense the emotions become.

Here is an excerpt from an interview I had that will illustrate the points just made.

Tom: When were you in Vietnam?

Paul: 1967 to 1968. I got hit February 14, 1968.

Tom: Where?

Paul: In Nui Bah Dinh. We were in there on a LRRP to do some reconnaissance for the 25th division.

Tom: Where in your body?

Paul: ...all over. I had second and third degree burns over the upper 40 percent of my body. Sharpnel right hand side of face, skull, I was shot three times, kneecap.

Tom: Bullets or fragments?

Paul: Both. Fragments from the waist up.

Tom: Was it a .51?

Paul: No, it was an AK-47. I got hit in the left ankle, right knee, left thigh, shrapnel right hand side, from the waist up—it was from a grenade. I think it was made in Czechoslovakia.

Tom: How did you get the burns?

Paul: They set the grass on fire and burned me. Trying to get me to come out—they wanted to have a party with me.

Tom: Start from the top.

Paul: We went in, right? They had a canopy [dense tree and foliage]....

Tom: How did you get in?

Paul: We rappeled in [slid down ropes from the helicopter].

Tom: Out of what?

Paul: I think it was an UH-4D if I remember right. We rappeled in, that was like 4:00 in the morning.

Tom: OK, how many went in?

Paul: There was 12 of us.

Tom: A whole team.

Paul: Yeah. There was a major, a captain, I can't remember all the guys now. At daylight we started to move. Thanks to the Air Force with their recon they said that we would run into light resistance, maybe VC. The 337th NVA regimental headquarters happened to be there. Needless to say, bad day. Everybody was killed but me. Because I was point [lead man].

Tom: You were let through the killing zone?

Paul: Yeah. Standard setup. You know that as well as I do. Uh, After I got hit, I laid in the woods for three-and-a-half days, something like that, four days, I lost track of time. I gave myself morphine.

Tom: You were fragged and shot.

Paul: And burned. You know what elephant grass is? They set it on fire to smoke me so they could butcher me. I didn't come out real quick.

Tom: What happened?

Paul: I'm on point. And we're talking daylight. About 5:30, 6:00 o'clock.

Tom: So it's light.

Paul: Yeah, it's light. They were waiting for us.

Tom: How long did you walk before you were hit?

Paul: Oh, shit. Maybe, anywhere from 3 seconds to 30 minutes. We were just getting our shit together. Evidently there was a leak. They were waiting on us.

Tom: You were walking point. How far away from your slack man [the man behind the point or lead man]?

Paul: I hit the grass. I was just going into the grass when we got ambushed. Then all of a sudden, you know, they hit them. I turned to go back.

Tom: What kind of fire?

Paul: Very heavy fire. AK's. Yea, heard a few grenades go off but they were ours. Fire fight lasted maybe three minutes. Maybe four. I'm not sure.

Tom: So you went back.

Paul: I started back and then I got hit.

Tom: What hit you first?

Paul: The gunshot hit me first. I got hit first in the left ankle. Then I went down. It was like I was in a dream. You know, it was slow motion. I got up to my right leg. I remember that clearly. Then I tried to set up. I was wanting to get back to my team. And then I got hit in the left thigh. And it wasn't real serious, just enough to knock me down again. Scrape—they call it a flesh wound. I got back up and the other one hit me just, well, damn near dead center in the knee but had a glancing blow and hit the bone. I went back down again. And then I remember the gooks coming out of the woods. They came after me. I got off in the grass, low crawl, dragging. Went into the grass and tried to set myself up to where I could do some business. Then all of a sudden it was real quiet, it was like in a church during a high mass. And then I remember smelling something burning, I was on fire. It may have been 30 seconds to 30 minutes, I'm not sure of time. I got hot, started burning, so I ran through the fire or crawled or whatever I done.... I think I ran. Out of the woods and crawled up under some bushes and stuff and foliage and that was it.

Tom: NVA?

Paul: NVA. They were already busy butchering what was left of the team. They had a bad habit of cutting our dicks off and stuffing them in our mouths.

Tom: Is that what happened?

Paul: I don't know. I didn't see it. I went into shock or whatever. Mother Nature's anesthetic.

Tom: So you didn't see it.

Paul: No. I couldn't get back to the team. Man, it was called self-preservation. Maybe I was chicken. I should have went back. But I didn't.

Tom: Why?

Paul: I was scared. And I don't think I could have really made it. Just to be honest. Because I remember looking at my arm, the flesh was hanging off of it, the skin. And this side of my face, it was, I was bleeding really bad. I don't know if I got the blood stopped or not before I passed out. I'm not sure. Three days later the 25th division picked me up. I remember the Medic saying, "This one's still alive." And then I passed out. I woke up in the 3rd Field Hospital.

Paul gave me the facts of the story. Probing the feelings is often more difficult.

Probing

While doing interviews with the trauma victims, it is helpful to be acutely aware of the subtle hints of survival guilt. As the interview continues, note the connection between death and guilt:

Tom: What did you do after Vietnam?

Paul: Worked in an airplane plant welding—the same thing every day. Then I drove an 18-wheeler and then became an embalmer. I was the best in restorative art in the state of New Mexico.

Tom: Why were you a mortician?

Paul: I know what it was—I was dealing with death again.

Tom: What do you feel so guilty about?

Paul: I don't feel guilty about a fuckin' thing. And even if I did, I wouldn't tell you, I would go tell the people that I feel bad about if, if I can find out where they're buried.

Tom: What's all this "if" shit?

Paul: What do you mean, if? If I could find out where they're at? I would. I let my partners down. I never made it back.

Tom: Tell me about it. What do you tell yourself?

Paul: I didn't make it back.

Tom: What do you tell yourself?

Paul: I was wounded, but I should have been with my partners. I don't want to talk now. You hear? All right? That's none of your business. Okay?

An additional technique to surface guilt is to use some type of audiovisual stimulus to provoke memories.

Using Media to Stimulate Discussion

Utilizing some sort of stimulus to provoke the survivor guilt has been helpful in individual work and is especially useful in the therapy in group work. I have used some emotion-laden material, such as the Viet Vet Video production, *Wall of Tears*, to get Vietnam veterans talking about the experiences that distress them the most. Another audiovisual I have used is the last episode of *M.A.S.H.*, where Hawkeye suffers from survivor guilt when a Korean mother smothers her child in a tense situation. I have heard several similar stories where that actually happened: from an intelligence agent during the Berlin crisis, an American U.D.T. sailor in North Vietnam during the Bay of Tonken "shoot-out," and a regular combat soldier hiding in a hut in Vietnam. It is much better to hear these stories in individual counseling than to have them erupt unexpectedly in group. It is my standard practice to ask group members whether they have seen anything in the media, read any books, or seen any movies that were distressing to them in order to get them to start talking.

Taking Time to Get the Story

Many stress victims are reluctant to discuss their guilt feelings or the trauma that they experienced. It is often necessary to spend several hours with them to uncover the traumatic situations involved. The following transcript is an interview with a Vietnam veteran. He had an abreaction after about 3 hours of interview. The material that came forth in that interview had been long suppressed, and was so dramatic that when it came out he vomited.

John: I'm a little leery of going to the Vet Center because there's a lot of Marines there and...it's one thing to talk about what you did over there, but it's another thing to say something you didn't do or should have done. I don't want to get anybody mad or ticked off.

Tom: Because.

John: Well, I got people hurt, you know.

Tom: How?

John: Well, you know, I didn't fire.

Tom: What difference would that have made?

John: A lot of difference.

Tom: Why?

John: Because I didn't fire.

Tom: How long was it between seeing movement and when the RPG [rocket-propelled grenade] hit?

John: About five seconds.

Tom: Do you think that four of five seconds would have made any difference?

John: Yeah.

Tom: You think you would have killed the NVA with an RPG before they squeezed it off?

John: ...I certainly don't know...all I know is I didn't do what I was supposed to do.

Tom: Afraid to fire? Or you just weren't sure?

John: I wasn't sure.

Tom: You didn't know where the two guys were from the LP [listening post]. The people on the line were alerted that there was movement, right?

John: Right. The jerk that was on with me fell asleep and the men on the lines were throwing rocks at us to wake us up. I woke up, you know, and all I remember was I got up and started running towards the lines.

Tom: What happened then?

John: I don't know what happened to the other two guys. I don't know what happened. I just got up.

Tom: Were they there?

John: I don't know. Don't ask me. [Crying] I don't know.

Tom: Tell me, John.

John: [Crying] I can't remember.

Tom: Tell me. What went on that night? What do you keep telling yourself? What are you seeing right now?

John: [sobbing/crying] They're all over us. [crying] They're all over us.

Tom: What do you mean, they're all over us? What are you seeing?

John: [crying] They were all over us. I, I don't know. I don't want to remember.

TREATMENT CONSIDERATIONS

One goal of counseling is to separate the rational or cognitive component from the emotional "grief" component. If you directly attack the survivor guilt you may not get anywhere. Trauma victims seem to have a great need to hang on to the guilt, so to make them accessible to treatment you must let them maintain that affective component while you attack the issue of responsibility. Often times I will make the comment, "Gosh, that was a horrible thing. That must make you feel very sad," to give words to their feelings of grief. People with survivor guilt really don't think that others can understand them. As you continue in treatment with them and continue to give them the affective part of the survivor guilt, the anguish will diminish over time. The intensity of their sadness begins to diminish as they begin to understand more about the trauma situation. The main goal in counseling with survivor guilt is to allow them to feel the sadness but to attack the issues of responsibility. There are a variety of ways of doing this, and the therapist is limited only by his or her imagination. Some suggestions are explored below.

Shared Responsibility

The technique of getting survivors to share responsibility for what happened starts with pointing out other factors involved in the incident itself. One of the factors may simply be one of time and space: they may have been in the wrong place at the wrong time; they may simply have been victims of a random act. Many people who have been raised in organized religions tend to feel that what happened to them was paying them back for some past sin. With war victims, you focus on the fact that the war was responsible for the deaths; the war was responsible for the situation in which the trauma occurred. You do not necessarily try to absolve them of all responsibility, depending on their trauma situation.

Cognitive Restructuring

Survivors of trauma tend to remember the traumatic situation in an unchanged way; their initial perception of the event is the way they continue to view it, as if the traumatic event were frozen in their memories. The healing process involves thawing those memories and looking at them realistically. Because the memories have a very negative focus, the goal of cognitive restructuring is simply to look at the original trauma in a different light.

For example, a SEAL (Navy special warfare teams who are highly trained to work behind enemy lines) whom I was treating was the assassin for his SEAL team; he was an excellent shot. He called himself a "murderer." In discussing the concept of a "murderer" with him, I suggested that in fact he was a "killer," a less pejorative and more accurate term. What he was doing was not illegal and was in fact not only condoned but ordered by his seniors. It was a major breakthrough in therapy when he started to call himself simply a "killer" instead of a "murderer."

The first step a client seems to go through in cognitive restructuring is one of confusion. That is a very positive sign that he or she is beginning to doubt the original perceptions of the situation and is realizing that perhaps the trauma has other aspects that have been ignored, forgotten, or devalued. I make a point of letting my clients know why this confusion is a good sign, a sign of change. When dealing with survivor guilt, it is important to find out what kinds of words people use to talk to themselves when they are thinking about the trauma situation, and to help change these words.

Clergy Referral

Often times, Veterans have lost their religious beliefs in going through war. Trauma victims' religious beliefs are often either strengthened or weakened. They frequently say, "Where was God when I needed him/her?" (Please refer to Jacob, this volume, or to Walter Capps' book, *Vietnam the Unfinished War*, [1982] for suggestions.) I urge all trauma counselors to have some contact with a clergy in their community. It is most important to have a clergyman who can listen to these rather dramatic and sometimes gruesome stories in a nonjudgemental and practical way, but with a sensitivity to the theological implications for the victim.

THE MESSAGE IS: THE VICTIMS DID THE BEST THEY COULD

The bottom line of many of these concepts is to leave the survivor of trauma feeling that he or she did the best job in the situation that could have been done considering the circumstances and the resources available in the situation. As victims start to realize this, they often feel a need to do some form of restitution such as reaching out to other trauma survivors or making themselves available to the media for discussions about their experiences. One way to help them get to this point is to ask them how long they need to continue to make themselves suffer. Certainly the trauma survivor feels that no amount of retribution or restitution can make up for the loss of a friend or loved one, and perhaps the best they can do for that lost person is pull themselves together and make their own lives positive and productive.

TECHNIQUES/SPECIAL POINTS

We have observed a variety of techniques that have been found useful with many individuals suffering survivor guilt.

Age/Moral Development

Many people suffering from survivor guilt can be helped substantially if the trauma happened when they were young and their youth becomes a subject for discussion. Many Vietnam veterans were quite young when the trauma occurred and they acted in a way that is now causing them the stress. With them, as with other young trauma victims, pain revolves around self-punitive survivor guilt that results from the way they behaved during the trauma; I discuss with them the moral development of adolescence. Essentially, adolescent idealism means that people in their late teens and early twenties hold to very high moral standards. They tend to see the world as black and white, but when they find themselves in a trauma situation such as war they soon learn that there are many gray areas. Nonetheless, they still judge themselves years later rather harshly because their moral development was frozen in time. Now they need to look at the moral aspects of their behavior in light of their further experiences in life; point out that now they know life is not fair. Adolescent idealism holds that life is fair, that good things should happen to good people, and bad things should happen to bad people. Clinging to this adolescent belief system obviously leads to a very self-punitive position.

Included in the discussion of age in relation to the trauma, it must also be noted that there were often massive amounts of peer pressure from others in the group. For instance, many combat units in Vietnam would cut off the ears of the enemy or slit the throat of the dead enemy soldier and "patch them" with a unit patch so that the enemy who found the bodies of their comrades would know who killed them. Other rituals occurred, such as cutting off and braiding the hair of dead enemy women or sleeping in a body bag, that were locally designed and generally unknown to persons in command authority positions.

Empty Chair/Reversal

Gestalt techniques tend to be particularly effective in dealing with survivor guilt when one can pose such questions to the client as, "If Joe were here and alive now, sitting in that chair, would he blame you for your actions or if you had died instead of Joe, would you blame him for your death?" One is limited only by one's imagination in using such reversal techniques as writing a letter to a person who did not survive a trauma or to a dead relative with whom there is unfinished business.

Time

As discussed earlier in the chapter, a person in a trauma experiences a warp in the perception of time. Events seem to unfold in slow motion, and retrospectively the person tends to think that they had more time to make decisions than they actually had. It is important to clarify how much time was actually available, how quickly the decision had to be made, and that given the information they had, they (not someone else) were in the best position to decide how they should act and likely did the best they could. It is also important todiscuss the amount of experience they had had in similar trauma situations; if they had been in combat for six months, one would expect a different type of response than if they were on their first day in combat. Very similar parallels can be drawn with police officers and other emergency workers.

Technical Aspects

In working with victims who have on-the-job traumas, such as military, police, medical and other emergency workers, it may be very important to look at a trauma from a very technical sense. Did they in fact act correctly in that situation? Did they react according to procedures and standard policies? I have found in working with police, military, and medical persons that in certain trauma situations they have found themselves having to make decisions that are normally made by persons much higher up in the line of authority. One example is the young soldier who must call artillery fire because all of the officers are dead and the forward observer team has been wiped out; he gives the wrong coordinates and fires on friendly troops. Part of his therapy was to point out to him that the fire command was checked by two different organizations before the firing was actually done, and there were at least two other organizations whose job it was to clear the coordinates, which they did. He was therefore able to share some of the responsibility for the friendly fire with other units.

Pride

It is helpful to maintain a positive focus and glean as many positive aspects of the person's behavior (during the trauma) as possible. The therapist continually looks for things in clients that can reinforce pride in their unit, their profession, or their behaviors. A client who felt guilty about following the drag marks of his friend for three days and finally finding him freshly killed could be helped only by being commended for recovering his friend's body. Sometimes this pride can be encouraged by making comments like, "If that had been me, I would have been pleased that you had gone to that much effort to try to save me and that you recovered my body for my family."

Symbolic Memorials

There are many ways to ameliorate the guilt that someone else was killed in a trauma. We have found that many of our trauma victims have used arts and poetry to express some of the feelings they've had towards the missing person or their feelings about the involvement in that situation. In working with suicidal people with survivor guilt, some of the better interventions have included the communicating that, "As long as you are alive, the memory of the victim remains." With some trauma victims, it may be necessary to visit the graves of buddies or loved ones who died, or review newspaper or other media reports of the trauma; Vietnam veterans may need to look at the Book of Friends (a registry of all those who died in Vietnam), see the video tape, *Wall of Tears*, visit "The Wall," or the DAV Vietnam Memorial in Angel Fire, New Mexico, or participate in some other forms of recognition that someone actually did die. In group therapy, we frequently have some sort of memorial symbol at the last group of the series. It has been as simple as having a moment of silence and as complex as having a ceremony of lighting candles, talking about the death of a friend, and burning his or her name into a piece of plywood with a map of Vietnam sketched on it.

Healing and Purification Rituals

Wilson (1986) describes the role of the Native American Sweat Lodge as a form of group therapy for combat veterans. In my personal experience and observations, this can be a potent and dramatic healing experience when utilized in conjunction with more traditional forms of therapy.

SUMMARY

One of my clients was a medic in Vietnam. In October 1967, after losing many men in Vietnam, Jim went to a small village near where the action had been and wiped out the entire village by himself. The anniversary date has always been particularly important for Jim. He had been out of treatment for approximately a year when he called to remind me that his anniversary date was approaching and requested a meeting with me on that day. He told me that he was going to come in full combat gear, and I reminded him that I felt particularly uncomfortable with that idea and suggested that he wear civilian clothes. He said he didn't know what he was going to do, but we made our appointment. The next morning, Jim came into my office wearing a three-piece suit. The following transcript is typical of Jim's journey in attempting to deal with his survival guilt.

Tom: What helps deal with guilt? When guys keep showing up repeatedly like bad pennies, it means they've not been able to deal with their guilt.

Jim: That's true, I agree with you. I would say that I've totally solved the guilt. I think I've probably got a handle on it, and recognize it for what it is. For me, at least, it was so many years ago, October—, 1967, it was a bad scene, it happened, and made such an impression on me that it ruined me for so many years. Being a kid, an 18-year-old kid at that time, it made such an impression on me that I didn't know how to deal with it so what did I start doing? I started striking out to make up for my failure.

Tom: You started drinking.

Jim: I started drinking. To get over that pain. But seeing for the first time, actual, actual total obliteration of a human body and I couldn't do anything about it.

Tom: As a medic.

Jim: As a medic. So, as those years passed, when I'd strike out and I'd drink, it all went back to a clearing, went back to a village and I had to make up for the deaths that I felt that I caused and I had nothing to do with it. As I didn't fire the bullets, I didn't fire the rockets, the mortars, or anything. Recognizing that now puts me at ease. It's taken a long, long time to understand it for what it is. And for what it did. I volunteered to go. I went. Maybe I didn't *really* know what I was getting into because....I'm a soldier, I'm the best, I'm conditioned for this. By God, I individually can stop this war. Just like every other soldier, I was thinking the same thing but we never said it. My job wasn't to kill. Introspective... my job was to fix.

Tom: But you did kill.

Jim: I did. And maybe that's what hurt me more than anything. The fact that I did kill. Me? Taking a human life? Me? There's no rhyme or reason to that. I'm not that way. I'm not a murderer. I'm not a killer. I'm just a kid, but I turned out to be a man, a hard-core, hard-faced individual.

Tom: And what you did lately was to tape record all of your recollections about that day in the clearing.

Jim: That day in the clearing. And I can talk about my pain. I can't speak for others, I can only speak for myself and the pain that I have been going through, for so many years. ...The pain! Going to see the docs and having them talk about it and so forth and getting into groups, that's great, but I'm still within myself because I make the decision, you don't make the decision, the group doesn't make the decision, I make the decision.

Tom: Does the group help in talking about it?

Jim: It brings it out....

Tom: Makes it available for you to deal with? Or gives you ways of dealing with it? Gives you different ways of looking at it?

Jim: It gives me the opportunity to hear how others are doing it.

Tom: OK, like when Joe finally said, "I did the best job I could to try to save John."

Jim: But he didn't say that, we had to tell him.

Tom: But he finally said that, he recognized it. And did that do something for you?

Jim: Yeah.

Tom: So you got some vicarious learning from it. You said, "Wait a minute, maybe that works for me. Maybe I can take a look at it and see if I did the best job I could."

Jim: I got to go along with that.

Tom: Because you hadn't thought of that before by yourself over the last seventeen years.

Tom: Want to read your poem?

Jim: Sure. I may cry a little bit but it's over.

"*Another Soldier Down*"

Heat of the day,
A heavy mugginess fills the air.

Survivor Guilt

Clothes drenched with sweat and the sound
swoosh, swoosh.
Commands yelled in quick order.
To the sides everyone,
watch the flanks.
Joe, give me the damn phone.
Those sons o bitches.
The sound is gone with stillness all
around...
Then a moan, then a scream.
Doc...Doc
I grab my bag because there's
another soldier down.
Now it's dusk with
Coolness but mugginess still lingers
Entering heavy jungle foliage
Commands passed quietly. Keep alert.
Booby traps heavy in this area.
We'll sit in about two clicks and wait for
Caldwell's orders....
Doc, stay close.
We do as told.... then a sound fifty yards
ahead....
Twang...scream from point...help...
Hit a punji—voices gurgle
Grab my bag.
Lieutenant yells "Trap, ...Hold
position..."
I move anyway cause all I know is
Another soldier down.
Early morning. Chilly. Think awful
strange for such a hot country. Move to an
edge of a clearing.
Point man taking right out on evac...
Don't know if I did right...
Never saw holes like those before.
Ears perk up. Hear blades and choppers
come in.
For an evac, Jeff, didi [hurry away] *and*
take them.
To LZ. Others guard perimeter
HQ says activity heavy on all sides.
Be alert.
Evac hovers. We start forward and all
hell breaks loose.
Ratatat-tat. Swoosh. Ping. Ping.
Chopper twenty-five, thirty yards away.
Two, maybe three, other ships above.
Covering fire from ground and above ground
"WHOMB," evac blows.
Bodies and screaming.

Grab my bag. Another soldier down.
Later, hot again, a heavy mugginess in the air.
The stench of death wraps around like a blanket.
Shambles inside, confusion and anger and fear.
Yet, I know when I hear...
I'll grab my bag.
Another soldier down.

Jim: That's reality. There's more to that poem. Because of my shambles, confusion and anger, fear, I went to a village to make up in the sense of an eye-for-an-eye and a tooth-for-a-tooth. But I couldn't write that essay.

Tom: Have you?

Jim: In my mind. And I think it's best where it's at. The day will come I'll put it to a piece of paper.

REFERENCES

Bard, M., Sangrey, D. (1986). *The crime victim's book*. New York: Brunner/Mazel.

Capps, W. (1982). *The unfinished war: Vietnam and the American conscience.* Boston: Beacon Press.

Cobb, S., Lindemann, E. (1947). Neuropsychiatric observations. *Annals of Surgery.*

Horowitz, M.J. (1976). *Stress response syndromes.* New York: Jason A. Ronson.

Wilson, J.P. (1983). *Vietnam veteran on trial: Relationship of post-traumatic stress disorder to criminal behavior.* Volume three, *Behavior science and the law.*

Wilson, J.P. (1986). Native American healing and purification rituals: Implications for the treatment of post-traumatic stress disorder of Vietnam veterans. Cleveland, Ohio: Cleveland State University, unpublished manuscript.

CHAPTER SIX

THE PSYCHOPHARMACOLOGIC MANAGEMENT OF POST-TRAUMATIC STRESS DISORDER (PTSD) IN VIETNAM VETERANS AND IN CIVILIAN SITUATIONS

John F. Yost

Since the initial publication of this book, our knowledge of post-traumatic stress disorder (PTSD) has been broadened by our extensive experience in treating more than 3,000 veterans who suffer from PTSD, and our increasing work with a large number of civilian patients who have been involved in several different kinds of traumatic events. Auto accidents are clearly the most common of these events, but we have treated victims of aircraft accidents, physical assaults, on-the-job injuries, sexual assaults, shooting incidents experienced by police and security officers, mining accidents, bridge collapses, fires, gas explosions, and more recently, robbery victims.

The third edition of the *Diagnostic and Statistical Manual* ([*DSM-III*], American Psychiatric Association [APA], 1980) of the American Psychiatric Association has classified the diagnostic category of PTSD under the anxiety disorders. It has been our experience that the anxiety is frequently complicated by the coexistence of a significant clinical depression. In a large number of civilian post-trauma situations, the condition is often further complicated by the presence of a chronic pain syndrome. My discussion will include a brief review of the nature of anxiety and depression, focusing specifically on the pharmacologic agents I find useful in the management of these disorders. I will briefly address the issue of pharmacologic management of chronic pain syndromes.

The *DSM-III* diagnostic criteria for post-traumatic stress disorder are as follows:*

1. The existence of a recognizable stressor that would evoke significant symptoms of distress in almost everyone.
2. Reexperiencing of the trauma as evidenced by at least one of the following:
    a. Recurrent and intrusive recollections of the event.
    b. Recurrent dreams of the event.
    c. Sudden acting and feeling as if the traumatic event were recurring because of an association with an environmental or ideational stimulus.
3. Numbing of responsiveness to or reduced involvement with the external world, beginning some time after the trauma as shown by at least one of the following:
    a. Markedly diminished interest in one or more significant activities.
    b. Feeling detached or estranged from others.
    c. Constricted affect.
4. At least two of the following symptoms that were not present before the trauma:
    a. Hyperalertness or exaggerated startle response.
    b. Sleep disturbance.

*See Appendix A of this book for proposed revision.

c. Guilt about surviving when others have not, or about behavior required for survival.

d. Memory impairment or trouble concentrating.

e. Avoidance of activities that arouse recollection of the traumatic event.

f. Intensification of the symptoms by exposure to events that symbolize or resemble the traumatic event.

> [The acute subtype of PTSD presents with:] (1) the onset of symptoms within six months from the event; (2) duration of symptoms of less than six months' time. [The chronic or delayed type presents with] either of the following or both: (1) duration of symptoms for six months or more (chronic); (2) onset of symptoms at least six months after the trauma (delayed). (APA, 1980, p. 238)

If the severity of the associated symptoms of depression and anxiety are of sufficient magnitude, you should make the diagnosis of anxiety or depressive disorder, in addition to the primary diagnosis of PTSD (see Newman, this volume).

One difficulty I have experienced in the diagnosis of PTSD in civilian situations is determining the magnitude of the stressor. Obviously, no one questions the magnitude of the stressor in a major auto accident where significant physical injuries occur, or in a propane explosion where an individual may suffer burns over 50 percent of his or her body. But what about the relatively common auto accident of a minor rear-end collision in which there are only subjective findings of "whip lash?" I have appeared in court as an expert for the prosecution where the defendant who was charged with driving while intoxicated was claiming virtually all the subjective symptoms of PTSD following a minor rear-end collision. My primary diagnosis would be an alcohol abuse disorder and, additionally, a maladjustment to adult life.

A second issue for concern is the duration of the delay between the time the traumatic event occurred and the onset of the classic symptoms of PTSD. Those of us who work with World War II veterans are aware of the long delayed reaction time peculiar to the disorder. Van Dyke and Associates (1985) report a classic case of a World War II veteran whose symptoms first occurred more than 30 years post-combat. Recently, we have worked with a Korean war veteran who flew missions in a B-26 aircraft. He was shot down twice and eventually became a POW. He returned to civilian life in police work and rose to a position of considerable responsibility in a major western city. His only complaint for many years was chronic sleep disturbance, which he "treated" with alcohol. Eventually, he talked about his war experiences with another Korean war veteran while they were at a conference. Traveling home on a commercial airplane, he experienced, for the first time, a severe physiologic reaction resembling anaphylactic shock. He felt he was in a B-29 in Korea. He continued to have these reactions periodically, along with flashback phenomena, in spite of several psychiatric hospitalizations and numerous medications. Finally, he was referred to our clinic and is now doing quite well in group and individual counseling with only low doses of anti-anxiety agents for sleep.

As a general principle, I feel psychotropic medications in both civilian and military stress syndromes should not be prescribed as a matter of routine. They should be used to treat those symptoms of anxiety, depression, and sleep disturbance that seriously interfere with other modalities of treatment and so impair the individual that he or she cannot function adequately in the work place or in daily social activities.

If a substance abuse problem exists, the primary focus of treatment should be to correct this difficulty first before proceeding to deal with anxiety and/or depression. Unfortunately, all too many victims of trauma turn to alcohol as an agent to relieve anxiety or promote sleep. Even if the individual did not abuse alcohol before the traumatic event, he or she may find it provides some symptom relief in the denial phase of the disorder (see Sandecki, this volume). Do not neglect to carefully elicit a history of substance use and other medications the individual might be taking before proceeding with anti-anxiety or antidepressant medication.

ANXIETY AND POST-TRAUMATIC STRESS DISORDER

The *DSM-III* classifies anxiety disorders into the following four major groups:

- Anxiety states (panic disorders, generalized anxiety disorder, obsessive-compulsive disorder);
- Phobic disorders (agoraphobia with or without panic attacks, social phobia, simple phobia);
- Post-traumatic stress disorder (acute and delayed subtypes);
- Atypical anxiety disorder.

The relationship of PTSD to the other anxiety disorders is not fully clarified. Both "anxiety" and "panic" reactions are reported in PTSD. Several studies report conscious fear associated with PTSD, and it is becoming increasingly common to see studies with significant percentages of patients with PTSD who experience panic attacks and agoraphobia with panic attacks.

Anxiety may be simply defined as a pervading feeling of apprehension or dread that may or may not be associated with immediately stressful or fearful stimuli. Anxiety and fear frequently overlap. Fear is usually associated with a clearly discernible and immediate cause, and the response is rapid and congruous to the degree of threat. In contrast, anxiety generally refers to an overreaction to real danger or to an attenuated fear and dread response without any clear source of danger. Anxiety may take such forms as acute situational anxiety related to a stressful event (divorce), or traumatic anxiety following an unexpected, tragic event, such as surviving a fatal auto accident or being the victim of an armed robbery. We may also see free-floating anxiety associated with no discernible event.

Both objective and subjective symptoms are associated with the anxiety state. In addition to severe dysphoria, the individual may experience a variety of physical symptoms such as headache, dizziness, gastrointestinal distress, chest discomfort, nausea, tremulousness, and palpitations. The behavioral concomitants would include restlessness, nocturnal dyspnea, irritability, fatigue, insomnia, and distractibility.

Anxiety, of course, is commonly associated with clinical depression, heart disease, cancer, chronic brain syndromes, alcohol withdrawal, asthma, and many other acute and chronic medical disorders.

Recent epidemiologic data indicate that between 7 percent and 18 percent of the American population meets the diagnostic criteria for primary anxiety disorders at any point in time.

The debate over the biologic etiology of anxiety continues. At a recent symposium on anxiety disorders in Madison, Wisconsin, David V. Sheehan proposed that genetic and laboratory data strongly support the hypothesis that much anxiety, panic disorder in particular, is a metabolic disease, possibly involving chemoreceptor dysregulation. Isaac M. Marks, Professor of Experimental Psychopathology at the Institute of Psychiatry, University of London, who was at the same symposium, disagreed, citing growing evidence of the familial nature of anxiety disorders, and noting that familial and genetic are not necessarily the same thing. Sheehan pointed out that in family studies, 20 percent of first-degree relatives of panic disorder patients also have anxiety attacks and that the figures rise to 39 percent when more aggressive investigations are made. Twin studies are reported to show higher concordance for panic disorders among monozygous than dizygous twins. Typical ratios from studies are 41 percent to 4 percent, 30 percent to 9 percent and 34 percent to 17 percent.

Lactate sensitivity has emerged as the most dramatic marker for anxiety disorder.

Several compounds have been reported to be useful to relieve the symptoms of PTSD: alcohol, the benzodiazepines, the tricyclic antidepressant agents, lithium carbonate, beta-blockers, alpha-adrenergic agents, antipsychotic agents, and MAO inhibitors. In my experience, the safest and simplest of the available psychotropic agents for anxiety are the anti-anxiety agents, specifically the benzodiazepines. Seldom, if ever, do I use these agents alone; most often, the patient is in individual and/or group psychotherapy. I will list the currently available benzodiazepines, both generic and trade name, and the usual daily dose:

Table 1. Usual Daily Dose of Benzodiazepines.

Generic Name	**Trade Name**	**Dose/mg**
alprazolam	Xanax	.5-5.0
chlorazepate	Tranxene	15-60
chlordiazepoxide	Librium	15-100
diazepam	Valium	5-60
flurazepam	Dalmane	15-60
lorazepam	Ativan	2-6
oxazepam	Serax	15-120
prazepam	Centrax	20-60
temazepam	Restoril	10-30
triazolam	Halcion	.25-1.0

All these drugs are effective anti-anxiety agents and three (Dalmane, Restoril, Halcion) are marketed as hypnotics. They are differentiated only by their onset of activity (oral absorption rates), and their properties of lipid solubility, which in turn may influence some of their pharmacokinetic properties *in vivo*. Unfortunately, the commonly used concept for length of effect, the elimination half-life, does not necessarily predict duration of action. Benzodiazepine action may be terminated by at least three mechanisms, according to David J. Greenblatt (speaking at the second annual psychopharmacology update conference in Boston, October 1984), two of which are pharmacokinetic, while the third involves a functional change in the receptor mediating drug action. In pharmacokinetic terms, benzodiazepine action may be terminated if the drug disappears from its receptor site. The *first* mechanism is by drug distribution: the drug egresses from its site of action in the brain and is taken up into peripheral storage sites, principally in adipose tissue. The *second* is biotransformation or clearance: the drug disappears from the receptor site as it is irreversibly biotransformed by the liver.

The receptor or molecular *(third)* mechanism for termination of drug action is independent of the first two pharmacokinetic events and is sometimes termed "acute tolerance" or acute adaptation. Acute tolerance operationally describes the observation that the receptors become less sensitive to drug effects as the duration of exposure to the drug becomes longer. Current data suggest that distribution rather than clearance is the most important pharmacokinetic terminator of the action of benzodiazepines after single doses. Thus, the extent of distribution, rather than the half-life of elimination, is the major determinant of duration of action of benzodiazepines. Tables 2 and 3 illustrate the relative rates of absorption and distribution (termination of action) based upon lipid solubility of the various benzodiazepines.

Table 2. Oral Absorption Rates of Benzodiazepines.

Drug	**Time of Peak Plasma Concentration**
A. Rapid	Less than 1.2 hours
1. diazepam	
2. chlorazepate	
3. flurazepam	
B. Intermediate	1.2 to 2.0 hours
1. triazolam	
2. alprazolam	
3. lorazepam	
C. Slow	2.0 to 3.0 hours
1. oxazepam	
2. temazepam	
D. Ultra Slow	More than 3.0 hours
1. prazepam	
2. diazepam (slow release form)	

Table 3. Degree of Lipid Solubility—Greatest to Lowest

diazepam
desmethyldiazepam (from chlorazepate)
triazolam
desalkyl-flurazepam
alprazolam - temazepam
lorazepam
oxazepam

In using the benzodiazepines, some thought should be given to the desired effect. For example, diazepam (Valium) is the most rapidly absorbed from the gastrointestinal tract after oral administration and may produce an unwanted drowsy or "spaced-out" feeling in some individuals. On the other hand, temazepam (Restoril) is very slowly absorbed and may *not* be useful as a hypnotic in someone who needs rapid onset of sleep.

Once a determination has been made to prescribe a benzodiazepine for severe anxiety, the choice of a particular drug is based upon rapidity of action, duration of action, history of sensitivity to a particular drug, and, if available, family history of drug response.

Valium (diazepam) is the most rapid acting in oral dosage. Some patients like this effect; others feel "spaced-out" and fear loss of control. Most data suggest that the effective total daily dosage for most patients is 30-40 mg. I have seldom used doses in excess of this amount. Once a steady-state plasma level is reached (one to two weeks) on three-times-a-day dosage, the drug can be given twice daily. It has been my experience with a large number and variety of anxious patients that if the individual has no history of drug abuse (including alcohol), he or she seldom abuses this benzodiazepine.

When to discontinue the diazepam remains a controversy. Obviously, many patients who get relief of anxiety and who gain from other therapies will want to stop the drug. A gradual tapering is always important to prevent severe withdrawal effects. I know of no way to predict which patients can discontinue the drug and function optimally and which ones will have a recurrence of disabling symptoms and need to remain on medication for longer periods of time. I have several patients who have been maintained for several years on dosages of diazepam varying from 5 mg to 30 mg daily with no apparent adverse effects. Many are employed in high functioning jobs and have been promoted while in treatment. In other words, I am not afraid patients will become habituated to the benzodiazepines and not deal with their anxiety in other ways.

The main side effect of the benzodiazepines is an initial drowsiness, to which the patient quickly adapts (three to five days). Patients should be warned of this and other side effects when they start the new drug. There have been reports of reduced motor coordination and memory impairment at therapeutic levels, but I have rarely seen this in clinical practice.

Alprazolam is a unique benzodiazepine that appears to have, in addition to anti-anxiety effects, significant antidepressant effects, according to John P. Feighner (1982) of the University of California, San Diego, School of Medicine. My clinical experience agrees with his observations. In a clinical situation where depression is present in addition to anxiety, alprazolam is a good choice to start. The side effects are minimal and response is usually apparent in 10 days. We have also found Ativan (lorazepam) to be a useful benzodiazepine. It is intermediate in onset of action and slowly eliminated, making it useful as both a hypnotic and an anti-anxiety agent.

I am not impressed with the antihistamines or betablockers as useful anti-anxiety agents for most patients. I do not use the barbiturates because of the danger of oversedation and the narrow margin of safety between effective dose and toxic dose. I would not use the antipsychotic agents for anxiety because of the significant risk of tardive dyskinesia. The benzodiazepines are useful agents to prescribe in combination with other agents in the treatment of chronic pain syndromes, which often accompany civilian traumatic accidents.

POST-TRAUMATIC STRESS DISORDER AND DEPRESSION

Depression frequently accompanies other symptoms in PTSD and often meets the *DSM-III* criteria for depressive disorder. Most researchers find symptoms of depression periodically in a variety of post-traumatic stress disorders. Usually, the depression is not severe enough to be diagnosed as primary depression or major depressive disorder, and it is accompanied by anxiety. Symptoms include feeling sad or blue, being excessively worried or fatigued, feeling tense, being lonely, having trouble concentrating, lacking interest in sexual activity, and, sometimes, having suicidal ideation.

Depression in our experience is a relatively common finding in persons who meet *DSM-III* criteria for PTSD. Most of the current antidepressant medications have been used effectively.

The following is a list of currently available antidepressants and their usual dosages:

Table 4. Usual Dosages for Tricylic Antidepressants.

Tricyclic Antidepressants	**Usual Daily Dose** (mg)
imipramine (Tofranil)	100-200
amitriptyline (Elavil)	75-200
desipramine (Norpramin)	100-200
nortriptyline (Pamelor)	50-150
doxepin (Sinequan)	75-150
protriptyline (Vivactil)	15-40
trimipramine (Surmontil)	75-200
"Second-Generation" Antidepressants	
maprotiline (Ludiomil)	75-125
amoxapine (Asendin)	200-300
trazodone (Desyrel)	100-300
Monoamine Oxidose Inhibitors	
phenelzine (Nardil)	15-60
tranylcypromine (Parnate)	20-40
isocarboxazio (Marplan)	10-30

Again, as with the benzodiazepines, there is no one antidepressant better than all the others. Side-effect profile, individual response, and family history are helpful in choosing an antidepressant. If severe sleep disturbance is present and you want to use a single agent, then the more sedating agents, doxepin, amitriptyline, and trazodone, are useful. In the presence of marked anxiety, we have found doxepin (Sinequan) quite useful and at times have given daily dosages up to 300 to 400 mg per day for short periods of time.

I seldom use Asendin, since there have been reports of tardive dyskinesia as a long-term effect. Imipramine, one of the older drugs, is still one of the more useful antidepressants in our experience.

I have never had to use MAOI drugs such as Nardil in veterans with PTSD. I have used these agents, on occasion, in other cases of treatment-resistant depression with quite good results.

One must be patient when using antidepressant drugs, since most of them have rather slow (two-to-three weeks) onset of action. Dosage must be gradually increased to maximum levels for a sufficient length of time before one can say the drug worked or failed. If it failed, I would encourage the patient to try at least two more drugs of a different class before giving up. Successfully encouraging the patient to persist usually requires a strong therapeutic alliance between patient and physician.

After the patient has responded to the antidepressant, I like to reduce the drug to maintenance levels and treat for at least 90 days before gradually withdrawing the drug. If an exacerbation quickly occurs, then another treatment period of six months is indicated. Again, I know of no way to determine which patients may need longer term maintenance with these drugs. Fortunately, several studies have shown the safety of these agents in long-term maintenance.

Unfortunately, most antidepressant drugs have some rather unpleasant side effects that the physician must carefully explain to the patient if treatment is to be successful. Initial sedation may last up to five days, and can be useful in those patients with sleep disturbance.

Be cautioned about orthostatic hypotension (that is, when a sudden change in position produces lightheadedness and fainting), especially in older patients. Generally, if a patient tolerates the drug without troubling side effects for the first week, a gradual increase in dosage to obtain maximum effect is indicated. Unfortunately, we frequently see patients who are treated with subtherapeutic dosages and are labeled treatment-resistant. Once maximum therapeutic dosage is achieved, the patient should remain on the drug a minimum of six weeks before a gradual reduction of dosage is considered.

Although the antidepressant medications work best on patients with major depressive episodes, the use of antidepressants in other categories of depression still warrants our attention. The full benefits from most antidepressant drugs occur after the patient is on therapeutic dosages for three or four weeks. However, we often see a quicker improvement in sleep. But, if sleep disturbance and anxiety are problems, I often add a benzodiazepine, such as 2 mg of Ativan, an hour before bedtime.

Chronic pain is a fairly frequent complication of civilian traumas. Interestingly, we often see the chronic pain syndrome (pain persisting beyond six months of the original injury) in those situations where the original trauma was minimal and without significant medical findings. Unfortunately, we seldom see the patient within six months of the injury; more often, it's after the first year or later, by which time the symptom is quite fixed and has been reinforced by repeated medical consultations. Still, we can often intervene successfully by educating the patient about the psychological aspects of his or her pain and by giving the patients anti-anxiety and/or antidepressant medications. We are currently working with an industrial medical group to try to identify those patients who may be developing a pain syndrome within the first two to three months of their traumatic injury. It's still too early in our experience to tell what, if any, success we will have.

In some difficult chronic pain syndromes with significant psychogenic pain, we are having some success with (male and female) chronic pain groups that meet weekly for an hour-and-a-half. Currently, my co-therapist in these groups is a specialist in internal medicine who is especially interested in and sensitive to the psychological aspects of chronic pain. Again, I would emphasize that the pharmacotherapy of the symptoms of PTSD, especially severe anxiety, depression, and chronic pain syndromes, is best carried out in a setting where a variety of behavioral and other psychotherapies are the primary focus of treatment and pharmacotherapy is a significant addition to these ongoing treatment strategies.

REFERENCES

American Psychiatric Association. (1980). *Diagnostic and Statistical Manual of Mental Disorders III.* Washington, D.C.: American Psychiatric Press.

Feighner, J.P. (1982). *Modern Problems of Pharmacopsychiatry, 18*, 198-212.

Van Dyke and Associates. (1985, September). *The American Journal of Psychiatry, 142*:9.

CHAPTER SEVEN

POST-TRAUMATIC STRESS DISORDER AND SUBSTANCE ABUSE: TREATMENT PROBLEMS, STRATEGIES AND RECOMMENDATIONS

J. Michael Jelinek
Tom Williams

INTRODUCTION

Post-traumatic stress disorder (PTSD), acute, chronic, and/or delayed, is a diagnostic category in the *Diagnostic and Statistical Manual of Mental Disorders III* (American Psychiatric Association, 1980). PTSD is a cluster of symptoms that includes depression, intense anxiety, explosive aggressive behavior, emotional numbing/anesthesia, guilt, intrusive imagery, and sleep disturbances. Vietnam combat veterans appear to be particularly vulnerable to this disorder (Blank, 1982; Figley, 1978; Penk *et al.*, 1982; Williams, 1980; Wilson, 1980).

PTSD is not a disorder exclusive to combat veterans. Individuals or groups who experience catastrophic events such as terrorist activities, rape, automobile accidents or natural disasters (the Mount St. Helens volcanic eruption, for example) (Adams & Adams, 1984) can display PTSD symptoms.

DIFFICULTIES IN ASSESSING COMBAT VETERANS

A number of research studies conclude that Vietnam combat veterans exhibit substantially higher levels of alcohol consumption than do light combat veterans, Vietnam era veterans who did not go to Vietnam, military veterans from other wars, and nonveterans. In general, research indicates that Vietnam combat veterans engage in more continuous, sustained drinking patterns, engage in binge drinking more frequently, and drink to change mood. Many combat veterans appear to use alcohol as an anti-anxiety agent that induces a form of psychic numbing (Boscarino, 1979, 198l; Horowitz, 1979; Lacoursiere, Godfrey, & Ruby, 1980; Nace *et al.*, 1980; Robinowitz, Penk, Cannon & Fowler, 1982; Wilson, 1980; Wilson & Prabucki, 1983).

PTSD is frequently accompanied by a substance abuse problem; this tends to confuse the intake process. Although this chapter focuses on the interplay of PTSD and alcohol abuse, other substances follow a similar pattern. Barbiturates, tranquilizers, stimulants, and opiates may be substituted for alcohol or they may be accompanying problems.

Atkinson, Henderson, Sparr, and Deale (1982) outline several sources of difficulty in the assessment process with PTSD veterans. Intake pitfalls pertinent to combat veterans who are abusing alcohol are discussed below.

The "Silent" Veterans

The veterans who have made contact to "check us out" and find out about this PTSD "stuff" are often socially isolated, distrustful, cynical, unemployed, and suspicious of any affiliation we might have with the military or the Veterans Administration. They complain of experiencing existential crises relating to career achievements, interpersonal relationships, or general unhappiness. Creating a satisfactory therapeutic relationship is difficult because many veterans come to the initial interview after consuming substances.

Many combat veterans appear to be self-medicating with alcohol. They often use alcohol to suppress PTSD symptoms (Wilson, 1980). It is possible that they are consuming alcohol in an effort to maintain control through inebriation and its consequent psychic numbing that helps to thwart the capricious shifts of intrusive thoughts, anxiety, depression, and explosive anger that veterans believe are at times uncontrollable.

Veterans often have negative ideas of psychotherapy partly due to past experiences in the military or with the Veterans Administration. They are reticent, rather than engaging, in part because they fear that the therapist is going to force them to reopen the proverbial war-related "can of worms," which could result in their being helplessly out of control of surging emotions. Alcohol enables veterans to maintain a non-sensate focus towards therapy.

Combat veterans have learned from previous drinking experiences that they can mask adverse symptoms of PTSD (Lacoursiere *et al.*, 1980; Nace, O'Brien, Mintz, Ream and Meyers, 1980). A study conducted by Samaritan Village, Inc. (1982), a private drug and alcohol program, found that most of the patients in their sample believed that the military environment condoned or encouraged alcohol and drug use. Military recruits away from home, placed in uncontrollable environments, exposed to military authority and discipline, frequently utilized their sole recreational resource—the serviceman's club. Alcohol was readily and cheaply available to these teenage warriors (Williams, 1979). Many veterans discovered alcohol to be an effective stress-reducing technique. Combat veterans refined this stress reduction technique in dealing with battlefield stress. The military reinforced this coping strategy: successful combat operations were frequently rewarded with increased liquor rations. Many veterans used alcohol to enable them to socialize with peers and maintain acceptable behavior. Explosive anger at an unseen enemy or an uncontrollable situation could be temporarily diffused by consuming alcohol. During post-military adjustment, many veterans continued to use alcohol to suppress socially unacceptable behaviors (e.g., fighting, angry verbal altercations, etc.) and the symptoms of PTSD. As one veteran explained, "Give me a dark room and a bottle of whiskey and the nightmares won't bother me at all." Alcohol appears to be a social lubricant that has facilitated many veterans' reentry into mainstream society.

Often these "silent" veterans are caught up in a vicious cycle of alcohol abuse. Over time, combat veterans using alcohol to suppress symptoms find that their tolerance to alcohol increases, resulting in a need to increase consumption to achieve the desired effects. This frequently results in alcohol-related problems such as unemployment, financial difficulties, and impoverished interpersonal relationships. Many try to control alcohol problems by reducing consumption, going "on the wagon" or switching to other drugs (marijuana, sedatives, etc.). This often leads to an exacerbation of the original PTSD symptoms, resulting in increased alcohol usage to regain control. The abuse cycle is renewed, and the veteran becomes alcoholic.

The Antisocial Veteran

Although many emotions are suppressed, combat veterans have no difficulty in expressing anger or explosive rage. For some, the anger is directed toward family members, co-workers, or supervisors; others have sublimated their rage toward inanimate objects. Alcohol is only partially successful when used to suppress symptoms of PTSD. Anger, depression, and impulsiveness occasionally surface (Lacoursiere *et al.*, 1980).

We have found two different ways of understanding explosive anger in combat veterans. In the first, we concur with Blank (1979) who states that violence or unpredictable explosions of aggressive behavior, upon minimal or no provocation, sometimes have a dissociative stereotyped quality, as if a former event were being re-enacted. Many combat veterans have suppressed painful recollections of traumatic events in combat. Various internal or external stimuli, reminiscent of the traumatic event, are exacerbated by alcohol. These veterans appear to be reliving actual experiences (these have been called flashbacks). In every case that we have encountered, alcohol has been involved in the dissociative break. Sometimes the quantity of alcohol consumed has been small.

A second way we understand explosive anger in combat veterans is to view it as a potent learned coping strategy. Explosive acts of aggression towards co-workers or a "target of opportunity" in a bar serve to reduce stress or negative emotions.

Many combat veterans viewed situations in an all-or-none dichotomy (e.g., action versus non-action). The soldier in battle frequently would endure prolonged periods during which he had no control over when he could discharge pent-up stress. When given approval for action, he did so in an aggressive manner to relieve the stress. This style of thinking of stress management has carried over into post-military life. Many combat veterans go for prolonged periods of time without managing environmental or psychological stress in an adaptive manner. But as pressure from multiple stressors increases, we have found many veterans resorting to some sort of physical violence while abusing alcohol. Alcohol seems to be a trigger for an overt conditioned response to stress (see Agosta and McHugh, "Family Violence," this volume).

A major assessment problem, when encountering what appears to be anti-social behavior in combat veterans, is that a personality disorder could be diagnosed although PTSD may be more accurate (see Newman, this volume). A thorough intake evaluation should be employed to differentiate between possible personality disorders and combat veterans with PTSD and accompanying maladaptive behaviors.

DIAGNOSTIC PROBLEMS IN TREATING SURVIVORS

The polymorphous, non-distinct clinical appearance of PTSD has occasionally resulted in survivors' problems being misdiagnosed as personality disorders (Walker, 1981), neuroses (Van Putten & Emory, 1973), or psychoses (Van Putten & Emory 1973; Williams, 1980). Different diagnostic criteria should be used systematically to screen for syndromes other than PTSD. PTSD may be mixed with or masked by other disorders. The major risk of assuming PTSD to be the sole cause of behaviors characteristic of other diagnostic categories is that some clients with other diagnoses may be deprived of specific treatments of known effectiveness (Sierles, Chen, McFarland, and Taylor, 1983). Excessive diagnostic parsimony that could reduce multi-problem cases to a single diagnosis is a disadvantage to the client and could negatively affect the treatment outcome.

Biased clinicians contribute to diagnostic difficulties. Some psychiatrists and psychologists doubt the validity of PTSD or consider it a very rare phenomenon. Despite the overwhelming evidence of competent research projects that validate PTSD, the psychodynamically trained psychiatric community tends to cling to predispositional factors. An opposite bias can be directed towards veteran therapists who see PTSD in every veteran. Therapists who are sensitized to PTSD may elevate the importance of that disorder and minimize or neglect additional psychopathology.

TREATMENT STRATEGIES

Treatment begins with the first contact. Every effort should be oriented toward "hooking" the veteran and capitalizing on the motivation that prompted him to seek treatment. Haley (1974) has stated:

> Establishment of a therapeutic alliance for this group of patients is the treatment rather than the facilitator of treatment. It is critical that in every sense the therapist be "for real," a "real person" more so than a transference figure, and a "real person" respectful of the veteran's strength and concerned about but not "put off" by their psychopathology. (p. 195)

Combat veterans can be very difficult upon first contact. They are generally distrustful, suspicious, and have a very poor self-concept (Williams, 1980). They will key on style and tone, in addition to content of speech, lines of questioning, or your assertiveness, in order to justify their withdrawing from therapy, thus reinforcing their sense of helplessness.

It might be advantageous to keep the first contact warm, open, and relaxed. Ask the veteran about units he served with, where he served, and how his life is going right now. Try not to hesitate in answering any questions from the client. Self-disclosure and openness by the therapist may be key factors in joining with the client. Many veterans are isolated and very cautious, concealing themselves, their thoughts, and their emotions from others. Being aloof, distant, or authoritarian may exacerbate the veteran's paranoia or hostility and sabotage the therapeutic alliance. Using an open and self-disclosing style demonstrates to the veteran your genuineness and is a potent model to be emulated.

In our experience, being a veteran greatly enhances this initial joining process. Having access to a veteran who could make telephone contacts with prospective clients might facilitate the intake and could also help screen the content of combat incidents to ensure their validity. Nonveteran therapists, male and female, can and have worked very well with veterans. Their motives for working with veterans may be questioned and confrontation may occur more frequently, but potential conflicts may be diffused if the therapist is open and acknowledges veterans' questions. Nonveteran therapists may never understand the complex events that occur on an ambush or night patrol, but they can understand the breadth of emotions—fear, anger, helplessness, guilt—that many combat veterans experienced. In some cases, paradoxical techniques can be used to enhance motivation in combat veterans. Many believe that their situation is so hopeless there is no way anyone can help. You could inform these clients that you know of no magical cure or pill that will solve their problems. You might acknowledge the severity of their problems and the inadequacy of their solutions. We have found it helpful to suggest that they try a new solution. Active involvement in a therapy program oriented towards traumatic experiences is frequently a solution that many veterans have not tried.

PTSD INTAKE

PTSD is rarely presented as a discrete entity unclouded by other psychopathology. Alcohol abuse has been a key accompanying disorder with many survivors. The first assessment task that we perform is a detailed life history. Investigating pre-trauma, trauma, and post-trauma variables can greatly assist the clinician in differentiating between a personality/somatic/affective disorder and an individual who had a normal childhood/adolescence and was overcome by conflicts experienced during the traumatic situation.

The role that alcohol plays should be ascertained. Those who had a family history of alcohol abuse or who abused alcohol before the trauma can be differentiated from those who began to abuse alcohol after the trauma. The PTSD intake acts as a screening measure for further alcohol abuse assessment.

Inconsistencies, gaps, or observed behavioral abnormalities detected during the initial intake evaluation can be used to facilitate the selection of psychological and/or neurological testing measures.

Developing rapport during the intake interviews is necessary to reduce discomfort in the veteran and to solidify the joining process. Use the client's language and try to dispel myths about therapy; reinforce emotional sharing and disclosure. It may help to let the clients set their own pace during the intake assessment. We have found it helpful to conduct the intake evaluation over two or three sessions and avoid rapid-fire data collection. One may find the intake sessions very helpful in getting to know the clients, letting them know you, and enhancing the transition into a therapeutic alliance.

Williams (1981) has devised a detailed intake evaluation that is helpful in organizing large amounts of data and guiding the evaluation process (Table 1). Each client is asked to talk about his childhood, family, military service, and post-military adjustment. The evaluation format provides structure to the assessment and assists questioning when the client makes omissions in the life history. Additional information from military records, veteran organizations, schools, and families is requested when appropriate. The goal of the intake assessment is to get a clear view of the client's life situation. Specific questions to be answered include: the extent and severity of PTSD, additional disorders, level of functioning, and prognosis. Try not to be strict and formal in following this guideline, but fill it in as the client talks. They do not respond well to "filling out forms." Be warm and inquisitive. You might ask the veteran to teach you about his experiences.

The interview provides information to aid diagnosis, assists in the selection of psychological/neurological tests, and gains a holistic picture of the veteran's development. In the "classic" case of veterans experiencing PTSD, one typically learns that they had a happy childhood, good family relations, and adapted well to environmental and psychological stressors. In school, they adapted to structure, got average grades, made friends, and had a paper route. In high school, they dated, socialized with friends, and experienced no major or minor involvements with school or police authorities. These veterans usually enlisted to "do their part for the country," because their fathers/uncles/ brothers served, or to make a better life for themselves. After the war, the veterans describe a very different picture of their lives. Unemployment, divorce, interpersonal relationship difficulties, legal problems, and alcohol abuse comprise a sad litany for many combat veterans.

Table 1: Intake Evaluation

PTSD Life History Format	**Potential Question Areas**
1. Identifying Data	
2. Presenting Problem	
3. Pre-service Data	
a. Family	Parental marriage data, birth order, siblings, holidays/vacations, family activities, relocations, financial situation, family violence/discipline/alcohol-drug usage.
b. School (Elementary-High School)	Transition to structured environment, peer activity, grades, school activities, neighborhood activities, family support in schooling, police or educational disciplinary actions, alcohol/drug abuse, sexual activities. Social activities in high school—dating, friendships, social networks, school clubs, honors, sports, disciplinary problems (school, police, family, work).
c. Employment	Earliest job, types of employment, conflicts with school or family, use of profits (e.g., for dating, auto, family, alcohol, etc.), co-worker and supervisor relationships.
d. Interpersonal	Girlfriend, married, friendships, intimacy, sexual activity.
4. Military Service Data	
a. Military Induction	Which service, how inducted (volunteer, draft, court referral), motivations, goals, family history of military service, career-oriented.
b. Basic Training	Transition to military environment, friendships, awards, promotions, disciplinary action, stress factors, drug/alcohol use, AWOL.
c. Advanced Training	Military occupational specialty, schools, grades, awards, promotions, social activities, friendships, disciplinary actions, alcohol/drug use, stress management.

d. Wartime Service	How notified of duty and reaction, alone or by unit to war zone, leaves, perception of first day in-country, unit assigned to, duties performed (same as specialty?), area assigned, friendships, drug/alcohol use.
5. Most Emotional and Resistant Portion of Interview	Describe combat situations/traumatic events, loss of friends, wounded in action, atrocities seen or participated in, dates of combat, units, feelings (e.g., guilt, shame, fear, anger, etc.), relations with civilians in combat zone, unit solidarity vs. individual phenomena, hospitalizations, evacuations, promotions, was veteran a doctor/medic/corpsman/nurse or assigned to graves registration?
a. Post-war	Medical treatment after war, evacuation process, hospitalizations, arrival and reception in USA, discharge (honorable, etc.) military treatment upon discharge, military duty and adjustment if remained in service, feelings upon return and reception, PTSD symptoms, alcohol/drug use, stress management.
6. Post-service Data	
a. Initial Readjustment	Family reception, friends, dating, employment, PTSD symptoms, alcohol/drug use, stressors.
b. Interpersonal Relationships	Marriage, divorce, friendships, social network, isolation, contact with other veterans.
c. Employment History	Type, number of jobs, relocations, quit/fired from jobs, co-worker and supervisor relations.
d. Legal Difficulties	Police, governmental agencies, social services, compensation, divorce, bankruptcy, arrests.
e. Medical Problems	War injuries and deterioration, Agent Orange, V.A. compensation and treatment problems, exposure to radiation, malnutrition, ex-POW.
f. Drug/Alcohol Use	Role of alcohol/drugs, type, frequency, self-medicating.

SUBSTANCE ABUSE ASSESSMENT

Crisci (1983) has assembled a comprehensive substance abuse form that can be used to assess the role of alcohol/substance abuse in post-trauma clients; it is presented below as Table 2.

Table 2. Substance Abuse Form

This form consists of five sections, and data can be collected during one session. Data from the preceding evaluation can be used to augment or shorten this assessment.

1. History of Present Illness

a. A brief narrative of the client's use of substances—when it started, initial use pattern—did the pattern change or escalate up or down? When? What was the drug of choice—what is the current drug of choice?

b. Have they experienced withdrawals, blackouts, DT's, seizures?

c. Do they have any medical problems that are being exacerbated by substance use or that would inhibit the use of Antabuse?

d. Has anyone in family had substance abuse problems? Include some questions to assess sexual functioning in relationship to substance use.

2. Significant Substance Use/Abuse Information

a. Detailed information on history of substance abuse. Screen for: alcohol, marijuana, cocaine, amphetamines, barbiturates, tranquilizers, opiates, PCP inhalents, hallucinogens, "crack."

b. Collect normative data for each substance to include type, age/year started, age became a problem, initial frequency and amount, current frequency and amount, last use and specific additional comments.

3. Descriptive Mental Status

a. Describe appearance, general behavior, attitude, mood, affect, speech, thought process and content.

b. Physical appearance often is a cue to the veteran's intensity of abuse.

c. Observe for shakes, shifting in seat, shaking of foot, flushed face, red eyes.

4. Living Arrangements/Activities of Daily Living

a. Are they in an environment that supports a substance-free lifestyle?

b. Are they living alone or with a significant other?

If living with someone, does the other person use any substance?

c. Is their life centered around substance use or do they use any available leisure time for other activities?

5. Assessment

a. Include an assessment of strengths, assets, problems and needs, the clients' perception of problems, and list problems to be addressed during treatment.

TREATMENT PLANNING

The information gathered from the above evaluations is used to differentiate among three types of combat veterans. The first is the combat veteran experiencing PTSD without a substance problem. The second is the veteran who began abusing substances in war to relieve stress and has continued to self-medicate with alcohol. The third type is a veteran who has had a life-long drinking pattern and, frequently, a family history of alcohol abuse. Differentiating between these types of veterans is very important for treatment planning. We have found it very counterproductive to mix these different types of veterans into one therapy group. Their primary issues/goals differ greatly, and this can inhibit group cohesiveness, direction, and productivity.

Clients with PTSD who are substance free are perhaps the easiest to work with. PTSD symptoms are easily discussed and they are able to reexperience the emotional content of the trauma and work through the many emotional issues.

The veteran with PTSD and substance abuse during and after war requires a different treatment approach. Several areas need to be clarified. Is the alcohol abuse compounding the PTSD symptoms? Is the veteran experiencing alcohol-related problems above and beyond his PTSD? Is the alcohol abuse masking underlying symptoms of PTSD? Does alcohol abuse appear to be isolating the veteran or is it a tidy explanation for frequent unemployment and poor interpersonal relationships? Is alcohol abuse perpetuating the PTSD symptoms? Have the veterans managed to self-medicate themselves into a "maintaining" state?

This second type of veteran may admit alcohol abuse and agree that it is a problem. With these veterans, PTSD appears to be the primary issue and alcohol is a secondary issue. In our experience, we have found it helpful to place these veterans in a therapy group where the primary focus is on PTSD, and alcohol abuse is worked with as an inhibiting factor for their treatment progress. Veterans who are self-medicating with alcohol can be placed with substance-free veterans in group therapy as long as the primary focus is on PTSD. As PTSD symptomatology decreases in intensity and frequency, we have found that many combat veterans reduce or eliminate alcohol consumption.

The veteran with life-long substance abuse is also treated differently, and should be strongly encouraged to enter a drug/alcohol detoxification program. We recommend that a monitored Antabuse program be initiated before placing this type of veteran into therapy. For example, the Veterans Administration hospital in Denver has a clinic where veterans can enter a drug/alcohol rehabilitation program. We urge veterans to enter such a program and inform them that therapy for PTSD will accompany their alcohol treatment. The primary treatment orientation for this group of veterans is alcohol abuse education and detoxification. PTSD therapy is secondary. Research (Lacoursiere *et al.*, 1980) has suggested that alcohol suppresses PTSD symptoms (e.g., reduces anxiety, relaxes muscles, induces sleep, and suppresses REM activity, etc.). Often veterans who begin the detoxification process soon exhibit a rebound effect in their PTSD symptoms (e.g., increased number and duration of nightmares, increased anxiety and hyperalertness, etc.). After the primary goal of reducing alcohol abuse is achieved, the treatment of PTSD may become primary.

Pharmacologic therapy is often employed with this third type of veteran. Yost (1980 and this volume) discusses the pharmacological treatment of Vietnam combat veterans and highly recommends that these individuals reduce or abstain from alcohol consumption during therapy. He recommends that Antabuse be used as an adjunct to ensure no alcohol consumption while the patient is being treated for anxiety. Alcohol will confound pharmacological therapy (e.g., use of benzodiazepines, tricyclic antidepressants, etc.) and should be monitored throughout the treatment process.

CLINICAL ILLUSTRATIONS

Three case histories may clarify these classifications: case example 1, Tom, who has PTSD without alcohol abuse; case example 2, Greg, who has PTSD with alcohol abuse; and case example 3, Jim, who has had life-long alcohol abuse and who has PTSD.

Case Example 1

Tom is a 34-year-old Chicano Vietnam combat veteran. He is currently filing for a divorce from his wife and has retained custody of his children.

Tom was raised by an extended family network in the southwest. He was the youngest of five children and remembers many happy times with aunts, uncles, and his family. He was raised in a small community and socialized extensively with his peers. He did well in school and sporting activities. He received no disciplinary action at school or in the community. He tried beer in high school but got sick and did not use alcohol thereafter. He dated frequently and worked part-time in a grocery store. Tom enlisted in the Marines to see the world, learn a trade, and do his duty in Vietnam.

Tom adjusted to service life and enjoyed the challenging situations he experienced in the Marines. He was an expert marksman and was promoted in advanced training. Tom did not smoke or drink and received no military discipline during his enlistment. Tom served two tours in Vietnam as a "grunt" (frontline combat soldier) stationed near the DMZ. He saw extensive combat and lost several friends. He did not use alcohol or drugs in Vietnam. He tried marijuana once but was upset and confused by the drug. "I didn't need that stuff, man, I wanted to make it through my thirteen months in one piece," he remarked. Tom was wounded once and volunteered for a second tour to do more for the friends he had lost. Tom was discharged and returned to civilian life to get back to being "normal."

He married his high school girlfriend, got a job with a large corporation, and began to isolate himself. "I didn't feel comfortable not knowing where my wife was at all times, something bad might happen," he remarked. Tom had frequent nightmares, intrusive thoughts, and bouts of explosive rage. Instead of using alcohol, Tom immersed himself in his work. Tom was fired after 12 years because of an argument with a supervisor. His life began to unravel. Marital problems and PTSD symptoms intensified. Tom entered therapy when his wife left him. Tom has been in individual, family, and group therapy for six months. He has made a marked improvement and is beginning to resolve issues related to Vietnam and his failed marriage. His alcohol consumption consists of a glass of wine on holidays or when he gets together with family members.

Case Example 2

Greg is a 35-year-old Vietnam combat veteran. He is married, employed, and not abusing alcohol.

Greg grew up in a rural midwestern town and was the second oldest of five children. Neither of his parents drank and Greg remembers many family holidays and vacations. He was an average student in school academically and excelled in athletics. He played baseball, football, and basketball, socialized with neighborhood friends, and did not experience disciplinary problems. In high school, Greg lettered in two sports and was class president one year. He dated a girl for two years and thought about marrying her after high school. He socialized with his male friends and together they rebuilt a 1957 Chevrolet. He remembers trying beer, but in general, his friends didn't smoke or drink. Greg enlisted in the Marine Corps because his father and uncle served in World War II, and he wanted to do his part. Greg did not experience any disciplinary action from school or police authorities.

Greg enjoyed his Marine Corps training and he did well in his military courses. He was assigned to Vietnam in October 1967 and served as a "grunt" in Northern I Corps. Greg's first duty was at Con Thien, a small Marine fire base. In November, 1967, Con Thien came under enemy attack. The battle around Con Thien was the largest engagement of the Vietnam war to that date. Nearly 800 B-52 flights dropped 22,000 tons of bombs, and fighter-bombers and naval warships pummeled the area in one month's time. Greg began to smoke cigarettes and discovered that alcohol was the only way to get away from the bombings. "You couldn't ever forget it but alcohol made it go away for a while," he remarked. An enemy rocket killed every man in Greg's squad. Greg was wounded twice and he served later at Khe Sanh and Dong Ha in intense combat operations. By the end of his tour of duty in Vietnam, Greg described himself as a robot devoid of feelings.

At first, Greg made a successful readjustment to civilian life. He had a steady job, was dating a woman and thinking of marriage. But nightmares and intrusive thoughts of Con Thien intensified, and Greg increased his drinking to get away from the thoughts and to sleep. For the next ten years, Greg functioned with the assistance of alcohol. In November 1980, Greg experienced a very powerful anniversary reaction from his time at Con Thien and contacted our office to enter therapy. PTSD was diagnosed and treated primarily. Greg spent 18 months in individual and group therapy dealing with PTSD issues/symptoms. When he terminated from therapy, Greg was not drinking to sleep or suppress PTSD symptoms. As the PTSD issues were resolved, Greg remarked, "In the past the alcohol helped me make it, but now I find that it's no longer necessary."

Case Example 3

Jim is a 40-year-old Vietnam combat veteran. He has been divorced twice and is again married. Jim described a life-long history of alcohol abuse.

When Jim was four years old, he remembers his parents' bridge parties where he got a lot of attention, a small glass of beer and a bit of cheese. His father made his own beer and Jim had either beer or wine with his meals. His grandfather and three uncles were known alcoholics in his hometown. When Jim was in the ninth grade, he worked in a grocery store where he could obtain beer. He went out with older friends who could drive and he would drink a couple of six-packs. His parents objected to the driving and requested that he drink at home. Jim went to a private Catholic high school and was placed on probation for drinking. "We got high because we would forcefeed ourselves booze when we had the chance," he remarked. Jim believed that drinking was a way to be mature. "You had to be 21 to vote and drink, we grew up young," he remarked. Jim attended college where he drank two or three times a week. He was arrested for illegal possession of alcohol when he was 19.

When Jim was in basic training, he would go to the PX to buy beer and sit in the sun. "Whenever we got time off, we would go to town and get drunk because there was nothing else to do," Jim remarked. By the end of advanced training, Jim was drinking "pretty much every day." When Jim arrived in Vietnam, he thought he should stay straight and he would reward himself with alcohol when he got home. He worked in a medical dispensary, and engineers built an EM club next door. "I began to drink every day to keep my nerves down, not to get drunk," he stated. Jim didn't drink when he went out on combat operations, but he would reward himself with a binge when he returned. Jim remembers a powerful hangover on the day he left Vietnam.

Jim's wife gave him three bottles of whiskey as a welcome home present. He believed that he had a year to relax and enjoy booze. Jim drank heavily for three years, then his wife left him. Jim returned to Vietnam as a medic with a private corporation. He remained in Vietnam for 15 months and got drunk every day. "I was drinking to stay calm, to get to sleep, to avoid people, to not think," Jim remarked. When Jim returned to the U.S., he lived for the "life of Riley," drinking every day. He was drinking in the morning to get going and began to believe that his alcohol consumption was out of control. Between 1971 and 1975, Jim entered 15 different alcohol programs but dropped out of almost all of them. Jim has been a member of AA since 1975, but occasionally goes on binges. He has been hospitalized on several occasions after a drinking binge. Jim started a monitored Antabuse program when he entered therapy. "The only way I can deal with Vietnam is when I'm dry," he remarked. In the past, alcohol was a friend that kept him calm and made life easy. Jim is utilizing new stress management techniques to deal with stressors and is actively involved in individual and group therapy on PTSD issues.

TREATMENT CONSIDERATIONS

PTSD is a crucial and precipitating cause of alcohol abuse in trauma survivors. Alcohol abuse may begin secondary to PTSD and might continue by itself after the PTSD is treated. Alcohol use should be monitored throughout the treatment process to ensure maximum gain and long-term treatment effects.

Many survivors have been using alcohol as a primary stress-reducing coping strategy. Many are very resistant to abandoning this cheap, available, effective, albeit inappropriate, coping strategy. New alternative coping strategies should be incorporated into the treatment process as soon as possible. Breathing exercises, progressive muscle relaxation, visual imagery, physical exercise, peer support systems, and bibliotherapy are explained and encouraged as options to alcohol. Stress management is difficult to teach to many combat veterans because they appear to like increased levels of stress. Pointing out the negative effects of alcohol must be consistently addressed and all new attempts to manage stress in an adaptive manner should be highly reinforced.

RECOMMENDATIONS

1. PTSD is rarely presented as a distinct entity. Alcohol/substance use, somatoform, affective and/or other disorders may coexist with PTSD symptoms.

2. Survivors may display features characteristic of personality disorders, neuroses or psychoses when first encountered in a clinical setting. Many are socially isolated, distrustful, cynical, and suspicious. Building the therapeutic alliance with combat veterans begins with first contact. Openness and self-disclosure are necessary in forging a therapuetic relationship with traumatized persons.

3. A thorough intake assessment is necessary to differentiate between PTSD and/or other disorders. Pre-trauma, trauma, and post-trauma variables will assist the clinician in assessing the severity and validity of PTSD.

4. Differentiating between PTSD clients without substance use, those who use substances to suppress PTSD symptomatology, and those with a life-long history of abuse is important for treatment planning. For the first two types of clients, the primary focus of therapy is PTSD, while alcohol abuse education is primary for the third type. PTSD may become the primary therapy focus for those who have completed a detoxification program.

5. Alcohol abuse is a frequent companion to PTSD. Alcohol may be suppressing, exacerbating, or perpetuating PTSD symptomatology. Understanding the role of alcohol in the maintenance of PTSD will facilitate treatment planning.

6. Alcohol consumption appears to be a potent stress-reducing strategy for many. New stress management techniques should be introduced to veterans as an alternative to alcohol.

7. When alcoholism and PTSD are diagnosed, the alcoholism is life-threatening and therefore the primary diagnosis and a major focus of treatment.

It is unfortunate that the scientific understanding of PTSD has become the object of a "turf war." Proponents of premorbid pathology versus proponents who highlight the impact of trauma in the etiology of PTSD have yet to resolve their differences and they may not for years to come.

REFERENCES

Adams, P.R. & Adams, G.R. (1984). Mount Saint Helens' ash fall: Evidence for a disaster stress reaction. *American Psychologist, 39,* 252-260.

American Psychiatric Association (1980). *Diagnostic and statistical manual of mental disorders* (3rd ed.). Washington, DC: American Psychiatric Press.

American Psychological Association (1983). *Publication Manual of the American Psychological Association* (3rd ed.). Washington, DC: Author

Atkinson, R.M., Henderson, R.G., Sparr, L.F., & Deale, S. (1982). Assessment of Viet Nam veterans for post-traumatic stress disorder in Veterans Administration disability claims. *American Journal of Psychiatry,* 139, 1118-1121.

Atkinson, R.M., Callen, K.E., Reaves, M.D., & Drum mond, D.J. (1984). Veterans Administration mental health services for Viet Nam veterans. Accepted for publication in *Psychiatric Annals.*

Blank, A.S. (1979, September 24-28). First training conference papers, Viet Nam veterans—Operation outreach. St. Louis, MO: U.S. Veterans Administration.

Blank, A.S. (1982, November). Apocalypse terminable and interminable: Operation outreach for Viet Nam veterans. *Hospital and Community Psychiatry, 33.*

Boscarino, J. (1979). Current drug involvement among Viet Nam and non-Viet Nam veterans. *American Journal Drug and Alcohol Abuse, 6,* 301-312.

Boscarino, J. (1981). Current excessive drinking among Viet Nam veterans: A comparison with other veterans and non-veterans. *The International Journal of Social Psychiatry, 27.*

Crisci, J. (1983). Suggested Substance Abuse Intake and Assessment. Unpublished assessment measure, Park Place, 1810 Gilpin, Denver, CO 80218.

Del Vecchio, J.M. (1982). *The 13th valley.* New York: Bantam Books, Inc.

Escobar, J.I., Randolph, E.T., Puente, G., Spivak, F., Asamen, J.K., Hill, M., & Hough, R.L. (1983, October). Post traumatic stress disorder in Hispanic Viet Nam veterans: Clinical phenomenology and sociocultural characteristics. *The Journal of Nervous and Mental Diseases, 171,* 00-00.

Figley, C.R. (Ed.) (1978). *Stress disorders among Viet Nam veterans.* New York: Brunner/Mazel.

Goodwin, J. (1980). The etiology of combat-related post-traumatic stress disorders. In T. Williams (Ed.), *Post-traumatic stress disorders of the Viet Nam veteran.* Cincinnati, O: Disabled American Veterans.

Haley, S.A. (1974). When the patient reports atrocities. *Archives of General Psychiatry, 30,* 191-196.

Horowitz, M.J. (1979). Psychological responses to serious life events. In V. Hamilton & D.M. Warburton (Eds.), *Human stress and cognition.* New York: Wiley & Sons.

Lifton, R.J. (1973). *Home from the War.* New York: Simon & Schuster.

Lacoursiere, R.B., Godfrey, K.E., & Ruby, L.M. (1980). Traumatic neurosis in the etiology of alcoholism: Viet Nam combat and other trauma. *American Journal of Psychiatry, 137,* 966-968.

Nace, E.P., O'Brien, C.P., Mintz, J., Ream, N., & Meyers, A.L. (1980). Adjustment among Viet Nam veteran drug users two years post service. *American Journal of Psychiatry, 137,* 966-968.

President's Commission on Mental Health (1978, February 15). *Report of the special working group: Mental health problems of Viet Nam era veterans.* Washington, DC: Author.

Robinowitz, R., Penk, W.E., Cannon, D., & Fowler, D.R. (1982). Psychological assessment of combat-related post-traumatic stress disorders among substance abusers entering treatment . Unpublished paper presented at the VAMC, Dallas, Texas.

Penk, W.E., Robinowitz, R., Roberts, W.R., Patterson, E.T., Dolan, M.P., & Atkins, H.G. (1981). Adjustment differences among male substance abusers varying in degree of combat experiences in Viet Nam. *Journal of Consulting and Clinical Psychology, 49,* 426-437.

Samaritan Village, Inc. Veterans Study (1982). Unpublished survey. Samaritan Village Inc., 118-121, Queens Boulevard, Forest Hills, NY.

Shatan, C.F. (1978). Stress disorders among Viet Nam veterans: The emotional content of combat continues. In C.R. Figley (Ed.), *Stress disorders among Viet Nam veterans: Theory, research and treatment.* New York: Brunner/Mazel.

Sierles, F.S., Chen, J., McFarland, R.E., & Taylor, M.A. (1983). Post-traumatic stress disorder and concurrent psychiatric illness: A preliminary report. *American Journal of Psychiatry, 140,* 1177-1179.

Van Putten, T., & Emory, W.H. (1973). Traumatic neurosis in Viet Nam returnees. *Archives of General Psychiatry, 129,* 695-698.

Webb, J. (1978). *Fields of Fire.* Englewood Cliffs, NJ: Prentice-Hall, Inc.

Williams, T. (Ed.). (1980). *Post-traumatic stress disorder of the Vietnam veteran.* Cincinnati, O: Disabled American Veterans.

Williams, T. (1979, April). Viet Nam veterans. Unpublished paper presented at the University of Denver, School of Professional Psychology, Denver, CO.

Williams, T. (1981). PTSD assessment form. Unpublished assessment measure. Post-Trauma Treatment Center, 12361 East Cornell Avenue, Aurora, CO.

Wilson, J.P. (1978). Conflict, stress, and growth: The effects of the Viet Nam war on psychosocial development among Viet Nam veterans. In C.R. Figley and S. Leventman (Eds.), *Strangers at home: Viet Nam veterans since the war.* Praeger Press.

Wilson, J.P, Prabucki, K. (1983). The relationship of post-traumatic stress disorder to drug and alcohol use among Viet Nam combat veterans. Unpublished paper presented at Cleveland State University, Cleveland, O.

Yost, J. (1980). The psychopharmacologic treatment of delayed stress syndrome in Viet Nam veterans. In T. Williams (Ed.), *Post-traumatic stress disorders of the Viet Nam veteran.* Cincinnati, O: Disabled American Veterans.

CHAPTER EIGHT

COUNSELING CONSIDERATIONS IN WORKING WITH DISABLED VIETNAM VETERANS[1]

Gary E. May

BACKGROUND

The legacies of U.S. involvement in Vietnam have been well-documented. Particular attention has been paid to the effects that it had on combatants (Blank, 1982; Figley, 1978, 1985; Figley & Leventman, 1980; Laufer et al., 1981; Wilson, 1977), but there remains a rather glaring omission of useful, thoughtful information about service personnel who were wounded while serving in Vietnam. The number of wounded exceeds 303,000, half of whom required hospitalization.

The war in Vietnam swelled the ranks of severely disabled individuals in America. Because of the guerrilla nature of the warfare in Vietnam, the likelihood of serious injury was quite high, and, because of advances in medical and transportation technologies,[2] the survival rate for the severely wounded was higher than in previous U.S. wars. Two-and-one-half percent of those hospitalized in Vietnam died. In World War II, this figure stood at 4.5 percent. Battle deaths for the U.S. Army in Vietnam for the period July 1965 through June 1969 were 21.9 per thousand troops. In Korea, this figure was 43.2 per thousand. In Europe during World War II, from June 1944 through May 1945, battle deaths reported were at 51.9 per thousand troops. Military personnel wounded in Vietnam were likely to sustain more serious injuries and were far more likely to survive those injuries. For example, service personnel in Vietnam suffered amputation or crippling wounds to the lower extremities at a rate that was fully 300 percent higher than in World War II. The rate of multiple amputations during Vietnam was 18.4 percent, in comparison to World War II's 5.7 percent (Starr, 1973; Veterans Administration, 1985). The Veterans Administration reported that as of December 1983, 587,032 Vietnam-era veterans were receiving compensation for service-related illness or injury; of these, nearly 6,700 incurred anatomical loss of a limb and nearly 11,000 suffered the loss of the use of a limb. The record seems to be that great care was taken for the physical well-being of wounded soldiers in Vietnam.

However, attention to the psychosocial aspects of disability were largely ignored in the rehabilitation process. Indeed, the focus in the acute phases of rehabilitation was on the physical, vocational, and economic issues in the veteran's recovery. Long stays in a military hospital were not conducive to the identification and expression of feelings or emotional reactions to serious disability: there was a premium on stoicism and maintaining a "John Wayne" image.

The experience of the thousands of these primarily teenaged citizen soldiers gave new meaning to the ubiquitous recruiting slogan of the '60s, "The Marine Corps builds men." For many, this slogan became literally true as they were faced with learning to adjust to a drastically altered body and body image, and to live with their "hardware" and "adaptive aids" or compensate for the damage to or lack of "original equipment." The emphasis was on technology and physical rehabilitation; little attention was given to the psychosocial aspects of disability.

This "high-tech" environment notwithstanding, many disabled Vietnam veterans did form informal rap groups during their periods of hospitalization. These groups were generally organized around needs for camaraderie and companionship; very little work of psychological or therapeutic substance was accomplished. When powerful feelings did emerge, there seemed to be a tacit agreement to ignore them. Ready availability of prescription drugs and alcohol also served to numb the intensity and effects of very powerful emotions. Moreover, hospital staff gave scant attention to assisting in this informal process: many involved with providing ongoing direct care to seriously wounded veterans were anticipating their own upcoming assignments with infantry units in Vietnam. Denial seemed to be a very useful defense mechanism for everyone.

The continuation of the military orientation in the military hospital system had powerful implications for the seriously disabled veterans. Standardization and routines are highly valued in the military and they were no less important in its hospital system. This approach (which included requiring each new hospital arrival-patient to complete a very detailed uniform and equipment questionnaire) ignored obvious individual differences and variations in the physical state of the new arrivals. Bilateral, above-the-knee amputees report being asked for boot size and inseam measurements upon arrival at each new treatment facility (indeed, such is this author's experience). This "cookie-cutter" approach may have had some bureaucratic benefit for the military supply components, but for the victim, it solidified feelings of resentment, bitterness, loneliness, and alienation. For some, these feelings have endured for many years.

However, the hospital setting did provide a safe and secure place where disabled Vietnam veterans were in many ways shielded from some of the more direct and abrasive expressions of public disdain for the U.S. role in Vietnam. It also provided an environment where confrontation with the "normal world" could be conveniently delayed if not avoided altogether. For some, dependency on this safe and secure place developed to the point that they resisted leaving the hospital.

Not only does this disabled population carry the stigma of disability, they also were left to struggle with reconciling themselves to their role in Vietnam. In searching for the answer to very tough questions ("Why did all this happen to me? Why does no one seem to understand or appreciate me? What does the future hold for me?"), many found despair and hopelessness. Even years after their return from Vietnam, many disabled Vietnam veterans find that these issues and concerns are still potent. As a consequence, those working in counseling relationships with these veterans must be aware of and sensitive to these questions to help ensure an effective therapeutic relationship.

CLINICAL CONSIDERATIONS

The young men who returned from Vietnam as seriously disabled veterans had started their tours as reasonably healthy, physically functional, and generally unimpaired individuals who had internalized such ideals as physique, physical power and prowess, good looks, and wholeness. The sudden onset of an adventitious, serious impairment shattered many of their chances for attaining these valued ideals.

They had also internalized many of the negative stereotypes that are used to characterize the physically disabled in this society—such attributes as mental retardation, stupidity, fragility, poor judgement, dependence, asexuality, unemployability, etc. Indeed, those who were wounded by a "booby trap" began to think of themselves as fitting the negative stereotypes. Thus, the wounded veterans faced not only being unable to realize certain ideals, but the additional insult of seeing themselves in unflattering terms.

Abandonment of previously valued standards is not a short-term proposition nor should it be seen as a wholly desirable goal, but some conceptual shift is required so that these valued characteristics are perceived as asset values rather than comparative values. That is, unattainable, premorbid standards need not be abandoned, but redefinition and reframing are useful, and the veterans need to identify new ways to attain these standards. When working with disabled clients, it is important to remember that the nature of the interactions is different (not necessarily better or worse); this difference must be understood and acknowledged by the counselor. Let us consider the effects of the negative attitudes that are often held by the able-bodied population toward persons with disabilities. (For an excellent overview of the origins of these attitudes, see Livneh, 1984). Generally, these attitudes stem from a variety of sociocultural origins and as a result of diverse psychodynamic influences, childhood influences, anxiety-provoking unstructured situations, aesthetic aversions, threats to body image and integrity, minority group comparability, the fact that disability is a reminder of death, and individual personality variables. Specific manifestations of these negative attitudes are discussed below.

Interaction between a disabled person and a nondisabled person is stilted and characterized by reduced length of interaction, reduced eye contact, motor inhibitions, fewer smiles, restricted range of discussion topics, and a feeling of discomfort (Kleck, 1966, 1968, 1969). This dynamic is equally present for both parties in the social interaction (Comer & Piliavin, 1972).

Disabled persons perceive themselves as members of minority groups, which, in fact, they are. Their behavior is a manifestation of this status and of society's attitude toward them (Yamamoto, 1971). Society uses disabilities to establish parameters for "normality," and the resulting prejudices are exacerbated by labeling and arbitrary categorization. Prejudice toward disabled persons reflects the degree of intolerance extended towards them, and the degree of social distance that one desires to place between himself and those with disabilities (Satilios-Rothchild, 1968). Rehabilitation counselors may play into this self-perpetuating cycle by failing to understand clients who do not respond as expected to ablebodied values; the disabled, disheartened by this lack of understanding, become convinced of the futility of attempting to "become rehabilitated" (DuBrow, 1965; Wright, 1960).

The professional involved with disabled clients needs to avail himself of every opportunity for effective, positive, ongoing contact so as to maintain a positive attitude toward impaired persons. The counselor must be sensitized to the social and affective areas of discrimination against the disabled. Education, sensitization, honest and nondefensive orientation can do much to maximize the potential for effective interaction. Counselors must be versatile, using both their own creativity as well as that of others (including clients) to assist the client. Recognition of special needs and openness to new learning are critically important (McDowell et al., 1984).

The importance of a positive attitude toward persons with visible impairments cannot be overstated; it has been found to be closely related to the development of close interpersonal contacts with disabled persons in personal, social, educational, and vocational settings (English, 1971). Quality rather than quantity of contact seems to be the most critical factor. This seems particularly true where both parties can work together in relatively egalitarian statuses. People with low levels of aggressiveness, high self-concepts, low levels of anxiety, high needs for social approval, and a good ability to tolerate ambiguity have been found to be most accepting of people with impairments (English, 1971).

Many authors report that mental health professionals find it difficult to sustain ongoing therapeutic contact with trauma victims (Haley, 1978; Lifton, 1978; Roche Report, 1982), in some measure because very evocative material is elicited that sometimes triggers powerful emotions for the counselor. Such evocative material includes the description and reaction to the partial disintegration of the body as well as the functional and cosmetic consequences of trauma. Counselors should be prepared to make frequent use of a support system that both acknowledges the intensity of this work and allows for its effective expressions.

Accounts of the recovery of disabled Vietnam veterans (Cleland, 1980; Downs, 1978, 1984; Kovic, 1976) are quite excellent and effective in identifying some of the major adjustment issues from a very emotional and personal perspective. These and similar works can and should be read by anyone who proposes to become or is currently involved in counseling disabled Vietnam veterans, and much can also be gained from listening to disabled clients as they describe their experiences. Counselors who have the integrity and sensitivity to accompany the disabled client as he recounts his experiences are particularly effective.

ASSESSMENT FRAMEWORK

Assessment is a method for gathering, evaluating, categorizing, organizing, and presenting information so as to accurately describe the subject of the assessment. The process is obviously heavily dependent upon communication. As has been discussed above, there are many barriers to effective communication with a disabled person. Difficulties involve a lack of a frame of reference for both the disabled and nondisabled, difficulty in telling "the story" about the disability and its effects in an understandable manner, and incongruous expectations between the disabled and nondisabled. (For a compelling first-person account of major communication barriers and their effects, see Zola, 1984.) Some framework, or frame of reference, must be used to organize and rationalize the assessment process.

Much has been written about needs assessment and diagnosis for Vietnam veterans (Figley, 1978, 1985; Keane, Fairbank, Caddell, Zimering & Bender, 1985; Scurfield, 1985; Wilson, 1977). Typically, the foci are pre-military, military, post-military, and current adjustment and functioning. These areas are very important and must be explored thoroughly in order for one to gain a comprehensive, accurate, and helpful understanding of the person in the situation. For the disabled person, it is useful to explore several other areas with particular emphasis on the effects of the disability. The importance of gender, racial, and ethnic differences must also be considered.

Siegelman, Vengrof, and Spanhel (1984) have suggested a conceptual framework for assessing physical impairment that centers around the impairment's effect on life functions; it is a useful general outline for understanding the role the disability plays in an individual's life. (This framework is depicted in Figure 1.) When built on a foundation of thorough understanding of Vietnam veteran issues, this framework systematically focuses attention on the effects of the disability.

Impairment

The assessment process begins with an identification of the impairment and the specific circumstances that surround it. Obviously, one area that should receive considerable attention is the circumstances and conditions under which the veteran became disabled (Dew, Lynch, Ernst, Rosenthal, & Judd, 1985). Specific questions to be answered include, "How did you get into the military? (drafted, enlisted, etc.) What did you know about what was going on in Vietnam? What were you doing? How did it happen? Was anyone else injured or killed? Had you had any other close calls? What is the first thing you can recall after being wounded? Who was around? How were you removed from the field? Where were you taken for treatment? How long were you hospitalized?" The purpose initially is to ascertain as much as possible about "the event" and the veteran's immediate reaction to it. As the relationship progresses, similar information and reactions should be elicited regarding later experiences with intermediate stops through the medivac/hospital system.

Obviously, the pace at which this questioning proceeds is largely determined by the status of the therapeutic relationship with the veteran. This is particularly true in the early phases of the relationship. This line of questioning is frequently experienced as relatively nonthreatening by the veteran. The theme is a description of events first, followed by an exploration of their the cognitive/emotional impact.

Life Function Limitations

The next area for investigation is the extent to which limitations are imposed on general life functions: health, social-attitudinal, mobility, cognitive/intellectual, and communications. Effects of the disability on bodily systems must be determined as well as the amount of energy expended coping with pain and simply staying alive. Limitations or alterations in sexual expressions and reproduction also warrant considerable attention (Diamond, 1984). It is important to determine the extent to which the veteran avoids activities that would threaten life or well-being (or that he perceives would threaten them).

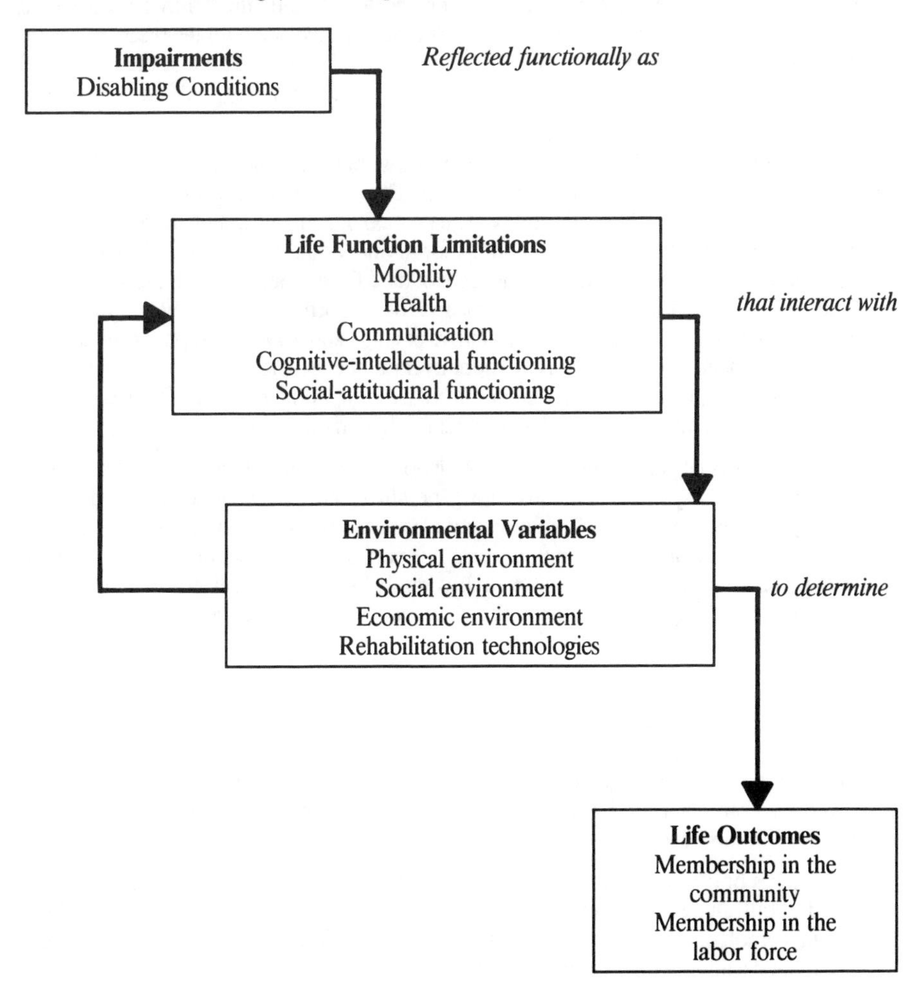

Figure 1. Disability model.

Social-attitudinal adaptation entails the veteran's general assessment and evaluation of himself and his situation as it pertains to his disability. If the degree to which the veteran "accepts" his disability is problematic, it may be helpful to suggest a reorientation of the concept of "acceptance." For many, acceptance implies giving up or giving in (Malec, 1985). The notion is repulsive, and frequently results in the veteran's adopting a bitter, angry, and distancing attitude. Attempts to eliminate this anger are almost certain to fail; however, it is important to acknowledge this anger and help the victim identify ways of using it constructively through additional training, group membership, social activity, advocacy, social activitism, and the like. Anger is a very powerful and fearsome emotion for many veterans who often fear "losing control" to the point of violence. Consequently, this emotion is overcontrolled and muffled by many. The therapeutic task is to "normalize" the process by which this anger develops, help the client understand it and, most importantly, identify constructive means for its expression.

It is equally important to understand the orientation of the veteran's family or primary support system in these areas (Featherstone, 1981; Rustad, 1984; Stanton & Figley, 1978). To what extent does the support system perpetuate a dysfunctional, isolating mode for the veteran, perpetuating the veteran's role as a "sick" person? Should the family be considered in the counseling process to a major extent? Those closely involved with the disabled person are affected in many ways by his experience. If no one really took the time or the risk to find out from the veteran what it all meant to him, it's quite likely that the family, too, was overlooked.

To understand the disabled veteran, a counselor must appreciate the impact of the disability on mobility. It is especially important to determine the degree to which mobility has diminished since the onset of the disability. The process of aging in conjunction with serious disability has potentially serious implications for an individual who, as a healthy teenager, sustained a serious injury in Vietnam, was "rehabilitated" and outfitted with the appropriate mobility and sensory aids, resumed what passed for a "normal" life for several years, and now sees his stamina, strength, acuity, agility, energy, and mobility slipping away. Not surprisingly, concern about decreased mobility and the general level of functioning is growing among disabled Vietnam veterans who are now in their 30s or 40s (Tice, 1985); this concern should not be dismissed as routine midlife crisis.

Cognitive, intellectual, and communication functions also warrant exploration. Any limitation in manipulating symbols, remembering, generalizing new learning, sending and receiving messages, and exchanging information and ideas have obvious implications for rehabilitation and day-to-day interaction and survival. It is particularly important to note changes in these areas as reported by the veteran or his family. A neurological evaluation may be warranted if any change is noted; however, depression may also be the probable cause for these symptoms.

Environmental Variables

Variables in the environment that both affect and are affected by limitations in life functions also warrant examination. The physical, social, economic, and rehabilitative environment are included in this general area.

Major changes or disruptions in any of these areas demand attention. Information should be obtained about change in residence, family structure, economic circumstances (laid-off, fired, quit, demoted, etc.), and involvement with rehabilitation. Some veterans must change employment because of their inability to continue with strenuous labor; feelings of remorse, anger, and hopelessness frequently accompany the forced changes.

It is often necessary to mobilize the family or other support system to encourage and assist the veteran in using available public and private resources to meet new challenges. Counselors must be at least generally aware of the availability of resources in any of these areas, and should have specific information about how and to whom to make a proper referral.

It is important to understand the veteran's knowledge and use of adaptive aids. A major focus here should be on whether the veteran has had recent contact with competent and caring technicians who work with prosthetics and sensory aids. Many veterans, having "recovered" from their wounds in a crowded, confused, and overworked military or VA hospital have had very negative experiences with using various adaptive aids. Fitting, fabrication, and training in the use of adaptive aids were frequently done as rapidly as possible and with poor results; many veterans decided to have nothing more to do with such adaptive aids. The veteran's decision in this matter must be respected—there are serious limitations in using any prosthetic device—but it is helpful to at least explore the decision.

Life Outcomes

All these areas together help determine "life outcome." Although the paramount considerations here are the quality of the veteran's membership in the community and in the labor force, there are other "life outcomes" for disabled Vietnam veterans because the level of VA compensation for the most seriously disabled is such that gainful employment is not mandatory. The fact that this is possible and desirable for some should be acknowledged and accepted by the counselor. The client should not be encouraged to judge "productive and useful" only in terms of "gainful employment"; his goals and aspirations should be considered against more typical cultural norms. When work-ethic (or any other) values seem to be setting the tone for the counseling process, the veteran is likely to feel that the pattern of insensitivity and callousness—already all too familiar—is merely being played out again to a slightly different tune.

IMPLICATIONS FOR TREATMENT

The overriding aim in the counseling process is that the veteran work toward normalization (Park, 1975). This implies a rational attempt to assess and address the circumstances that exacerbate and perpetuate the negative stereotypes that have alienated and isolated those with serious impairments from the rest of society. These stereotypes may be found at all levels of society and seriously impede effective rehabilitation and assimilation. In the absence of a knowledgeable, compassionate, and empathetic clinician, the disabled Vietnam veteran seeking assistance will likely encounter another episode of the "cookie-cutter" phenomenon—an experience that has been ineffective or damaging in the past.

For the variety of reasons outlined above, disabled persons are frequently reluctant to seek needed assistance. The disabled Vietnam veteran not only has these concerns but also feels "burned" by the system (Klein, 1981; Starr, 1973) and may be so disheartened as to believe that genuine help simply cannot be found.

Outreach efforts for this population must reflect sensitivity and understanding of their specific and unique needs; they must be convinced that their circumstances will be acknowledged and understood. A person or program purporting to understand and care about the needs of disabled Vietnam veterans may have but one chance to connect: outreach, no matter how sophisticated, cannot compensate for a lack of substance and integrity. A comprehensive outreach program that includes prominent symbols of disability is desirable; literature should depict disabled individuals; public presentations should include disabled speakers and pertinent disability issues; facilities must be accessible and barrier-free. Finally, condescending and patronizing approaches do not work. In general, an attitude of understanding and acknowledgement must be consistently conveyed as a integral part of an overall outreach and service delivery plan, and the involvement of the disabled person in formulating an outreach strategy is an invaluable asset.

Groups

The group is a very powerful and useful vehicle for the veteran to reach out to and connect with his peers in a safe, controlled environment. It offers an opportunity for him to interact effectively with nondisabled persons in a mutually supportive and caring atmosphere.

In groups with a seriously disabled veteran, extra care must be taken by the facilitator; it is not uncommon for nondisabled group members and the facilitator to ascribe to the disabled veteran "powers and abilities far beyond those of mortal men." That the veteran has mastered the limitations and constraints imposed by his disability is frequently generalized by the group to imply that the veteran has equally surmounted all life's problems (including symptoms of post-traumatic stress disorder, marital conflict, economic or employment difficulties). The facilitator must be vigilant for the development of this dynamic and be prepared to introduce it as a topic for immediate consideration by the group. The group facilitator must ensure that each group member maintains a unique identity that includes both an ability to and need for help. The seriously disabled counselor should be vigilant for behaviors that establish him as the standard for measuring adaptation and coping. Many clients equally or less seriously disabled may express concern that they are not really trying hard enough or coping well with their disabilities as they have not achieved as well as their counselors. The group may also attempt to "disqualify" the counselor (disabled or not) because he or she can't really understand what it's like to be disabled or as disabled as some of the members. In any case, the counselor should be alert to group dynamics that involve projection, disqualification, depreciation, exclusion, distancing, and avoidance with regard to either the group leader(s) or other members.

Individual Therapy

Individual sessions can be very useful, especially during the early stages of the development of the relationship when much of the focus is on assessment and planning. This time can be used effectively to discuss the specific impacts of the disability, and is also a good time for the counselor to identify and convey to the disabled client the limitations and interpersonal stresses disabled people encounter in society. These difficulties should be presented as a normative process and not a function of intrapersonal maladies/limitations/deficiences. Effective individual therapy can also be very useful for screening and to supplement ongoing involvement in a group.

Family Therapy

Involvement of the veteran's family usually is desirable. Such involvement is especially indicated when there is evidence that either the family of origin or of procreation is blunting the veteran's efforts towards independence and relative autonomy (Ireys & Burr, 1984). Even when there is no evidence of dysfunction, family involvement can facilitate understanding of both general and specific issues related to the veteran's involvement in Vietnam, his disability, and his current adjustment in all areas. It is important, too, to find out how the family was notified of the veteran's injury, as it was often very abrupt and the details very meager. Little support and sanction was offered for the family to acknowledge and assess the impact of the disability on their lives.

SUMMARY

Counselors should be prepared through education, sensitizations, and support to work with disabled clients. Differences in the nature of the relationship with the disabled client must be considered, with important emphasis on the clients' search for identity, meaning, and direction in their "new lives." Allowances must be made for considerable individual variation as to what constitutes satisfactory adjustment. It is not useful to view the population of disabled Vietnam veterans (or any population, for that matter) as a single, monolithic group—there are striking individual differences in beliefs, orientation, adaptation, outlook, and needs. Rather, these men and women are a collection of unique individuals with a powerful common experience that can serve as a beginning point in understanding, assessing, and addressing needs.

NOTES

1. The words disabled, handicapped, or impaired will be used interchangeably to identify the population of wounded Vietnam veterans. I am aware of the considerable discussion over the relative merits and deficiencies of each of these terms and their variations. Much of the discussion seems to center around identifying terminology that conveys a "positive" image or outlook, primarily to assuage anxiety among the "temporarily ablebodied." While recognizing the importance of labels, I think the volume and intensity of the debate detracts unnecessarily from critical clinical needs of the disabled population.

2. Congressional testimony in 1969 noted the variations in the time lapse between being wounded and being treated for abdominal wounds in recent U.S. wars. In World War II, for example, transportation time averaged 10.5 hours; in Korea, this time was shortened to 6.3 hours. In Vietnam, less than three hours (2.8) lapsed, and it was not uncommon for wounded soldiers to arrive at a very sophisticated field medical station in twenty minutes or less.

REFERENCES

Blank, A. S. (1982). Stresses of war: The example of Vietnam. In Goldberger & Breznitz (Eds.), *Handbook of stress: Theoretical and clinical aspects* (pp. 631-644). New York: Free Press.

Cleland, M. (1980). *Strong at the broken places.* Waco, Texas: Chosen Books.

Comer, R. J., & Piliarin, J. A. (1972). The effects of physical deviance upon face-to-face interaction: The other side. *Journal of Personality and Social Psychology, 23*(1), 33-39.

Dew, M., Lynch, K., Ernst, J., Rosenthal, R., & Judd, C. (1985). A causal analysis of factors affecting judgement to spinal cord injury. *Rehabilitation Psychology, 30*(1), 39-46.

Diamond, M. (1984). Sexuality and the handicapped. In R. P. Marinelli & A. E. Dell Orto (Eds.), *The psychological and social impact of physical disability* (2nd ed.) (pp. 207-220). New York: Springer.

Downs, F. (1978). *The killing zone.* New York: Norton.

Downs, F. (1984). *Aftermath: A soldier's return from Vietnam.* New York: Norton.

DuBrow, A. (1965). Attitudes toward disability. *Journal of Rehabilitation, 31*(4), 25-26.

English, R. W. (1971). Correlates of stigma toward physically disabled persons. *Rehabilitation Counseling Bulletin, 2*(4), 1-17.

Featherstone, H. (1981). *A difference in the family: Life with a disabled child.* New York: Basic Books.

Figley, C. R. (Ed.). (1978). *Stress disorders among Vietnam veterans: Theory, research and treatment.* New York: Brunner/Mazel.

Figley, C. R. (Ed.). (1985). *Trauma and its wake: The study and treatment of post-traumatic stress disorder.* New York: Brunner/Mazel.

Figley, C. R., & Leventman, S. (Eds.). (1980). *Strangers at home: Vietnam veterans since the war.* New York: Praeger.

Haley, S. (1978). Treatment implications of post-combat stress response syndromes for mental health professions. In C. R. Figley (Ed.), *Stress disorders among Vietnam veterans.* New York: Brunner/Mazel.

Ireys, H. T., & Burr, C. K. (1984). Apart and a part: Family issues for young adults with chronic illness and disability. In Eisenberg, Sutkin, & Jamsen (Eds.), *Chronic illness and disability through the life span: Effects on self and family* (pp. 184-209). New York: Springer.

Johnson, L. (1980). Scars of war: Alienation and estrangement among wounded Vietnam veterans. In C. R. Figley & S. Leventman (Eds.), *Strangers at home: Vietnam veterans since the war* (pp. 213-229). New York: Praeger.

Keane, T. M., Fairbank, J. A., Caddell, J. M. Zimering, R. T., & Bender, M. E. (1985). A behavioral approach to assessing and treating post-traumatic stress disorder in Vietnam veterans. In C. R. Figley (Ed.), *Trauma and its wake* (pp. 257-295). New York: Brunner/Mazel.

Kleck, R. (1966). Emotional arousal in interaction with stigmatized persons. *Psychological Reports, 19*, 12-26.

Kleck, R. (1968). Physical stigma and nonverbal cues emitted in face-to-face interactions. *Human Relations, 21*(1) 19-28.

Kleck, R. (1969). Physical stigma and task oriented interactions. *Human Relations, 22*(1), 53-60.

Klein, R. (1981). *Wounded men, broken promises: How the Veterans Administration betrays yesterday's heroes.* New York: Macmillan.

Kovic, R. (1976). *Born on the fourth of July.* New York: McGraw-Hill.

Laufer, R. et al. (1981). *Legacies of Vietnam: Comparative adjustment of veterans and their peers.* Washington, DC: U.S. Government Printing Office.

Lifton, R. J. (1978). Advocacy and corruption in the healing profession. In C. R. Figley (Ed.), *Stress disorders among Vietnam veterans.* New York: Brunner/Mazel.

Livneh, H. (1984). On the origins of negative attitudes toward people with disabilities. In R. P. Marinelli, & A. E. Dell Orto (Eds.), *The psychological and social impact of physical disability* (2nd ed.) New York: Springer.

McDowell, W.A., Coven, A.B., Eash, V.C. (1984). The handicapped: Special needs and strategies for counseling. In R.P. Marinelli and A.E. Dell Orto, (Eds.), *The psychological and social impact of physical disability* (2nd ed.) New York: Springer.

Malec, J. (1985). Personality factors associated with severe traumatic disability. *Rehabilitation Psychology, 30*(3), 165-172.

Park, L. D. (1975). Barriers to normality for the handicapped adult in the U.S. *Rehabilitation Literature, 36*(4), 108-111.

Roche Report. (1982). Uncovering post-traumatic stress disorders. *Frontiers in Psychiatry, 12,* 6.

Rustad, L. (1984). Family adjustment to chronic illness and disability in mid-life. In Eisenberg, Sutkin, & Jansen (Eds.), *Chronic illness and disability through the life span: Effects on self and family* (pp. 222-245). New York: Springer.

Satilios-Rothchild, C. (1968). Prejudice against the disabled and some means to combat it. *International Rehabilitation Review, 19*(4), 8-10.

Scurfield, R. M. (1985). Post-traumatic stress assessment and treatment: Overview and formulations. In C. R. Figley (Ed.), *Trauma and its wake* (pp. 219-257). New York: Brunner/Mazel.

Siegelman, C. K., Vengrof, L. P., & Spanhel, C. L. (1984). Disability and the concept of life functions. In R. P. Marinelli and A. E. Dell Orto (Eds.), *The psychological and social impact of physical disability* (2nd ed.) (pp. 3-14). New York: Springer.

Stanton, M. D., & Figley, C. R. (1978). Treating the Vietnam veteran within the family system. In C. R. Figley (Ed.), *Stress disorders among Vietnam veterans* (pp. 281-291). New York: Brunner/Mazel.

Starr, P. (1973). *The discarded army: Veterans after Vietnam.* New York: Charterhouse.

Tice, C. (1985). Personal Communication. (Team Leader, Veterans Center, Eugene, Oregon and National Co-Chairman for The Working Group on Physically Disabled Vietnam Veterans.)

Veterans Administration. (1985). *Initial report of the working group on physically disabled Vietnam veterans.* Washington, DC: Veterans Administration.

Wilson, J. P. (1977, 1978). *Identity, ideology and crisis: The Vietnam veteran in transition* (Part 1 & 2). Cleveland State University.

Wright, B. (1960). *Physical disability: A psychological approach.* New York: Harper Row.

Yamamoto, K. (1971). To be different. *Rehabilitation Counseling, 14*(3), 180-188.

Zola, I. K. (1984). Communication barriers between "the able-bodied" and "the handicapped." In R. P. Marinelli & A. E. Dell Orto (Eds.), *The psychological and social impact of physical disability* (pp. 139-148). New York: Springer.

CHAPTER NINE

AMERICAN PRISONERS OF WAR—
AN OVERVIEW

Steven Oboler

Recent renewed interest in former prisoners of war (POWs) can be traced to the 444-day Iranian hostage crisis between November 1979 and January 1981. The 52 American embassy personnel were returned as heroes and whisked away for much-publicized repatriation evaluations and secluded R & R. While technically not prisoners of war at the time, the hostages were treated in much the same way as were prisoners in previous wars. Legislation passed by Congress in August 1981 amended existing laws to provide prisoner of war benefits to active duty military personnel who were detained by a hostile government under circumstances that are comparable to those found during periods of war. Thus, the 10 embassy guards in Tehran have now been accorded exPOW status.

The larger issue concerns the status of over 85,000 living exPOWs from WW I, WW II, Korea and Vietnam. The purpose of this chapter is to provide an overview of the POW experience, especially the current physical and mental health of America's aging exPOW veterans, focusing on our experience at the Denver VA Medical Center. In another chapter, Ron Langer discusses the psychiatric symptomatology, and outlines therapeutic strategies in treating exPOWs on both an individual and group basis.

THE POW EXPERIENCE

Although recent news and movies have focused on Vietnam POWs and those missing-in-action (MIAs), almost 95 percent of all surviving exPOWs date from WW II: 78,914 of the 83,430 total. Of these surviving WW II exPOWs, approximately 87 percent were interned in Europe and 13 percent in the Pacific Theater. In contrast, there are only 3,562 surviving exPOWs from Korea and 618 from Vietnam.

Table 1. Number of POWs and MIAs in Four Wars.

	WWI	WWII	Korea	Vietnam	Total
Captured & Interned	4,120	130,201	7,140	766	142,227
Died While POW	147	14,072	2,701	114	17,034
Returned to U.S. Military Control	3,973	116,129	4,418	651	125,171
Alive 1/1/86	336	78,914	3,562	618	83,430
MIA	3,350	78,773	8,177	2,453	92,753

Source: Stenger, 1986.

Even before the Iranian hostage crisis in October 1978, Congress mandated a study of the health care needs of, and disability compensation awarded to, American prisoners of war. The results were published by the Veterans Administration (VA) in May 1980 in *POW: Study of Former Prisoners of War* (required reading for anyone treating POWs, and the source of much of the material for this chapter). It contains this summary of some of the important elements of the POW experience:

> Prisoners of war face a sense of loss: loss of self-determination, loss of hope, loss of knowledge of home and the chances for repatriation. Many POWs have lived for months and years with a crushing sense of doom, seeing themselves and their comrades dying from myriad diseases, starvation, exposure, misguided bombardments, lack of medical care, and murder by firearms, bludgeon, bayonet and the beheading sword. They have faced forced marches on bare subsistence rations or none at all, while exposed to intense cold or heat, often brutalized along the way, prodded by bayonet or attack dogs, and left to die if too injured or weakened to keep up. They have been victims of war crimes such as torture and mutilation, beatings, and forced heavy labor under inhumane conditions. Many prisoners who were severely injured by combat prior to capture had little hope of any but the most meager medical attention, at times none at all.(p. 23)

In addition to severe deprivation of food, housing, clothing, and medical care, POWs face terrible spiritual deprivation—months and even years of little or no contact with the outside world. Winston Churchill (1939), recounting his experiences as a prisoner in 1902, during the Boer War in South Africa, described it vividly:

> It is a melancholy state. You are in the power of the enemy....You must obey his orders, await his pleasure, possess your soul in patience. The days are very long; hours crawl by like paralytic centipedes....Companions quarrel about trifles and get the least possible enjoyment from each others' society. You feel a constant humiliation in being forced in by railings and wire, watched by armed guards and webbed about with a tangle of regulations and restrictions.

Treatment of POWs has varied greatly from war to war as well as from camp to camp. It is affected by a variety of factors, including:

- Mankind's varying concept of the value of life;
- The economic and logistical capacities of the captors;
- The belief that reprisals are a "legitimate" activity;
- Adherence to or rejection of international covenants on human rights;
- Climate and geography; and
- The whim of the individual captor. (VA 1980, p. 23)

These differences in treatment are strikingly reflected in the range of POW deaths in captivity in WW II: from just over 1 percent among 93,000 European Theater POWs in contrast with 40 percent among 29,000 Pacific Theater internees. American defenders of Bataan were so weak and debilitated from months of heavy combat that there were more POW deaths in the first few weeks following the fall of Bataan and gruesome death march than during the entire war in the European Theater. In addition, thousands more Americans died in transit on overcrowded, unmarked "hell ships" that were bombed and torpedoed while transporting POWs from the Philippines to Japan and Formosa. Three recently published books dramatize the grim conditions endured by Pacific Theater POWs: *Death March* by Donald Knox, *Some Survived* by Manny Lawton, and *Surrender & Survival* by E. Bartlett Kerr (see reference list). Sgt. Forrest Knox, a survivor of a "hell ship" trip to

Japan, describes his experience in *Death March* (Knox, 1981):

> How do I describe a packed, hot, filthy, stinking ship's hold that turned slowly into a madhouse? We called them "Hell Ships." They were. Most of the guys won't or can't talk about them....
>
> As a guy goes crazy he starts to scream—not like a woman, more like the howl of a dog. We were locked in a hold together, 500 of us. We're in there solid, wall to wall. Tight, so you couldn't put your feet between people when you tried to walk. I don't know how to describe the heat, there was no way we measured temperature. We were all practically naked by that time, because we had taken off everything in order to cut down on the heat. It must have been 120 or 125 degrees in that hold. The Jap's favorite trick was to cut off our water. It was bad enough in other places when they did this, but there, in this oven, when they cut it off, guys started going crazy. People running, people screaming....The Japs told the colonel to tell us to be quiet. He shouted down, "Be quiet or the Japs will completely cover over the hatch with canvas...."
>
> With the temperature we were in, if they'd closed off that little air we got, I don't know how many of us would have been alive by morning....The next guy that went by screaming they caught and killed....The crazy ones, they howled because they were afraid to die, but now the ground rules changed. If they howled, they died. The screaming stopped. The running stopped....The Japs didn't cover the hatch.

On the other hand, the popular impression (conveyed by the likes of television's "Hogans Heroes") of life in German prisoner of war camps, *stalags,* is that conditions were quite humane. These impressions are based primarily on accounts of the International Red Cross' inspection of "show camps" that were used to impress visitors that Germany was abiding by the Geneva Conventions, and on reports of life among aircrew members, who were treated with respect by the Germans because of their admiration for aviation and their use of pilots as an intelligence source. However, the average American POW, a foot soldier, not an airman, was interned in *stalags* that did not abide by even the minimum standards for POW treatment set forth in the 1929 Geneva Convention, which both the U.S. and Germans had signed. Less well-publicized than the Bataan death march were the many forced marches by POWs across Germany during the winter and spring of 1945. The Germans did not want to surrender to the advancing Russians on the Eastern Front and moved thousands of POWs westward toward American lines in forced marches lasting from a few days to almost 3 months (American Ex-Prisoners of War, 1980; O'Donnell, 1982; Spivey, 1984).

In Korea, the conditions of capture and internment were unquestionably harsh, as none of the participants, including the U.S., were signatories to the articles of the 1949 Geneva Convention. Seven thousand one hundred and forty American POWs were captured in Korea and 38 percent died in captivity. The Korean POW experience differed somewhat from earlier wars: it was the first large-scale use of propaganda and indoctrination directed at all captured military personnel. Attempts were initially made to weaken prisoners' physical resistance by keeping them cold and hungry, and to break down military organization by separating POWs into groups according to rank and race. Next, attempts were made to weaken psychological resistance through compulsory group and individual indoctrination programs. Unlike WW II in Germany, where Air Force POWs were generally treated more humanely than Army foot soldiers, aircrew captives in Korea received the harshest treatment, with constant interrogation, solitary confinement, and coerced "confessions" (VA, 1980, pp. 35-38).

American POWs in Vietnam were a distinctive group. The majority were pilots (Air Force, Navy, and Marine) and were somewhat older and more educated than American POWs captured in other wars. Most faced much longer periods of POW internment than did Americans in earlier wars, an average of almost 5 years (or 1800 days) in Vietnam, compared to 347 days for European Theater POWs, 1,148 days for Pacific Theater POWs, and 737 days for Korean internees. The Vietnamese did not consider captured personnel military prisoners, but rather "war criminals" to be dealt with harshly. Prisoners were publicly paraded, pressured into making broadcasts of alleged confessions, and physically and psychologically tortured. Fifteen percent of the 766 Vietnam POWs died in captivity.

CURRENT HEALTH STATUS OF EXPOWS

Over the past several years, concern has been growing among exPOWs (primarily WW II and Korean) and their service organizations that former POWs are dying younger, are suffering more severe psychiatric disability, and are prey to "premature aging" more frequently than their nonPOW comrades-in-arms.

Documentation of the health status of returning POWs varied widely, from cursory exams on most WW II European Theater POWs to exhaustive 400-page, 26-section "Operation Homecoming" repatriation exams on the 650 Vietnam POWs. Despite the many gaps in our "baseline" repatriation information, results of the 1945 "Morgan Board" survey of the health status of over 4,600 returning Pacific Theater POWs (Morgan, Wright & van Ravenswaay, 1946) and publications of the health status of returning Vietnam POWs clearly document a tremendous range of clinical pathology. For example, the repatriation exams of 138 Vietnam naval aviators yielded a total of 1,685 diagnoses—an average of 12.2 per man—comprising 367 diagnostic entities (Berg & Richlin, 1977).

In addition to repatriation examinations, several physician POWs (from WW II and Vietnam) published studies on the medical consequences of their POW internment (Hibbs, 1946; Jacobs, 1951; Nardini, 1947), most of them about POWs interned in the Pacific Theater and written shortly after repatriation. These reports documented a number of malnutrition-related conditions, including the spectrum of thiamine deficiency—"wet" and "dry" beriberi—describing the edema, heart failure, optic atrophy, and peripheral neuropathy. The authors acknowledged that they had conducted only one-time studies that needed follow-up if definitive conclusions were to be drawn on the ultimate residuals of specific POW-related physical and psychiatric disabilities.

Unfortunately, follow-up studies for most of the identified short-term problems never materialized. Detailed information on the long-term effects of specific conditions—e.g., parasite infestation, hepatitis, beriberi, and cold injuries—in the various POW groups is not available. Regular follow-up examinations of some of the Vietnam POWs is continuing, but nothing has been published beyond their status at repatriation (VA, 1980, p. 143). The few available long-term follow-up investigations are broad epidemiological studies of a host of physical and psychiatric problems on samples of entire POW populations (Beebe, 1975; Cohen & Cooper, 1954; Keehn, 1976; Nefzger, 1970) and a number of poorly controlled, almost anecdotal reports in selected populations, the latter confined almost exclusively to British Pacific Theater exPOWs in WW II (Gibberd & Simmonds, 1980; Gill & Bell, 1980, 1981).

Based on these less-than-complete follow-up studies and the 1980 VA study comparing VA compensation received by former POWs with that received by nonPOW veterans, Congress enacted PL 97-37 in August 1981. This law, *The Former POW Benefits Act of 1981*, expanded VA eligibility of former POWs. The main provisions of this bill offered:

- Liberalized eligibility, changing the definition of POW from 6 months to 30 days in captivity;
- Entitlement to hospitalization and nursing home care without regard to ability to pay; and
- Lifelong presumption of "service connection" was established for 10 specific diagnoses if they become manifest at any time after repatriation, even if there is no record of such disease documented during active military service. Five of the 10 are malnutrition-related disorders:

  Avitaminosis
  Beriberi (including beriberi heart disease)
  Pellagra
  Malnutrition (including optic atrophy associated with malnutrition)
  Any other nutritional deficiency
  Chronic dysentery
  Helminthiasis
  Psychosis
  Any of the anxiety states
  Dysthymic disorder.

In addition, the law mandated standardization of exPOW examinations and was intended to maximize exPOW health and medical benefits, bringing some of the estimated 50 percent of all surviving exPOWs to the VA for evaluation.

FINDINGS FROM THE DENVER VA MEDICAL CENTER EXPOW PROGRAM

Late in the spring of 1983, I was appointed exPOW Physician Coordinator responsible for implementing the exPOW Protocol Examination Program at the Denver VA Medical Center. The new examination format—pioneered by Dr. Harold Morris and his staff at California's Loma Linda VA Medical Center and operational nationwide in all 172 VA medical centers since July 1983—consists of:

- Completion by the exPOW of a detailed 4-page medical history questionnaire about his POW experiences;
- A comprehensive general medical examination;
- A psychiatric interview;
- A social services evaluation;
- A battery of laboratory and x-ray studies; and
- An "exit interview" about two weeks after the evaluation to review the results with the exPOW and arrange any necessary follow-up.

Special audiology and eye clinic evaluations, as well as referral for dental care, are often done at the time of the initial general medical examination.

Over the past two-and-one-half years, my colleagues and I at the Denver VA Medical Center have had the opportunity of meeting with and examining over 200 exPOWs, more than half of all former POWs living in Colorado. Results of 190 consecutive exPOW Protocol Evaluations have been reviewed and reveal a high incidence of heart disease, degenerative arthritis—particularly spinal arthritis—and psychiatric pathology, predominantly anxiety disorders, including PTSD and depressive neuroses.

Not surprisingly, the majority of the 190 exPOWs served in WW II, with 121 interned in Europe and 50 in the Pacific Theater. An additional 15 were captured in Korea, 3 in Vietnam, and 1 was held hostage in Iran. I shall review some of the results of these examinations, focusing on the two largest groups, WW II exPOWs interned in Europe and the Pacific.

Peripheral Neuropathy

A common occurrence among malnourished POWs of all wars, but especially common in Pacific Theater POWs, is thiamine (vitamin B_1) deficiency, which manifested itself in two forms, "wet" and "dry." The "wet" form was characterized by cardiac failure and edema, while the "dry" form was heralded by a peripheral neuropathy, eloquently described by Manny Lawton in *Some Survived* (1984, p. 76):

> Anyone suffering with beriberi could easily be identified by his halting, cautious way of walking. Bent forward, standing on the outer edges of his feet with arms held outward for balance, he stepped lightly, as if tramping on nails. Being one of those victims, I knew why. With feet as painful as if the raw nerves were exposed, walking on a wood floor was painful. On the hard ground, where there were coarse sand and sharp pebbles, each step was sheer agony.

Among our group of 50 Pacific Theater exPOWs, 24 (48 percent) had objective evidence of a persistent peripheral sensory neuropathy on current examination. The majority complained only of mild numbness and tingling in the feet and ankles, but several had severe neuritic symptoms in both the upper and lower extremities, described as unpleasant "burning" or "electric" sensations, aggravated by movement and pressure. Among European Theater exPOWs, only 6 of 121 (5 percent) had mild peripheral sensory abnormalities. None of 3 Vietnam exPOWs and only 1 of 15 exPOWs captured in Korea had any current evidence of peripheral sensory defects.

Cardiovascular

In contrast to the frequent finding of a peripheral sensory neuropathy as a residual of "dry" beriberi, current cardiovascular residuals of POW confinement—whether secondary to "wet" beriberi, stress, or other nutritional deficiency—are much more difficult to identify with any certainty. Although the 1945 repatriation examinations of over 4,600 Pacific Theater POWs reported a significant number with edema and cardiomegaly (Morgan, Wright & van Ravenswaay, 1946), no long-term follow-up studies of these individuals were done, and available recent medical literature on chronic beriberi is confined to a few isolated case reports (Gill & Bell, 1980; Gill, Henry & Reid, 1980). Manifestations of chronic cardiac beriberi are characterized by biventricular failure with chronic congestive heart failure (Carson, 1982). It has been suggested that any chronic residuals of cardiac beriberi may be obscured by the co-existence of arteriosclerotic heart disease (Gill, 1983). A National Academy of Sciences/National Research Council morbidity study of WW II and Korean exPOWs, published in 1975, documented a significantly higher rate of hospitalization for arteriosclerotic heart disease in Pacific Theater exPOWs compared with matched nonPOW Pacific Theater combat veterans. No significant increases were documented for European Theater and Korean exPOWs (Beebe, 1975).

On current examination, hypertension and arteriosclerotic heart disease (including heart attacks and coronary artery bypass grafting) were frequent findings. Hypertension was diagnosed in 1 of the 3 younger Vietnam exPOWs, in 4 of the 15 exPOWs from Korea, 40 of the 121 WW II European Theater exPOWs, and 17 of the 50 WW II Pacific Theater group. None of the exPOWs had findings consistent with chronic beriberi heart disease and no definite connection could be drawn between these veterans' POW confinement and their current cardiovascular disorders.

Musculoskeletal Problems

Back injuries, including compression fractures and degenerative arthritis, are a well-documented sequel of high-speed ejections from aircraft in Vietnam exPOWs (Berg & Richlin, 1977). Among our group of three Vietnam exPOWs, two of whom were pilots and the third an Army footsoldier, all had significant spinal arthritis on current examination. The two pilots were injured on ejection from their disabled aircraft and the Army soldier was severely beaten on several occasions.

Current examination also revealed a high prevalence of spinal arthritis in both the European and Pacific Theater WW II exPOWs. Among European Theater exPOWs, the prevalence of back injuries was highest for aircrew members who parachuted from or landed with their disabled aircraft. The following is a typical history of such an injury, given by one of our patients:

> I was a B-17 waist gunner flying over Austria in February 1944 when we were hit. The plane was on fire when we were ordered to bail out. I didn't have my parachute strapped on tightly enough and the force of the chute opening popped my neck and back. I landed hard in some pine trees, cutting my leg. My back and neck hurt, but I was too scared about being captured and thankful for being alive to pay any attention to the pain.

Over the intervening 40 years, this veteran had recurrent episodes of neck and low back pain, culminating in the surgical removal of a ruptured disc 15 years ago. Despite surgery, the veteran continues to have frequent back and neck "aching" discomfort, with current x-rays revealing neck and low back degenerative arthritis.

On current examination, 63 of 121 (52 percent) of European Theater exPOWs had radiographic evidence of spinal arthritis. Twenty-nine of these exPOWS (24 per cent) had degenerative arthritis that could—from review of service medical records and/or compatible history—be related to the effects of POW capture or internment.

Although there has been little published information on the prevalence of osteoarthritis in Pacific Theater POWs, in 1981 Gill and Bell reported that 15 percent of 602 British Pacific Theater exPOWs had clinical and radiological evidence of osteoarthritis, with the "majority" having spinal osteoarthritis. These authors attributed an increased risk of arthritis in this group of exPOWs to "beatings and hard physical work."

In our group of 50 Pacific Theater exPOWS, 34 (68 percent) had current evidence of spinal osteoarthritis, with 23 (46 percent) felt to be related to the effects of POW confinement (i.e., beatings and injuries related to work in mines, steel mills, airfields, docks, etc.).

Among our group of 15 Korean exPOWs, 3 (20 percent) had degenerative osteorarthritis on current x-rays, 2 of which were related to the effects of repeated beatings during POW confinement.

Psychiatric

The 1945 "Morgan Board" repatriation examinations of over 4,600 Pacific Theater POWs gave the following summary of clinical impressions (Morgan, Wright & van Ravenswaay, 1946):

> A question which constantly recurred among the examiners was why this particular group survived. It was felt that, in a sense, this was a select group. Many factors doubtless played a part in survival. The factor of chance was important, since any man might have been on a torpedoed Japanese prison ship or slain in a fit of temper by some Japanese soldier....When the prisoners were asked for their opinions in this regard many of them stated that their confreres who had died when the going was difficult had in many instances "lacked the will to live." The "will to live" is an intangible phrase. It is difficult to define, but the men who did not give up were characterized by some of the following qualifications:
>
> 1. They had a never-failing hope of rescue.
> 2. They were possessed of a high morale and courage.
> 3. They were individuals who adjusted rather easily to difficult situations.
> 4. They were nonaggressive or at least were able to control a tendency to pugnaciousness which, if allowed to evidence itself, frequently resulted in summary death.
> 5. They were willing to eat anything, however disagreeable, if it might contain nutritional value.
> 6. They were willing to secure food by any and all means.

Findings on current psychiatric examinations reveal that this "will to live" exacted a high price from the futures of many of the survivors of POW internment. Forty-one of 50 (82 percent) Pacific Theater exPOWs were found to have psychiatric impairment on current protocol examination, with the majority, 30 (60 percent), suffering from anxiety disorders, most frequently (14 men or 28 percent) from post-traumatic stress disorder. Depressive disorders were found in an additional 9 veterans (18 percent).

Among European Theater exPOWs, 73 of 121 (60 percent) manifested significant psychiatric symptomatology; 40 (33 percent) were found to have anxiety disorders, of whom 13 (11 percent) met the criteria for the diagnosis of PTSD. An additional 25 veterans had depressive disorders, most frequently dysthymic disorder (21 men or 17 percent). Dementia was diagnosed in 7 (6 percent) of the European Theater exPOWS, compared to none in the Pacific Theater group and 1 of 15 in exPOWs from Korea.

In the group of 15 Korea exPOWs, 11 (73 percent) had psychiatric impairment on the protocol examination. Nine (60 percent) had anxiety disorders, with 7 (47 percent) diagnosed as having PTSD. One veteran was diagnosed as having dysthymic disorder.

Finally, in the three Vietnam exPOWS, PTSD was diagnosed in two; the third declined to undergo the psychiatric interview.

It should be noted that many of these diagnoses are based on a single 45-minute to 2-hour interview and review of available records. As has been discussed by Ron Langer in this volume, the diagnoses of PTSD and depression might well be even more prevalent with more in-depth interviews over a period of time.

In addition to the "facts-and-figures," we have learned many important lessons in working with this most interesting and deserving group of veterans. In the hopes that some of the situations we have encountered will help others who may have contact with exPOWs, I will review some of these points from the perspective of what we, the caregivers, need to practice. It is important to remember that these are illustrative anecdotes and generalizations, and certainly do not represent the feelings and actions of all or even most exPOWs.

Sensitivity

Shortly after our exPOW Protocol Program was established, I was called by a young physician who was completing his final year in our internal medicine residency program. A 70-year-old Pacific Theater exPOW had just left Dr. A.'s examining room in a very agitated state. Dr. A. explained that he had no idea what Mr. R.'s problem was, because as soon as Dr. A. entered the room to introduce himself Mr. R. jumped up, began jabbering unintelligibly, and left the office as fast as he could.

About two weeks later, I was able to locate Mr. R. and invited him to come to my office for a talk about the protocol examination. During the course of our interview, he apologized for his behavior with Dr. A., "It's just that I don't want to be treated by no Jap doctor." Dr. A. is a native Hawaiian of Oriental ancestry.

After 40 years, this type of response may seem irrational and immature, but to the exPOWs who saw their companions beaten and brutalized by the Japanese on Bataan, the Chinese in Korea, or the Vietnamese in the "Hanoi Hilton," this lingering anger is very real. And it is not confined to Mr. R., an elderly man of limited education. Consider the statement of Dr. John Nardini, a young medical officer in the Philippines at the outbreak of WW II and survivor of three-and-one-half years as a POW: "I want to ram every Toyota and Honda I see on the road. I know other POWs don't share my feelings, but they're wrong." Dr. Nardini is an eminent psychiatrist who has written extensively about exPOWs. He made this statement at an educational conference on exPOWs in Dallas, Texas in March 1985.

We now do our best to avoid sending exPOWs to staff who might be identified with captors (see Shovar, this volume).

Staff Education and Continuity of Care

A second incident, which also occurred early in our program, underscored the need for ongoing educational programs to familiarize our staff with the special circumstances of POW captivity, treatment, and subsequent medical and psychological problems.

When B.C. came to me for his exPOW protocol exam, I noted he had missed his last several appointments in our internal medicine clinic, and had run out of his medication for both his hypertension and degenerative arthritis. With some reluctance, he explained that his physician of many years—of whom he thought very highly—had recently transferred to another VA facility and he had been appointed to see an intern, fresh from medical school. "The intern was very nice and seemed bright enough, but when she asked me 'Where is Bataan? New York?' I saw red. Don't they teach these kids about history anymore?"

I recommend two books to our staff because they give a good overview of the conditions of POW internment: *POW: Study of Former Prisoners of War*, published by the VA and available from the U.S. Government Printing Office (VA, 1980) and *Prisoners of War*, published by Time-Life Books as part of their series on World War II (Bailey, 1981).

Former POWs seem to have more difficulty than most dealing with losses as they get older; the loss of job, of health, of a spouse, or a physician may hit harder than it would a person who had not been a POW. I do my best to refer exPOWs, new to our system, to our regular staff physicians and therapists (who will then follow them for many years) rather than to residents-in-training who only rotate through the VA.

Patience, Flexibility, and Trust

Many exPOWs have spent literally decades fighting for recognition from various governmental bureaucracies for injuries and illnesses incurred as a result of POW confinement. Other former POWs are hesitant to apply for benefits or even talk about their POW experiences because they feel that either no one will believe them or that they are not deserving of any special consideration because they were captured or because of their behavior while in captivity.

Addressing the crowds in London's Parliament Square on May 8, 1945, VE Day, Winston Churchill stated, "In all our long history, we have never seen a greater day than this." The POW wasn't there for the celebration, the recognition, or the appreciation. On the contrary, as Dr. Robert Obourn (himself a former Pacific Theater POW and now a staff psychiatrist at the Topeka, Kansas VA Medical Center) commented at the National Former POW Educational Conference in Dallas, Texas in March 1985:

> A POW is a mission failed. The exPOW lives with a sense of embarrassment. The tradition of the American Armed Services is one of pride and success. The POW cannot share in this. Although not his fault, having been a POW is a source of quiet embarrassment. POWs are quiet men and women, who seem very tolerant of the world around them.

A similar view was reflected at this same conference by Vietnam exPOW, Charles Stackhouse, a retired Navy commander now living in Texas: "POWs are a private group—a closed group. It's a group to which no one strives to belong. I didn't grow up wanting to be a POW."

The need for patience and flexibility was exemplified in our dealing with C.D., who had been a civilian construction worker on Wake Island, but who fought with American troops against invading Japanese forces in December 1941, and then endured almost four years of terrible hardships as a POW. Every night, C.D. relives some of the horrors of his POW captivity, but it was only in 1981, after almost four decades of struggle, that he and hundreds of other Wake Island civilians were finally granted veteran status and recognized for their valiant efforts on that island.

When C.D. first came to my office to discuss the exPOW protocol, he was bitter and hostile about the government in general and the VA in particular. I reviewed the nuts-and-bolts of the protocol, but soon realized that my explanation was falling on deaf ears. C.D. was communicating, but I wasn't really *listening* to him. Finally, I realized this and simply asked: "C.D. what can I do for you right now?" He calmed down immediately and said: "I can't pee and my glasses are broken. Can you help me?" I expedited appointments to the urology and eye clinics. Three months later, C.D. returned to my office ready to undergo the complete protocol evaluation. Not surprisingly, he was found to have severe PTSD and was one of my first referrals to Ron Langer's exPOW therapy group. In first dealing with exPOWs, action often speaks louder than words and helps build a lasting trust.

The Difference between Capture and Captivity

In general, the periods of greatest stress for most European POWs came when they were captured and near the end of the war during camp transfers. On the other hand, for Pacific Theater POWs, the long periods of captivity, with inadequate food, lack of medical care, and forced labor, resulted in much poorer general health at repatriation. While there is a tendency for psychological problems to be greater with longer periods of internment, the duration and extent of psychic scarring cannot simply be equated to the number of days in captivity.

For example, D.E. was a POW for only 9 days after his B-17 was shot down over Germany near the end of WW II in April 1945. His plane exploded in the air, and D.E. was thrown clear with his parachute smoldering and only partially deployed. He landed in a lake with an injured leg and was pulled to safety, half-drowned, by a German patrol. For the next week, he was repeatedly beaten during interrogation until he was liberated on April 17, 1945. He was treated for an ankle sprain and subsequently mustered out of the Air Corps in 1946, when he returned to his father's ranch in Kansas to raise cattle. D.E. wrote the following statement in support of his 1983 claim for benefits resulting from his military service:

> Several things happened to me while in the service of my country that I did not feel it necessary to talk about. I was brought up to believe that personal problems and humiliating experiences were solved by the individual, period.
>
> For that reason I had never mentioned to the Veterans Administration the many sleepless nights, the nightmares of an exploding B-17, or of screaming in the night and waking my wife. Nor did I mention the fact that I was flying first pilot when we were shot down and if I had been flying co-pilot, Lt. __________ would be alive rather than having gone down with the aircraft, and I would be dead. Neither did I mention the fact that I was beaten with rifle butts by the Gestapo in Hof, Germany.
>
> In June of this year, I went to an air show in Denver with two of my sons. On display was an old B-17G. I went aboard the aircraft and sat in the pilot's seat and it all came back. I lost control and completely broke down. Very humiliating.
>
> I am most proud of my service record....These facts are the truth. I am not asking for a handout. I only want what is just and fair.

D.E. was subsequently diagnosed as having PTSD and continues in therapy.

In contrast to D.E.'s short period of POW internment, E.F. endured 42 months of imprisonment after the fall of Corregidor in May 1942. He survived severe malnutrition and tuberculosis, which later resulted in a partial lung resection. He works as a real estate broker and is raising a family of 7 children. He did relatively well until about 1980, when increasing shortness of breath related to his old tuberculosis forced him to retire. During the Iranian hostage crisis, he found himself ruminating more and more about his own POW experiences, and finally was hospitalized for three weeks for severe depression and PTSD.

After discharge, he dropped out of treatment when his therapist unexpectedly died; subsequently, he avoided all contact with anything that reminded him of his POW experiences. At the urging of his family, after months of hesitation, E.F. finally consented to a protocol evaluation. The examining psychiatrist noted a great deal of survivor guilt: E.F. repeated on several occasions during the interview, "I could have done more," but was unable to be more specific (see T. Williams, this volume). At the time of the examination, E.F.'s wife related that his appetite was very poor and that he had lost over 40 pounds in the past two years. When asked about his weight loss, E.F. commented that he now weighed about what he did while a POW, 105 pounds, and that he "couldn't afford to eat; I need to save my money." E.F. was subsequently admitted to the psychiatry service for further evaluation and treatment of his weight loss and depression, and remained hospitalized for approximately two months.

A few months into the exPOW protocol program, I learned from the examining psychiatrists that many of the exPOWs they were interviewing seemed distant and were having difficulty expressing their feelings about their POW experiences. I reviewed this with exPOWs at the time of the exit interviews; they were somewhat apologetic that they couldn't be more open with the psychiatrists, but felt that it was almost impossible to share their feelings with a "stranger" in a short interview. They suggested that I better prepare exPOWs as to what they should expect when they come in for the protocol evaluation, particularly regarding the psychiatric examination. One POW asked me, "I'm not nuts, why do I need to see a psychiatrist?" I explained that many exPOWs have unresolved issues relating to their POW confinement and were now having difficulty adjusting to additional losses of getting older: loss of health, loss of jobs, loss of spouse and friends. He burst into tears and confided, "I'm having trouble with all of those things. I just thought psychiatrists were for crazy people."

Be There

Although I have focused on the exPOW protocol evaluation, it is important to emphasize that this is only the first step in really helping this most deserving group of veterans. By meeting with each exPOW when the protocol evaluation is initially set up, and then again on the day of the examination, and finally several weeks later to review the findings, I am trying to communicate my interest and concern and that I will do my best to maximize each exPOW's medical and compensation benefits. When we first meet, I give each exPOW my name and telephone number to be used at any time in the future. I make no extravagant promises, but I do my best to eliminate barriers and red tape, recognizing that many of these exPOWs have been shuffled around for years by an unresponsive system. A few minutes spent on the telephone arranging an appointment or clearing up some pharmacy glitsch goes a long way in really establishing our good intentions.

I encourage exPOWs to bring their wives and families to meet with me at the time of the final exit interview and keep copies of the completed protocol examinations in my office for easy reference. I talk frequently with staff physicians treating exPOWs and with Ron Langer, leader of two therapy groups, one for exPOWs and the other for wives of exPOWs. I meet on a weekly basis with the exPOW Service Officer and talk with interested service organizations. These are simple things, perhaps insignificant in and of themselves, but they help demonstrate to exPOWs that the system does care and will be responsive to their needs.

REFERENCES

American Ex-Prisoners of War, Inc. (1980). The European Story. (Packet No. 8). Arlington, TX: Author.

Bailey, R. H. (1981). *Prisoners of war: World War II.* Alexandria, VA: Time-Life Books.

Beebe, G. W. (1975). Follow-up studies of World War II and Korean War prisoners, II: Morbidity, disability, and maladjustments. *American Journal of Epidemiology, 101*, 400-422.

Berg, S. W., & Richlin M. (1977). Injuries and illnesses of Vietnam War POW, I: Navy POWs. *Military Medicine, 142,* 514-518.

Cardiovascular beriberi. (1982). *Lancet, 1,* 1287.

Carson, P. (1982). Alcoholic cardiac beriberi. *British Medical Journal, 284,* 1817.

Churchill, W. S. (1939). *A roving commission.* New York: Charles Scribner's Sons.

Cohen, B., & Cooper, M. (1954, September). *A follow-up of World War II prisoners of war.* Washington, DC: Veterans Administration.

Gibberd, F. B., & Simmonds, J. P. (1980). Neurological disease in ex-Far-East prisoners of war. *Lancet, 2,* 135-137.

Gill, G. V. (1983). Study of mortality and autopsy findings amongst former prisoners of the Japanese. *Journal of Royal Army Medical Corps, 129,* 11-13.

Gill, G. V., & Bell, D. R. (1980). Persisting tropical diseases amongst former prisoners of war of the Japanese. *Practitioner, 224,* 801-803.

Gill, G. V., & Bell, D. R. (1981). The health of former prisoners of war of the Japanese. *Practitioner, 225,* 531-538.

Gill, G. V., Henry, L., & Reid, H. A. (1980). Chronic cardiac beriberi in a former prisoner of the Japanese. *British Journal of Nutrition, 44,* 273-274.

Hibbs, R. (1946). Beriberi in a Japanese prison camp. *Annals of Internal Medicine, 25,* 270-282.

Jacobs, E. C. (1951). Oculo-oro-genital syndrome: A deficiency disease. *Annals of Internal Medicine, 35,* 1049-1054.

Keehn, R. (1980). Follow-up studies of World War II and Korean conflict prisoners, III: Mortality to January 1, 1976. *American Journal of Epidemiology, 111,* 194-211.

Kerr, E. B. (1985). *Surrender and survival.* New York: William Morrow and Company, Inc.

Knox, D. (1981). *Death march: The survivors of Bataan.* New York: Harcourt Brace Jovanovich, Inc.

Lawton, M. (1984). *Some survived.* Chapel Hill, NC: Algonquin Books of Chapel Hill.

Morgan, H. J., Wright, I. S., & van Ravenswaay, A. (1946). Health of repatriated prisoners of war from the Far East. *Journal of American Medical Association, 130,* 995-999.

Nardini, J. (1947). Vitamin-deficiency diseases in allied prisoners of the Japanese. *U.S. Naval Medical Bulletin, 47,* 272-278.

Nefzger, D. (1970). Follow-up studies of World War II and Korean War prisoners, I: Study plan and mortality findings. *American Journal of Epidemiology, 91,* 123-138.

O'Donnell, J. P. (1982). *The shoe leather express.* Salinas, CA: Ford.

Spivey, D. T. (1984). *POW odyssey.* Attleboro, MA: Colonial Lithograph, Inc.

Stenger, C. A. (1985). *American POWs in WW I, WW II, Korea and Vietnam: Statistical data concerning numbers captured, repatriated and still alive as of January 1, 1985.* Washington, DC: Veterans Administration.

Veterans Administration. (1980). POW: Study of former prisoners of war. Washington, DC: VA Office of Planning and Program Evaluation.

CHAPTER TEN

MEDICAL PROFESSIONALS AND PTSD

G. Phil Shovar

INTRODUCTION

Many medical professionals served in Vietnam in their various professional capacities. These were primarily physicians and nurses, but there were also various other specialty people such as physical therapists. Corpsmen, who had been trained specifically to do emergency medical work during battle but who, for the most part, had no previous medical experience, were also part of the team.

These medical people did not, or at least not often, actually participate in combat (except the line medical corpsmen). Nonetheless, they shared the same psychological, emotional, and moral experiences of the soldiers and others who used or were hurt by weapons. Within this group were nurses who lived with the product of war for 12 hours a day, 7 days a week. Moreover, they confronted dilemmas that were unique to them because they were in the war for peaceful purposes—to save and restore lives. However, many of them suppressed their own horror by telling themselves, and with some truth, that there were others who were worse off. They, the care givers, often the life givers, were trained to look to others' needs first, and to meet them.

During their education, physicians, nurses, and combat medics are taught to develop a high degree of clinical detachment. This detachment is necessary to keep clinicians' judgement from being clouded by emotional reactions. They are often taught: "Don't get personally involved or it will keep you from making the right decision when you need to." This denial of emotions either expands to encompass a denial of all feelings, or the mass casualties and long hours break down the self-imposed barriers that protect against emotionally reacting to the horror of combat medicine. The following anecdote reflects the former, and more common, phenomenon that will be discussed throughout this chapter.

Bonnie returned to the east coast after her year in an evacuation unit in Vietnam and found a job in the emergency unit of a hospital. She functioned well, sometimes rotating to other units in the hospital, including intensive care. She was getting on with her life; things seemed to be going well. She had a few minor medical problems, and even had surgery, but never seemed to suffer any painful memories or flashbacks. Eighteen years after coming home, Bonnie had major dental work done on her lower jaw. When she awoke from the anesthesia she "freaked out." She called a therapist who was also a former Vietnam nurse—and said she thought she had gone crazy. She was, in the words of the therapist, "a wreck." After two months of intensive therapy, Bonnie realized that her first Vietnam casualty had been a young man whose lower jaw had been extensively damaged and who needed a great deal of care and plastic surgery. Her own dental work—no doubt coupled with the "liberating" effects of anesthesia—brought it all back.

We hear little about the long-term psychological and emotional effects the war had on the care givers. Unfortunately, the process of shutting off feelings that served them well in battle has hardened for many of these care givers into a denial that they suffered at all, or were in any way affected. This accounts for one very substantial reason that the post-war needs of the medical professionals and nurses have gone largely unrecognized. But there is another, perhaps equally potent but far more insidious reason for the silence: many people who came back to careers in medicine are afraid to acknowledge that they have any residual psychological or emotional problem because they are afraid they may lose their colleagues' respect, or worse, their jobs or practices. It is only with considerable professional risk that members of these professions will even suggest that they are having emotional difficulties. It is important to remember what one writer has sagely pointed out:

> We [symbolically] eliminate the victims we are guilty of creating...by denying the existence of the condition from which they suffer. The endless debates over whether there is shellshock, combat neurosis or concentration camp survivors' syndrome fulfill our manifestation of denial...[of the event itself] and of the meaning of the event. Unfortunately, reality has the disagreeable quality of relentlessly asserting its existence. (Tanay, 1985, p.39)

Many medical people served in Vietnam as combat medics and corpsmen attached to units that were in direct contact with the enemy. Many of their treatment issues are identical to those of infantry soldiers, but their role as care givers sets them apart—in some ways—from the combat soldier. Most were inadequately trained to treat the massive injuries they saw daily. Few were well-grounded in tropical medicine, so they had little idea how to treat, or prevent, such conditions as immersion foot and tropical ulcers.

In this chapter, we will look at how many medical professionals experienced Vietnam, and how that experience has affected their lives and careers. Because there are no figures that will give us a statistical grasp on the magnitude of the problem, we can only discuss it in anecdotal terms. In a final section, some observations on therapy will be offered.

MEDICINE IN VIETNAM AND ITS AFTERMATH

Medicine has progressed to the point that with heroic measures, saving a life is often possible, even in the face of severe damage to most body systems. No longer is there the relief that used to be brought by an untreatable pneumonia. These heroic measures are usually taken by teams of trained people in the comparative calm of a well-organized hospital situation, which is where most medical personnel first learn about them. Not only is the hospital calm, in contrast to the field hospital, it is also comparatively impersonal—one is not likely to be treating people with whom one has developed a personal, sometimes intensely intimate, relationship. Moreoever, those who work in hospitals, even in emergency units, rarely experience the outrage that is constantly felt in battle—where a young man's injuries are so clearly not of his own making and so inescapably the result of someone else's intent.

Few of the medical people who went to Vietnam were prepared for what they would find—in terms of the number and severity of casualties or in terms of the threat to their own safety. As one nurse explained: "We thought the model was World War II. We thought we were going into a safe, demilitarized zone, behind the front lines and that the hospital would be respected by the enemy. No one told us in basic training that this wasn't so. My unit—the 71st Evac in Pleiku—was rocketed twice during my year [July 1967 - July 1968]. One rocket landed within 3 feet of my hootch and left a crater in the ground as big as this table [a good-sized table for two in a restaurant]." (Lungrin, 1986)

Medical personnel in Vietnam often had to work alone, or with very little assistance, making on-the-spot, life-and-death decisions with but little information. Nurses, as triage officers, were often responsible for determining the category of the casualty: immediate, expectant, or delayed. In practical terms, the "immediate" wounded were those who, if provided immediate care, could survive without seriously draining the resources of the medical unit. "Expectants" were so severely wounded that the likelihood of their survival was remote, and to try to treat them would mean tying up resources that could be spread over a larger number of "immediates." "Delayeds" could wait for some time—provided the nurse hadn't overlooked some small but potentially lethal problem. Once these determinations had been made, it was up to the nurse to designate a place for the wounded; those who were sent to the chapel were consigned to die.

As Canjar (unpublished) has pointed out: "Resources [in the combat hospital] must be utilized and expended efficiently and rationally...to maximize the highest survival rates ....Often the best means of maximizing the survivability of one soldier is to deny life support and comfort to another....Necessity and expediency must dictate moral choice." She further notes that health care specialists in war are never given the opportunity to altruistically risk their own lives in order that another's might be spared:

> [He or she] can only risk a life other than [his or her] own to save a life....It may be very difficult to reconcile [him or] herself in her own mind, much less in the minds of those who were not there and who do not understand that this was a fundamentally good act. The psycho-emotive stress of continued confrontation with these choices, and the hidden specter of oneself as the ghoulish adjudicator of pain and suffering, of life and death, cannot be overemphasized.

It is no wonder that Elizabeth, a Vietnam nurse, returned and enrolled in medical school, explaining that, "I didn't feel I knew enough over there and if I went to medical school, maybe I wouldn't make mistakes that could kill."

Elizabeth got through medical school without difficulty until she rotated into trauma medicine during her residency. She called me one night with a plaintive question and a sad story: "Am I going crazy?" she asked. "I have just been fired from my residency because I can't concentrate and remember things." She reported that the memories of Vietnam had come flooding back in the trauma unit, yet she was afraid to seek help or talk about her problem because she did not want to be labelled as a "crazy Vietnam vet." I advised her to try to find other nurses or a therapist who understood PTSD and how it relates to women, knowing that would be an almost impossible chore (see Sandecki, this volume).

Ed, a pathologist, handles his Vietnam experience in just the opposite way, insisting that he be called by his colleagues when there is any death by trauma or under questionable circumstances. While Ed has not yet faced the effects of his experiences as a surgeon in Vietnam, he is nonetheless organizing his life to constantly relive the "adrenalin rush" that combat work provided him.

Ed's "addiction" to action is not uncommon in returned vets; we call them "action junkies." But there are other, equally typical, response modes that go in the other direction—into isolation, withdrawal, depression, and substance abuse. Jim's story illustrates this response.

Jim was a young man who had been trained as a combat field medic at Fort Sam Houston. Within a month of completing his training, he was assigned to a medevac chopper and expected to make life-and-death decisions. On one run, Jim was trying to help a casualty who had had his spinal cord blown away along with a major portion of his abdominal contents; he had lost his left arm, and another medic had clamped off the arteries at the stump. The young soldier was conscious, but in great pain and very much aware that he had terminal wounds. Jim recognized Bob, a fellow medic classmate from Fort Sam Houston, as this mutilated young man. Bob begged Jim to undo the clamp and give him some morphine, rationally explaining that he knew he was going to die and didn't want to prolong the process. After agonizing soul-searching, Jim complied with Bob's wishes, and with similar wishes of other wounded men throughout the war.

Jim—and many others like him—have carried the burden of these decisions back with them, not realizing that what they had done was a long-standing and honorable military tradition—giving grace—that recognized that sometimes the kindest thing one can do for a fellow soldier is to help him die. Some, like Jim, have sought refuge in drugs and alcohol; others carry an enormous weight of survivor guilt that plagues them with self-doubt and depression. Jim had been in treatment for over a year with another therapist before I discovered the complete story of his having repeatedly "given grace" to fellow soldiers. In spite of its military respectability, this honorable tradition is also one whose social and emotional implications are immense, particularly for those who have been trained to give life, not death, as their greatest gift. (Jim benefited from the cognitive restructuring we did as he learned to understand and believe that what he had done had been the kindest, most compassionate, and honorable thing he could have done for a fellow soldier.)

Similar issues surface for those medical personnel who have had to use weapons, and the problem is compounded when the very enemy they shot becomes a patient for medical care.

Not only do these issues resonate personally for these returned care givers, but the facts of medicine in war rarely fit the facts of medicine in the community hospital. Vietnam nurses report having had difficulty with stateside physicians who refused to believe that they were responsible for the kind of triage operation described above. "How could you have done that, you were only a nurse?" captures the attitude. The combat medic is also subject to this type of response from nurses who weren't there. Such situations create one more reason to suppress the war experience, and consequently to deny its impact.

The problems of survivor guilt, described in this volume by Tom Williams, denial, and the range of symptoms that parallels the classic symptoms of PTSD combine to make many of our returned medical people in great need of psychological help and emotional support. Yet many of them do not seek it. Why?

COMPENSATION AND MILITARY RETIREMENT PROBLEMS

In this section, our focus is on the way in which the federal government (the Veterans Administration and the Department of Defense) works to grant compensation and/or treatment for service-related disabilities. For those readers who are not familiar with this system, a brief description will be helpful. In essence, in order to receive disability pay for service-connected problems, one must prove that the problem resulted from being in the service. In the case of physical ailments, this is generally fairly straightforward. However, in the case of emotional problems and symptoms, especially months or perhaps even years after the termination of service, the question is not so simple unless documented care was provided in the service or shortly after discharge.

VA rating boards, who award disabilities, place a heavy emphasis on combat-related stress. So immediately, a problem arises in seeking compensation and/or treatment for this disorder if one were not in active physical combat. While the VA does acknowledge a service connection for other extraordinary stressors, historically there has been great weight attached to the combat question. Thus, the initial source of the stress for those who were not in combat becomes a judgement call. While there are those who maintain that simply being in Vietnam was an extraordinary stress that resulted in what Canjar (unpublished) has called "psychic wounding," this does not necessarily meet the criteria for PTSD.

The difficulty in pinpointing the stress is compounded for medical professionals, whose "normal" professional life is filled with stress, with moral quandries, and with depressing events.

As noted elsewhere in this book, women who served in Vietnam face a particularly vicious

"Catch-22": since women are not considered eligible for combat, compensating women for PTSD would in effect acknowledge that they had been in combat, thus giving lie to the stated government policy that women would not be sent to combat. Thus, the political problems are particularly acute for women who need help for a constellation of symptoms that are quite like those experienced by combat veterans.

We are treating one nurse who fought with the Veterans Administration for five years before being given a 50 percent disability rating for her diagnosis of PTSD. Before this award was finally made, after considerable legal struggle, Janet ran a gauntlet of problems with diagnoses that refused to acknowledge the fact that she was suffering with all the classic symptoms of PTSD. One examining physician at the VA suggested in his report that Janet could not be suffering from PTSD because she had resigned for the good of the service (in effect, a dishonorable discharge). In fact, she had resigned from active duty and was commissioned as a reserve officer. Later she was diagnosed as having a narcissistic personality disorder—a diagnosis that was based on her assertion to the therapist that she was one of the best nurses in her specialty, as evidenced by the fact that she had been decorated three times for professional excellency and had received numerous letters of commendation and recognition. Apart from being one of the flimsiest "reasons" for making a diagnosis of such a personality disorder, this judgement also disavowed the legitimacy of Janet's wartime experience.

Another case that has come to our attention involves a white male nurse and a black female nurse who were in Vietnam for the same amount of time at the same hospital, and who both have gone back to school for advanced degrees in mental health to try to understand what has happened to them. Their post-Vietnam symptoms were almost identical, and both sought treatment from the VA. Jack, with the help of a competent DAV Service Officer, was able to have the diagnosis of "personality disorder" vacated from his record and replaced with a diagnosis of PTSD, thus making him eligible for treatment and compensation within the VA system. Marilyn, on the other hand, was stuck with a diagnosis of a personality disorder that originated in childhood, and therefore her problems are not compensated by the VA system. It strikes us as implausible that these two people with such different backgrounds until the war could have developed almost identical post-war symptoms, if the war experience were not the critical factor. We have to wonder whether the fact that Marilyn is a woman and black blinded the diagnosing physicians to the possibility that she could be suffering from the same problems as Jack.

While the system is increasingly less reluctant to consider PTSD as a legitimate diagnosis for "noncombatants," it has been a long and difficult struggle, and many people have been damaged in the interim. Ralph's story provides another case in point.

Ralph was a Military Reserve Registered Nurse field grade officer who notified military authorities that he had PTSD. He provided the appropriate documentation. He was ordered to report to a major military treatment facility for examination in uniform, which he did, being careful to put on his four rows of ribbons.

He was met by a man in civilian clothes who represented himself to be a doctor of psychology doing a clinical internship. Ralph much later discovered that this individual was a sergeant on active duty in another branch of the military who was working on a master's degree. When the sergeant determined that Ralph's problems were beyond his skill, he referred Ralph to an Oriental psychiatrist who specialized in adolescent psychiatry and who had never been in combat. (Here we must take time out to note that many combat veterans still harbor what might be called racism with regard to Orientals. Even those who have gotten to the point of not seeing every Oriental as a potential enemy still might find it terribly difficult to establish the kind of trust needed for a successful interview and evaluation. This is often related to the intensification of symptoms when reminded of the original stressor and avoidance of activities that remind them of that original stressor.) Although this psychiatrist indicated that he had read Ralph's records, nothing he did or said showed that he had any knowledge of Ralph's case. Ralph's attempts to get help were frustrated, and his response was to go into a deeper and deeper depression.

Joe had been a military physician's assistant providing medical support for an Army division of the rapid deployment force. He joined a rap group of Vietnam veterans for about six months, at which time he retired from the Army. Joe complained that over the past year he had been noticing changes in his behavior: he had a hard time dealing with his subordinates; he was having intrusive imagery of soldiers with massive traumas whom he had treated in Vietnam; he was troubled by these thoughts whenever he had to treat a trauma victim in his current work. He reported feeling a dread similar to that he felt during the war.

Joe frequently cried in the group, explaining that he could not have saved more lives because he lacked the proper training. (As we have noted, many lives were well beyond saving, even though a soldier may have been "alive" on arrival at a treatment unit.) Joe found the rap group wanting, and came to us for treatment. He reported decreased libido, sleep disturbances, and intrusive imagery that was becoming increasingly more graphic. It became clear to us that Joe was suffering from marked survivor guilt that focused around his perception of his "inadequate" skills. Although both Joe and his wife profitted from the separate treatment they received, Joe still felt unsettled, and could no longer trust the system. When he retired from the Army, he moved with his family to Texas to raise cattle in an isolated rural area. This highly skilled medical professional was lost to the profession because of the impact of PTSD and the limited therapy Joe was able to obtain. It is not possible to say with certainty that earlier and longer intervention would have altered the outcome, but there can be no question that it would have been preferable, as the two cases below seem to demonstrate.

Mary, a 44-year-old active duty field grade officer, was a nurse at a major military medical center when she was placed on a roster of nurses who would respond to combat requirements anywhere in the world. As part of this possible new assignment, Mary was required to qualify to fire the M-16. Since her sixteen-month tour in a Vietnam field hospital, Mary had been able to avoid any such duties, and she came to us for therapy saying, "I'm phobic about firing weapons."

She complained of long-term survival guilt, emotional numbing, intrusive memories of traumatic episodes, and interpersonal distancing—she had had no significant intimate relationships since the war. The requirement to learn to fire the M-16 intensified all of these symptoms, and she felt she had become dysfunctional at work with increased disruption to her thought processes and emotional ability (anger and tears at work). She reported sleep disturbances and nightmares about the war in which she kept seeing a room of "discarded American corpses."

We saw Mary for three months, allowing her to ventilate about the war and see the connection between having to learn to fire the M-16 and the intensification of her symptoms. She was treated with systematic desensitization around firing the weapon and with a mild anti-anxiety agent. She learned thought-stopping and relaxation techniques, and we worked with her until she was able to fire the weapon. After the firing, she reported a significant decrease in her symptoms and the medication was terminated. Unfortunately, there was no women veterans rap group that Mary could attend, but we would suggest such a course whenever possible.

George, a 36-year-old active duty physician in an Ob-Gyn residency at a military facility was referred by the chief of obstetrics because he seemed forgetful and indifferent to supervision. So severe were his problems that he was facing recycling through his residency or being dropped altogether.

He presented as depressed and angry with his supervisors, but he was also very concerned that his father, who lived one thousand miles away, was dying. This was creating intrusive thoughts of his father's death and conjuring memories of deaths he had witnessed in Vietnam, where he had received numerous decorations, including two purple hearts.

The fact that he was a well-decorated war veteran isolated him from his peers, who considered him "one of those crazy Vietnam vets." George made matters worse by wearing his decorations at every possible opportunity, believing that he had earned some respect and understanding.

George was instructed in the basic symptoms of PTSD, and explored how a current event—in this case, his father's dying—could exacerbate the symptoms. He was given a six-month leave from his residency and transferred to a hospital near his father. The sensitivity that was displayed by this transfer and the intervention that occurred before George's symptoms became such that he would lose his job saved a valuable and productive member of the medical community.

PROBLEMS WITHIN THE PROFESSIONS

Medical professionals suffering from PTSD are hampered within their professions as well as inside the treatment system. As we noted earlier, they are reluctant to admit to psychological problems for fear of professional censure, or worse. PTSD may affect one's ability to function under stress, and for some who served in Vietnam, certain medical situations recall the war in vivid and still unsettling ways, and flashbacks and nightmares may be exacerbated when one works in a medical setting. Medical professionals, regardless of whether they have combat experience, may suffer the classic signs and symptoms of PTSD when their work brings them face-to-face with events beyond the range of normal human experience.

In fact, the first of the diagnostic criteria for PTSD from *DSM-III* (Revised) (American Psychiatric Association [APA], in revision; see Appendix A to this book) is the "Existence of a recognizable stressor that would evoke significant symptoms of distress in almost everyone." The following case example illustrates this point for medical professionals who have not had previous combat experience, as well as those who have.

A Hospital Hostage Incident

Eddie was a severely depressed and suicidal patient on a ward overseen by Betty, a charge nurse who was thirty-five at the time of the incident and had no combat experience. Betty had decided that Eddie needed to be in seclusion for his own safety. She notified the attending physician that she had secluded Eddie, but the physician, apparently without having seen Eddie that morning, insisted that Eddie was not dangerous to himself or others, released him from seclusion, and allowed him to go out on a pass.

That night, Eddie returned with a magnum pistol, held the staff hostage, and threatened: "I'm going to blow my brains all over the unit to make you suffer." Although Betty's later perception was that she had been immobilized for a long time, other staff report that it was only a matter of a few seconds before she began talking with Eddie to try to defuse the situation.

The crisis lasted for about twenty minutes before help arrived. Eddie shot himself in the leg, but it was not until he had bled sufficiently to be incapacitated that staff were able to subdue him.

The attending physician, who was not present at the incident, later again certified that Eddie was not dangerous to himself or others, and released Eddie to leave the state. Eddie had bragged to the nursing staff that he knew how to make himself "look OK" with the physician, and that he would be back to "do the job right."

Two weeks passed, during which time Betty became increasingly dysfunctional and anxious on the job. It was at this point that she was referred for treatment, reporting only extreme rage at the inadequate responses of the hospital administration to the incident, especially the behavior of the attending physician. Betty used the defense mechanism of denial to repress the traumatizing fear she'd experienced during the incident. She denied, as well, any post-traumatic symptoms. Later, however, she agreed during therapy that she'd been concerned that she was "going crazy" because of her behavior at home and work, and because objectively she exhibited most of the symptoms of PTSD (Appendix A).

Treatment was extended to all staff who had been present during the hostage incident, two of whom, Harry and Bill, had been in Vietnam. Not surprisingly, the hostage incident profoundly affected both men, and rekindled memories of Vietnam.

Harry began having vivid, intrusive dreams that recalled his assignment as a clerk in full view of the graves registration office. "I used to see the remains brought in by truck and just dumped. Now I'm dreaming I'm being zippered into a body bag and the zipper is being closed over my face." (Under such circumstances, it is not uncommon for one intrusive image to be replayed again and again.) Harry had not ever had an opportunity to examine what he then expressed as his "disregard" for the dead. In subsequent treatment, he was able to understand that he had developed a perfectly normal defense against the emotional assault he experienced daily in Vietnam watching the dead being dumped from a truck.

At the time of Eddie's hostage-taking, both Harry and Bill felt themselves to be dissociated from the event: "It was like I was watching myself from several feet away, and I felt that if I didn't move, he wouldn't be able to see me."

All staff who were present at the event were offered treatment, which will be discussed in detail later, but it took two weeks for the offer to be made. What is important to note here is that during those two weeks, the staff, almost without exception, reported that they believed they were handling the situation well, denying that it had affected them in any profound way.

Nurses Lose Jobs, Credibility

Alberta, who had served as a nurse in Vietnam, returned home to work in the intensive care unit of a large western hospital as a registered nurse. Ten years later, in casual conversation with her supervisor, she remarked that she was having nightmares associated with her war experiences. She was summarily fired from her job, in spite of her superb work record, and the state board of nursing was notified that Alberta was dangerous and not safe to be allowed to practice. The state certifying board withdrew her license to practice. Alberta has filed suit for personal damages.

Joan had been an active member of a well-known certifying organization for many years, with a perfect record. But she came to recognize that her memory was impaired under stress, and she turned in her credentials to work within her specialty area, even though her ability to function under normal nursing conditions in no way suffered. She said that she didn't feel she could do what she considered lying if she maintained her specialized credentials above the level of a registered nurse. When she notified her professional organization that she could not ethically practice in her speciality area, she received a form letter that said, in part, that since she was impaired, "when you complete treatment for drug and alcohol problems you may reapply for recertification."

Joan threatened to sue the organization for casting doubt on her integrity and competence. Their reply was an apology, a retraction of the form letter, and a letter continuing her as a medically and honorably disabled member of the speciality within the profession.

As these stories circulate, it is not surprising that people are reluctant to admit that they are having emotional problems, even though there is no evidence to suggest that patients have been endangered.

Memory impairment seems to be the most common, and the most persistent functional result of PTSD in medical professionals. We have heard of many nurses who have given up nursing and sought employment in other fields because they felt they could not function—and some of these stories have another chapter that is lacking in compassion.

THE CONSPIRACY TO DENY

Frank, a combat physician, returned to practice in a small southern hospital. His co-workers noticed that he was increasingly edgy (probably an exaggerated startle response) and moved from one intimate relationship to another, all the while drinking more and more. He had denied to many staff members that he had been in Vietnam. Nonetheless, someone discreetly gave him Jim Goodwin's pamphlet, "Continuing Readjustment Problems in Vietnam Veterans" (a DAV publication).

Shortly thereafter, Frank went off on an "extended vacation," (he actually sought treatment) and returned with some important and positive personality readjustments.

What can we say about Frank? Factually, very little, as is sadly the case in many others like Frank who hope to get by on suppression and denial because of the difficulties and anxieties I described earlier in this paper. He did not know what was wrong and therefore denied that anything was wrong until provided with a rational, empirical explanation (that is, with a clear statement of the symptoms of PTSD).

Denial occurs at several levels—from the institutionalized denial that "noncombatants" are suffering anything that could be related to the war to the intensely personal denial that one is suffering at all—as we saw with Betty—to another level of institutional denial that there is anything to be suffering about (again, as in Betty's case).

It is frightening for anyone to find him or herself impaired in any way, but it is perhaps more so for those whose job involves saving and improving the lives of others, and who feel both burdened and exhilarated by the task. Thus, there is a high premium within the medical community on appearing to be functional and intact at all times, as the following story—told to me by a client when she was new to my town—illustrates.

Lydia had been seeing a psychiatrist on the east coast for an extended period. She told me that when she showed up for an appointment one day, the psychiatrist appeared at the door with both hands bandaged like catchers' mitts. Lydia gasped and asked, "What in the world happened to you?" The psychiatrist replied coolly, "Oh, nothing." Lydia felt foolish and embarrassed—clearly, there was something wrong with the psychiatrist's hands, yet the message that came through to Lydia was that her normal human concern was both unwanted and inappropriate.

I don't want to debate the unanswerable question of how self-revealing psychiatrists or other medical professionals think they should be with their clients, but only to point out that within these professions there is support and sanction for denying one's personal pains, perplexities, and frailties. Those working in mental health, particularly, are constantly alert to ensuring that they do not become involved in countertransferrence with their clients. Yet we have found, as therapists, that some amount of self-disclosure is good in working with medical professionals (and other groups, as well, with careful consideration), especially since their identification with us is so strong.

However, it would be both naive and foolish to fail to acknowledge that a certain amount of detachment serves the profession well, and it was all the more necessary in Vietnam. Indeed, many care givers report having "turned a switch" to shut off their feelings. The medicine that was practiced during the war set the stage for more-than-normal soul searching because expedience, not broad humanitarianism, was often at the bottom of the decision. How, then, can we help the helpers?

THERAPEUTIC INTERVENTIONS

As has been repeatedly reported, group therapy for survivors has been shown to be an effective form of treatment. But the clinician may find that it is very difficult to get together a group of medical people large enough to be effective. However, it may be quite possible to put together a "professional persons group," as we did in Denver.

This group consisted of clients who had been in various levels of combat. Two prerequisites for entering this group were that the participants had resolved most issues related to active combat, and that they were in a profession (medicine, nursing, education, accounting, business administration, etc.). The group agreed that their goal was not to "tell war stories," but rather to let professionals know that there were others out there who had similar issues and problems. We wanted to foster support from and for individuals of the same socio-economic and educational background because we have found it is often difficult for the medical professional to communicate with individuals of greatly divergent backgrounds (such as might be found in a typical combat group). We also wanted to avoid having the clinician in a group where he or she would assume a "helper" role.

Every effort should be made to help restore the battered self-concept of the medical professional who seeks help. Many feel they have lost everything they worked for and built. They often report feeling life is not worth living, and it is therefore important to carefully and continually evaluate the individual for suicidal ideation, and to determine whether he or she has a method. However, it should be remembered that hospitalization, except in the gravest of extremes, is not a good idea, as it will in many states compromise their professional licensure. Every skill the therapist has to keep clients focused on their own professional competence should be brought to bear.

As with other veterans, medical professionals may have firearms. Rather than trying to get them to dispose of their firearms, the therapist should make a deal with the veteran to surrender them temporarily to some third person whom the veteran trusts, with the understanding that they will be returned when the suicidal ideation has passed.

A client, now able to recognize when he enters such a depressive cycle, has a security vault in his home where he stores most of his weapons. When he recognizes he is entering such a depressive state, he will secure all the firearms in the house and give his wife the key, and she returns it only when he has improved. This veteran reports that he is not concerned with thinking out and acting on a suicidal process, because if his situation became that desperate, he would carry out his plan with or without firearms. He states he is more concerned with impulse control, and giving his wife the key to the gun chest provides a form of control.

Chronically anxious and/or severely depressed persons often respond well to prescribed medications (see Yost, this volume). These symptoms are associated with PTSD, and medication and psychotherapy are often the treatments of choice. However, it should be noted that clients with a medical background often are wary of taking psychotropic medications.

To overcome this reticence, cognitive restructuring is often helpful. I repeatedly note that if they had diabetes, it would not be inappropriate for them to take daily insulin. If they have what some researchers suggest may well be a chemical imbalance of seratonin metabolism that results in severe depression, then it is appropriate for them to take medication to control this. I point out that they are not abusing medication, and that the abuse lies in not taking what has been prescribed.

Cognitive restructuring is also valuable at another level, as exemplified by the work done with the hospital hostages. The group was seen by a team experienced in handling PTSD. One very important theme was that each staff member had done the best he or she could at the time, given the information they had and the circumstances. This theme cannot be overstated, nor can the "victims" hear too often that their reaction is normal—it was the situation that was extraordinary. Victims of very different traumas report similar feelings—the distancing, the immobilization, amnesia, pain, fear, and doubt of one's own judgement. The more quickly a group or individual can be helped to express and talk through these feelings, the less likely it is that the experience will come back to haunt them.

The need for trained therapists to debrief medical staff who have experienced a major traumatic event is becoming recognized as essential to effective functioning of the clinical unit. Unfortunately, litigation-conscious administrators sometimes place barriers to rapid intervention, but this attitude is diminishing as they realize, if nothing else, that early resistance to intervention may be setting the stage for future job stress problems and consequent compensation claims.

A recent *Harvard Business Review (HBR)* "Special Report" highlights this issue in a discussion of "Who Is Liable for Stress on the Job?":

> Job stress can cause physical illness and psychological disturbance with psychosomatic as well as phsyical changes. While stress is an inevitable part of living and working, excessive pressure costs dearly in ill health, lost productivity, and increased personal problems.
>
> A growing stream of research has confirmed the relationship between work place stressors and such illnesses as varying degrees of emotional distress without physical symptoms, cardiovascular conditions in varying stages, gastrointestinal disorders, respiratory disorders, and infection and medicine abuse.
>
> Some courts have concluded that management has a responsibility for employee well-being and have asked what steps the company has taken to help an employee cope with stress. (*HBR* 1985, p. 60)

The stressors need not be as dramatic as the shooting incident described. The cumulative stress of hospital work, especially for trauma teams, if not recognized and dealt with, can result in stress disorder.

In his chapter on "Survivor Guilt" (this volume), Williams reports that PTSD is treatable, not curable. It is very difficult for us as helpers, medical or psychological, to tell the clients that their condition is not curable. It is sometimes helpful to suggest that the bell curve reflects the probability of subsequent symptoms: some individuals on one end of the curve will be totally incapacitated, and it is obvious that a client is not at that end because he or she is in your office seeking help. Some individuals will never have a problem with symptoms, and obviously your clients are not on that end of the curve either, because they are in your office. Obviously, a client is somewhere on that curve, and I always suggest that he or she is on the end where minimal or no treatment will be necessary after the current intervention. Whether this is actually the case, I frankly cannot say, but it is appropriate to provide the client with positive beliefs. It is entirely possible these beliefs will be borne out when statistical analysis is applied.

Again, there must be positive affirmation to help rebuild the damaged ego of the medical profesisonal who is in therapy. We seize every opportunity to acknowledge the client's demonstrations of mastery within his or her profession as part of the process of rebuilding the often shattered self-confidence of the "impaired" care giver.

REFERENCES

American Psychiatric Association. (in revision). *Diagnostic and statistical manual of mental disorders.* Washington, D.C.: American Psychiatric Press.

Canjar, Theresa. (1986). Unpublished research proposal. Department of Sociology, College Park, Maryland: University of Maryland.

Glasser, Ronald. (1980). *365 days.* New York: George Braziller.

Lungrin, Connie. (1986). Personal communication.

Tanay, E. (1985). "The Vietnam Veteran—Victim of War," in Kelly, William E. (Ed.) *Post-traumatic stress disorder and the war veteran patient.* New York: Brunner/Mazel.

"Special Report." (1985). "Who Is Responsible for Stress on the Job?" *Harvard Business Review,* March-April.

Williams, Tom. (1980). *Post-traumatic stress disorder of vietnam veterans.* Cincinnati, OH: Disabled American Veterans.

BIBLIOGRAPHY

Parish, John A. (1972). *12, 20, & 5—A doctor's year in Vietnam.* New York: Dutton and Co.

Sonnenberg, Stephan M., Blank, Arthur S., and Talbott, John A. (1985). *The trauma of war stress and recovery in Vietnam veterans.* Washington D.C: American Psychiatric Press.

CHAPTER ELEVEN

WOMEN VETERANS

Rose Sandecki

BACKGROUND

During the Vietnam conflict (1964-1975), between 8,000 and 10,000 women served in Vietnam (out of some three million Americans in total). Most of these women served as nurses, but others worked in various other supportive services such as logistics, personnel, and finance. In addition to the women who served with military units, a large number of civilian women served with support organizations such as the USO, American Red Cross, American embassy staff, and the USAID. This chapter will focus on what happened to these women. Because much of what they experienced is best expressed in their own words, I have chosen to quote them extensively (while maintaining their anonymity unless they gave specific permission to use their names).

My knowledge of the trials and traumas that so many of these women faced during and following their service in Vietnam is both personal and professional. I served in Vietnam as an army nurse in 1967 and 1968. In 1981, I became the first woman Vietnam veteran in charge of a Veterans Adminstration Vet Center. The Vet Centers are outpatient mental health clinics specifically set up to provide psychological counseling, nationwide, for Vietnam-era veterans. As one of the few Vet Centers with women veterans on staff, we have been very active in outreach and therapy for this too-often-forgotten group of veterans.

DEMOGRAPHIC DIFFERENCES BETWEEN MALE AND FEMALE VETERANS

While there are obviously many similarities between the experiences of male and female Vietnam veterans, there are important differences as well. Most men who went to Vietnam were drafted. The majority of the women volunteered for duty in Vietnam. The average age of males during the war was 19 (as compared with 27 in World War II). Women veterans were generally older, ranging in age from 21-30. Most of these women had completed several years of college or nursing school before joining the military. It has been my experience that women who joined the military so they could get financial assistance for education, that is, the younger ones, developed more severe symptoms of post-traumatic stress disorder (PTSD) and remain somewhat easier to identify. The women who completed their professional training or college and worked for several years before volunteering for Vietnam appear to have less difficulty (or are at least less likely to seek help). While most of this chapter deals with the forgotten minority of women in the nursing profession, there is still a smaller minority who are even less recognized. These are the women who served in service support roles such as air traffic control, administrative support with major headquarters, and other "noncombat" roles.

GENDER-RELATED ISSUES

Women tend to identify themselves as nurtuerers, as offering maternal comforts. Women who were nurses in Vietnam felt strongly about taking care of others, and this was especially true of the women taking care of the young men (often referred to as boy-soldiers) in the Vietnam conflict. I often felt I represented the mothers of those young men at the time of their death in this foreign land. Mothers are responsible for bringing us all into this world and we generally think about our mothers at the time our life is ending. "It was my job, I had to be strong for my patients, ...for my junior nurses and enlisted men. If I would fall apart when an eighteen-year-old came in with both his legs amputated, I wouldn't be able to help the countless numbers of casualties who would be following him" (Sandecki, 1982). As nurses, we were taught to take care of others; the patients always came first. Those working in hospitals in Vietnam were instructed to protect their patients before seeking their own shelter during the frequent shelling or mortar attacks. Even though the Geneva Convention had identified hospitals as being neutral zones, the enemy frequently directed their mortars and rockets towards the airfields, which were usually located close to the hospitals. The hospital compounds were under indirect though real attack by the enemy.

Another important gender difference is that women generally do not think of themselves as veterans. Very few of them have taken advantage of their G.I. Bill, home loans, or medical care through the Veterans Administration. They learned to keep their horror stories to themselves for many years and continue to silently suffer. It was even more difficult for the women to identify themselves as being Vietnam veterans because of the negative images the country had about women who served in the military in the late 1950s and early 1960s. It was a common belief that a woman joined the service then only because she could not make a go of it in the outside world; she was commonly thought of as a lesbian or prostitute. Add to this the extremely negative image of the Vietnam veteran as a loser, or worse, and it is no wonder that these women would not identify themselves and risk further criticism and humiliation.

The general public had a false impression that these women were safe in Vietnam. They were led to believe that women never served in a combat situation. The Department of the Army classified women serving in Vietnam as "noncombatants."

> It seems most of the nurses I know have one horror story that represents Vietnam to them. Mine happened one night we'd been in the operating room about sixty hours. We were fatigued beyond words. We'd stretch out under the operating table on the floor for five or ten minutes between cases.
>
> The operating rooms were in round-topped quonset huts. There were little cubicles inside separated with shoulder-high partitions to make operating rooms. We were being hit pretty heavily at the time. A mortar round came in and hit the front part of the building and blew away our scrub sinks. We were running out of supplies and didn't see how we would be able to take any more casualties that night. And then another chopper came in to the pad—it was about two in the morning—and they brought this guy off the chopper. We could hear him even above the noise of the rotor blades, screaming....We could hear him coming in our direction on a stretcher, coming up the concrete ramp, up to the operating room. He had stepped on a land mine and had both arms and both legs blown off right at the trunk. His eyes had been blown away, but he was still alive and screaming all the way down the ramp. They wheeled him past us, put him down at the back and tried real hard to find a place to start an I.V., and to put him to sleep so they could try to save him in some way. All the while he was screaming, "Let me die, let me die!" We listened to that for it seemed like thirty minutes until finally everything got real quiet and we knew he had died.
>
> Somebody had a portable radio on a shelf. Bing Crosby was singing "Don't Fence Me In." After a little bit, everybody in the operating room started singing along,

> "Don't Fence Me In." All of us in our cubicles were crying, the doctors and the nurses. Everybody up and down that place was just totally wiped out by the incident.
>
> I think from that point on I just simply did not...it wasn't that I didn't care, but the only way I could deal with it was to simply shut everything out and not feel anything. I brought that home with me when I left Vietnam. (White, 1983)

Women were not issued weapons or given infantry duty, but the combat situation in Vietnam was unlike that of any other war. No military installation in Vietnam was safe from enemy attack. Because of this, most of the doctors and all of the medics were issued individual weapons. Nurses were very much discouraged from obtaining or carrying weapons (although male nurses sometimes had them). Female nurses were dependent on the men in the hospital compound to protect them. This caused a sense of vulnerability and role confusion; on one level the nurse was expected to exhibit unwavering strength and act as a role model, while on another level she was expected to depend on the men around her to save her life should the need arise. As one of my women veterans put it, "...it was different for the men, at least they had guns and could 'off' someone or something to vent their frustrations. The men would protect us. Ha!"

Ironically, while female nurses are not recognized as having been in combat (see Shovar, this volume), male nurses (who made up approximately 25 percent of the nurse corps in Vietnam) generally are. When they report the classic symptoms of PTSD, they are usually taken seriously. That male nurses who served in Vietnam understand how women veterans feel about this issue was brought home to me in a conversation I had with a highly skilled male nurse who became unable to walk into a hospital without experiencing intense anxiety following his tour in Vietnam. "If during Tet of 1968 I was blown out of bed by Chicom rockets, fired on with automatic weapons, and didn't know from one minute to the next if I would be killed while working in triage, and the government says I served in combat, then the WOMEN WHO WORKED BESIDE ME WERE ALSO IN COMBAT."

Gender-related role confusion, however, extended beyond issues of survival. As one of very few women in a totally male-oriented environment, a woman in Vietnam was subjected to the most extreme forms of sex-role stereotyping. She tended to be alternately treated as princess or prostitute. Male members of the medical team referred to this as the "queen for a year syndrome." Any western female was placed on a pedestal and subject to exaggerated attentions by men starved for affection from women of their own culture. As a result of these unrealistic attentions by males (who expected the women to function as super professional nurses one minute and super sweet and pliable nurturers the next), a real conflict was established. Junior female officers with very little experience suddenly had their limited off-duty time occupied by male senior officers with significantly more life experience. These women had been trained and educated to respond to the senior officer in a subservient role. The attentions of "authorities" were often more than the inexperienced young women should or could be expected to deal with. Young, and often frightened, is it any wonder that these women would turn to someone who could provide them with comforts, information, and some degree of the security that had been left behind with their families? Even nurturers require a certain amount of nurturing, and for a few hours at a time this could be obtained through relationships with the more experienced men of senior rank.

Unfortunately, the vast majority of these men had families of their own back home, so when they rotated home, or were reassigned, these young women were left to find another senior officer; these relationships, born to provide comfort for both the men and the women during the war, could not endure beyond the war zone.

For those who got involved in these fleeting but vitally important relationships, the return home was sobering on two counts. First, the women were afraid to allow themselves another possibly transitory attachment with its attendant hurt. Second, women were no longer in short supply in the states, and facing the competition for men was a rude awakening for those who had been the center of unending masculine attention in Vietnam. The effects were often devastating, setting the stage for even more emotional numbing and distancing when they would later establish their own families. Even for the minority of women veterans who did not involve themselves in such relationships, the intense pressure to socialize with male officers during their off-duty hours was a continual source of stress and role confusion—engendered by the expectations that they would "switch hats" (from hard-nosed professional to softly feminine) without missing a beat. These problems followed many home.

The demographic and gender-related issues discussed above must be kept in mind by the therapist in attempting to establish an initial rapport with a female Vietnam veteran. If she sees that the therapist already knows or understands some of these background issues, a sense of trust can begin to develop without the client's having to educate the therapist. (It has been my experience that women Vietnam veterans trust me because I was one of them, thus eliminating the need for them to enlighten me.) It is also important for therapists to examine their attitudes towards female Vietnam veterans; this means examining attitudes related to gender and those about the Vietnam war in general.

SIGNS AND SYMPTOMS

The signs and symptoms of PTSD in the female Vietnam veteran are similar to those in the male veteran (particularly men who served in the medical evacuation chain). These symptoms include flashbacks, nightmares, startle response, emotional numbness, etc., and are well covered in other chapters. I will attempt to highlight some of the aspects of these symptoms from the perspective of women Vietnam veterans.

Substance Abuse

A great many Vietnam veterans turned to alcohol or drugs upon their return from Vietnam in an attempt to alleviate painful memories of the war, and to counter disappointment of their reception at home. Many women were among them. I would like to quote from one such woman's story at length, because it typifies many of the symptoms and experiences of women Vietnam veterans.

> I'm a Vietnam veteran. No, I wasn't a young combat soldier. I am part of the "forgotten minority"—women. No I wasn't a nurse. Within the forgotten minority, is another minority. There was a small contingency of WAC personnel performing various administrative functions who also served in Vietnam.
>
> I was one of two WACs assigned to USARV Communications Center, working on shifts with about 40 male soldiers. We worked a minimum of 6 days a week, on 12-hour shifts; 30 days on days and 30 days on nights. Mostly we processed casualty reports and some highly classified information about troop movements.
>
> I was twenty years old when I went to Vietnam. I volunteered because of a strong sense of patriotism and because I had been raised to believe that along with freedom and its benefits, go responsibilities. I wanted to fulfill my obligation to my country, and I wanted to do something really important, something that mattered. I knew every job in a war zone was critical, and I knew how respected war veterans were.
>
> The first thing I learned was there is *no behind the lines*, there was no front line as

there had been in WWI, WWII, and Korea. The next thing I learned was that emotions don't belong. The first casualty I saw nearly gagged me. Injuries on television and in the movies were always so clean and neat. But I was told that I shouldn't react, and that I'd "better learn to control" my emotions or I'd never make it.

During the next year I learned to drink, heavily, to "control the emotions." Friends and I would also sneak off the compound occasionally to the infantry "stand downs." Stand downs were get-togethers with "grunts" who had just come from combat in the field. All they wanted was to have a few drinks, talk to a woman, and sometimes dance. We would also go to parties with the helicopter pilots who flew the "dust-off" choppers which brought in the wounded. We knew that at the next gathering some of them would be missing. We'd go as often as we could even though we invariably drew sniper fire along the way.

For one year, three-hundred-and-sixty-five days, I stuck it out. Finally, my year in hell was over. Finished. Thank God, I had survived. But it wasn't really over—a whole different kind of war was just beginning....

Back home...back to "the world"...to rejoin the everyday routine but with a new pride and sense of accomplishment. I had done my job, and done it well in an incredible situation, under dire stress, and was now coming home to my family and friends.

But there were no congratulations or pats on the back. Instead, there were insults, anger, isolation, and crazy accusations. My high school chums were now in colleges and universities either actively or quietly protesting against the war I had just returned from. And, they protested me—by arguing with me, rejecting my reasoning, discounting my experience, and finding me deserving of all the horrors I had endured for having been "stupid enough" to volunteer. My family tried to be protective and felt that any conversation of the war was unnecessary, morbid, and should be forgotten since it was all behind me now. I should get on with life...with reality. Reality? I began to feel that Vietnam with its everyday life and death situations was far more real. I began to resent people's problems that they felt were so important. I felt they wanted nothing to do with me since they were ignoring such an important part of my life, and so I wanted little to do with them. Drinking continued to be a good way to cope.

[After a year and a half of this], I made a decision. I had survived hell, I could survive this. I had been good at my job so I found a job in communications and started a new survival game. I even joined the Army Reserves hoping to find some lost part within me. I did however, tell a friend that I was going to commit suicide, but not in a conventional way—I would die of cirrhosis of the liver before my 35th birthday.

For the next nine years things were fairly normal.

Oh, I changed jobs three times, drank a little too much sometimes, still jumped at sudden noises and got knots in my stomach when helicopters were overhead, had a sudden violent temper, generally mistrusted everybody, and had occasional nightmares, but for the most part, things were fine. I was impulsive too, and would think nothing of jumping into my car for long unplanned drives. I needed to get away a lot.

Then, in 1981, one of the guys on my company softball team mentioned he also played on a Vet Center team. I told him I was also a Vietnam veteran. We talked a bit, and I called and went to the Vet Center. The group leader felt I was showing signs of delayed stress. I left. I was fine. I wasn't in combat, and I wasn't a nurse, how could I be having problems? I got furious, how dare he think I has having problems, everything was fine....

> The nightmares increased; so did the drinking. Then one night it happened. I was startled out of bed by a repetitious nightmare and there, above me, in my bedroom, was a helicopter loaded with wounded....I didn't know exactly how, but I managed to reason that there was no plaster from the roof around me, so it couldn't really be there. I looked again and it was gone. I went back to the Vet Center.
>
> Now, twelve years after Vietnam, I'm in private therapy, an early sobriety rap group as a recovering alcoholic, and looking forward to starting in a Vietnam veterans rap group. I can't speak for anyone else, but *this* Vietnam veteran is scared, angry, very hurt, tired, confused, and trying desperately to come back home from Vietnam. (Anonymous, published with permission of the author)

For a woman who served as a nurse in Vietnam and who has continued in the profession upon her return, substance abuse can be a particularly difficult issue. She probably has easy access to medication at work, which can lead to a drug abuse problem. Yet she is likely not to seek treatment for fear of losing her job. The stresses of her job are likely to resemble those she experienced in Vietnam, exacerabating her PTSD symptoms. She may use alcohol at home to "self-medicate." Several of my clients talk about drinking several glasses of wine at night to stop the nightmares or recurring dreams. She is probably a workaholic trying to recreate the adrenaline rush she experienced years ago taking care of the wounded. If she is still in the nursing profession, she most likely continues in the most stressful types of nursing, such as emergency room or intensive care unit work.

Survivor Guilt

This is a common symptom in the male vets (see T. Williams, this volume). In the female vets, it is not so much the sense of having survived when others did not as it is feelings of guilt over not having done enough to save more of the casualties—wounded men whose conditions were far worse than anyone would have imagined. (Due to the advanced medical technology of the 1960s and employment of helicopters to transport the wounded, the types of casualties in Vietnam were beyond the expectations anyone could possibly imagine: multiple traumatic amputations, severe burns, multiple fragment wounds, etc.) Even though vets in combat units saw much death and suffering in Vietnam, they did not deal with the numbers and recurrences of casualties on a daily basis seen by the people in the medical evacuation chain. At times, a lack of supplies (medicine, blood, or IV fluids) resulted in the death of a young man who otherwise might have lived.

Many nurses returned from Vietnam with a sense of guilt about their anger and hatred toward the Vietnamese civilians who also were treated in U.S. hospitals. I remember my own confusion over the Vietcong POW who was in the same ward (opposite bed) with the young 18-year-old G.I. with a bilateral amputation of both legs. They were both human beings who were in need of medical care, despite the politics of the war. Many of these women feel a sense of guilt for mistreating the Vietnamese patients and, yet, still refer to them as "gooks" today. It was not uncommon for the nurses to mistreat the Vietnamese patients and do it with a sense of humor (bouncing patients onto the operating room table, shaving the goatee of the local village chief, etc.).

Isolation

Isolation is one of the most prevalent PTSD symptoms; the female Vietnam veteran feels alone. No one could understand the nightmares, guilt feelings, and anger she experiences. After all, she was a nurse and nurses don't suffer any psychological trauma themselves; they are responsible for taking care of others. If she is currently employed and seeks mental health assistance, her job may be at stake. Women who are single parents and dependent on their work for themselves and their families will be even more resistant to seeking treatment.

The female veteran also exhibits feelings of anger and rage related to her experiences in Vietnam, but these feelings are often displaced. "I couldn't get along with my family, I couldn't get along with my fellow workers, and I couldn't get along with my friends. I was angry and I don't know who or what I was angry with" (White, 1982). Male veterans with PTSD may vent their rage in impersonal ways such as barroom brawls. Even though society does not condone public displays of aggression, such behavior is somehow acceptable for men, but not for women. Thus, instances of rageful outbursts in women more often take the form of abusing their own children, partners, or themselves (e.g., suicidal gestures, self-destructive behavior).

Emotional Numbing

Medical training teaches clinical detachment. Due to this and the unique nature of their work, these women became experts at shutting off the feelings in Vietnam. Picture a scene of the chaos involved in working with numbers of severely wounded casualties needing immediate medical treatment, screaming and moaning, several of whom will die in front of you, or perhaps are already dead. A young nurse becomes responsible for deciding who will be treated first, and who will be left to die, because the doctors are all occupied in operating on or resuscitating those who are already receiving treatment. This woman has little time to feel shock, depression, anger, or anything at all. She becomes an automaton, shuts down her emotions and works off the adrenaline pounding through her veins. This numbing, which helped her survive Vietnam, continues for many years upon her return home. *She is probably an expert at it today and as a result will not seek treatment for her PTSD.* As one nurse expressed it: "...it wasn't that I didn't care, but the only way I could deal with it was to simply shut everything out and not feel anything. I brought that home with me when I left Vietnam."

TREATMENT ISSUES

Like their male counterparts, most women Vietnam veterans were in crisis when they first contacted a therapist. Perhaps she has recently read something about Vietnam or seen a film that has activated some painful memories. It has been my experience that the recently published book, *Home Before Morning* by Lynda Van Devanter, propelled many women veterans to seek assistance. Several of my clients reported that they couldn't get past the first chapter without crying.

Once the female Vietnam veteran identifies herself, it is important that the therapist work to gain her trust. These women have only recently begun to admit their veteran status. They probably are at the stage where the male Vietnam vets were in the late 1970s when the first outreach program in the country was started by the Disabled American Veterans.

The initial phase of her treatment is individual therapy. If the therapist is not a Vietnam veteran her/himself, it is important that the client be informed about this nonveteran status. I recommend the nonveteran clinician become informed about the women's role in Vietnam by reading what literature is available.

Trust is one of the most important factors in the treatment of any Vietnam veteran. Transference issues are an important aspect of the therapy, especially if the therapist is male and the client female. For the female veteran, *intimacy* and *trust* will be the most difficult areas. Similar to her male counterparts' experiences, those to whom she became close in Vietnam left her. They died, were evacuated from her hospitals, transferred to another command, or were simply rotated out of country.

Military regulations forbid nurses, as officers, from any fraternizing with the enlisted personnel with whom they worked so closely, yet they were expected to be available during their off-duty time to socialize with male officers. Any woman who was not part of the group that partied at the local Officers Club became the target of vicious hospital rumors. *Rejection* in Vietnam continues to be an issue for her many years later, and one of her primary concerns may be that once she finally starts to seek help for her PTSD, her therapist will also reject her.

Due to the intense bonding in Vietnam, many of these women may have or still might be involved with other women. How do you as a therapist feel about gay or lesbian clients? Are you able to work through your own judgements or attitudes? If there is the least bit of homophobia or discomfort present, I recommend that you refer the client elsewhere, because she will perceive your attitude and trust will never develop between you.

Individual therapy should continue for at least 6-8 sessions. If the female veteran is involved in a relationship (whether heterosexual or homosexual), couples counseling may also be in order. After individual therapy is completed, the treatment of choice for the female veteran is group therapy. The ideal group consists of other women who served in Vietnam, but few such groups exist. If a women veterans group is unavailable, she should be placed in a group of medical personnel, medics, lab technicians, air evac flight crew members, dust-off pilots, etc. If this type of group is not available, then the combat vets group is the next choice. It is also important that both the individual and group agree to her being part of the group.

It is imperative that the therapist guard against the female veteran's falling into certain "traps" related to her Vietnam experiences. The therapist must avoid group or individual situations where men place the woman again in a caretaker situation by bombarding her with their war stories and trauma and expecting her to *once again* take care of them. It is not uncommon that the female vet in an all-male group will also attempt to place herself in the helper role, thus avoiding her own issues. If a woman veteran can come to grips with this issue, she, like a woman in one of my groups, is likely to say: "I'm tired of being the caregiver. I want to be cared for sometimes. I want to be held and comforted. I need it."

Never place a female Vietnam veteran in a group of significant others, partners, or wives of veterans. After all the energy it has taken for her to finally identify herself as a Vietnam veteran, it would deny her the opportunity to share her experiences with other veterans, the very people who can provide the vital context for healing her wounds from Vietnam.

Encourage the veteran to outreach to other women veterans. My personal philosophy is that those veterans who have healed through therapy have an obligation to help others recover. I encourage my clients (both female and male) to speak to local high schools, nursing schools, and other groups about their experiences in Vietnam, especially around holidays like Veterans Day and Memorial Day. The news media are always looking for veterans to tell their stories. Encourage her involvement with local veterans organizations. Even though several of the national veterans organizations still prohibit women from joining, organizations like the DAV and the Vietnam Veterans of America encourage female membership.

As discussed previously, substance abuse is a common problem among Vietnam veterans. Always ask the veteran about her patterns of substance use at some point during your initial sessions. If she is currently abusing alcohol or drugs, it is important that she seek treatment specifically for that problem. It is possible to work with a client who is in concurrent treatment as long as the program or individual therapist who is assisting in the substance abuse treatment is aware of her treatment for PTSD. Premilitary history can also be very helpful in guiding treatment. A history of alcoholic parents, physical abuse as a child, or a broken family usually indicates that issues other than Vietnam also need to be addressed (see Newman, this volume).

It is possible that a client will need to be hospitalized for her PTSD. There have been a number of specific PTSD inpatient units established in VA Medical Centers around the country and all of them treat women veterans. If she is hospitalized for PTSD, it is important that she follow through immediately upon discharge with supportive treatment with a therapist who understands her issues.

Individual therapy is necessary to assist her in talking about the painful experiences she has numbed for so long. Talk about the types of casualties she can still describe in detail. She will be watching your reactions and nonverbal responses. Talk about the good as well as the bad; the fun times as well as the mass casualties. Talk about how she feels towards the Vietnamese civilians and the enemy. Talk about the support or lack of support she had from home (families and friends, etc.): was she ostracized because she joined the military? What was her homecoming like?

Perhaps she can validate her experience by visiting the Vietnam Memorial in Washington, D.C., or the DAV memorial at Angel Fire, New Mexico, or any of the several Vietnam memorials throughout the country. Another restorative process is doing public presentations about her experiences in Vietnam, thereby taking an active positive approach to healing. It is through the efforts of the caring therapist that the female Vietnam veteran will feel good about herself and her role in Vietnam.

REFERENCES

Sandecki, R. (1982). Lecture presented to Region Six Vet Center Training Program, San Diego, California.

White, P. (1982). Personal communication.

White, P. (1983, May 15). *California Living Magazine.*

Van Devanter, L. with C. Morgan. (1983). *Home before morning.* New York: Beaufort Books, Inc.

CHAPTER TWELVE

THE VETERAN SYSTEM WITH A FOCUS ON WOMEN PARTNERS

Candis M. Williams

INTRODUCTION

Research and treatment efforts are now underway to complete the emerging picture of troubled, alienated, often marginally employed Vietnam veterans. But scant attention has been given to the repercussions of their problems on their wives and families—the group Figley (1978) has described as "secondary victims." If one accepts the premise that an impact on one part of a system (the system, in this case, being the veterans' families) will affect the entire system, then remedial efforts may fruitfully be directed to the entire system—the veteran's spouse (or significant others and other household members.) The Veterans Administration, through the Vet Centers, has made some attempts to address the treatment needs of the veterans' families, but much work remains to be done.

Although my use of a systems perspective would imply looking at the interaction patterns of all members of a family, including children, I am limiting the discussion to women partners in the interest of brevity. Even when the family unit does include children, the dynamics between the man and woman are likely to be the most crucial. (Nonetheless, I hope that many of the observations here may be applied more broadly to work with family, friends, job associates, and society at large.)

In this chapter, I will describe my experiences in working with women partners of troubled Vietnam veterans in the context of systems theory and veteran systems. The term "partners" includes unmarried women who are living with veterans as well as veterans' wives. Whether they are married to or living with Vietnam veterans, the problems do not seem to be significantly different.

Part One of this chapter, "The Veteran System," provides a rationale based on open systems theory for considering the troubled veteran within a social context, addressing the veteran's interactions with others, the effects on the others and their influence on his behavior. These may include a veteran's woman partner, children, parents, siblings, co-workers, friends and others who have some influence on him. It may also include the groups, organizations, community, and larger society to which the veteran belongs. The individual veteran or woman partner is considered a subsystem within the family system. I am loosely defining the family system as all those living within the same household, regardless of whether there are children. The primary systems represented here include the veteran or woman partner (subsystem), the family (system), and the society (suprasystem). A case is made for more closely examining the woman partner as a central, rather than peripheral figure of the veteran system.

In Part Two, "Support Groups: Description and Discussion," I discuss work with women partners that we have done in Denver. Most of this section describes our first two women's support groups, as well as the history and dynamics of some of the women who participated. Some assumptions regarding problems and treatment strategies, as well as data collected from the second support group, are also discussed.

Part Three, "Problems of Women," looks at the more general effects of sex-role socialization on women, as well as the implications for problems that women partners are experiencing—their commonalities and differences. Here the reader may question why I discuss specific treatment considerations before a more global exploration of women's problems. This ordering allows the reader to move from the problems of women and women partners, per se, into family dynamics and how the woman's position or experience affects the veteran system.

In Part Four, "General Considerations," I discuss the role of education in changing veteran systems. Our work in Denver is briefly summarized, and some recommendations for future outreach efforts are offered.

Much more attention needs to be given to looking at the veteran having adjustment problems as a member of several systems, the most intimate of which, and consequently the one most appropriate for primary consideration, is the couple. It is in this unit that intervention can have the greatest direct impact.

PART ONE: THE VETERAN SYSTEM

Psychology's historic bias has been to focus on the individual who has problems or is affected by an event. Such a selective focus essentially ignores the effects felt by those who are close to the "identified patient." It impairs the success of treatment because it does not involve significant others in the change process. A systems approach to conceptualizing problems and treatment helps to eliminate this bias.

In treating combat-related problems, the focus is on the veteran, usually a man, and the most likely therapist is also a man. War is male-dominated. In such a context, the role of the woman partner is generally not recognized. She is put in a peculiar position—she is not considered to have special problems herself nor to have problems related to her partner's poor adjustment. The fact that the woman is a product of a culture that views women as the supportive care givers compounds this lack of acknowledgment. Hence the woman is, or at least can be, in a unique bind with regard to her relationship with the veteran and her own mental health. Some attention to sex-role stereotypes is necessary for an overall understanding of the dynamics in the relationships under discussion.

An Open Systems Perspective

As has been described in many other chapters in this book, the Vietnam veteran's experience was very different from that of veterans of other wars, and the American experience with the Vietnam War was also unique. Public support for the war was in short supply, and servicemen and women were publicly maligned. This coupling of negative attitudes toward both the war effort and the veteran continued for many years after our disengagement. Attempts to forget the turmoil and humiliation of the war meant that we also ignored the veteran and his plight—or we cast him as the scapegoat. We labeled him as an untouchable and made him an outcast by not acknowledging his sacrifices, failing to help him find employment, and refusing to assist his reintegration into society.

This societal rejection, while pervasive, was not total: families and various segments of society were sympathetic and helpful in the Vietnam veterans' readjustment. But we have been largely apathetic toward the situation, wanting to put the war away and forget the whole episode.

Thus, to understand the problems of veterans, we must look at the social and emotional context that contributes to those problems. It is fruitless to search for pure causal variables. The dynamics of these multiple interactions must be explored. Such a perspective is central to open systems theory, which emphasizes the interdependence of individuals, families, groups, organizations, and social systems. An action or event in one segment affects and is affected by countless other segments to some degree.

Certain principles operate in this process regardless of whether we focus on an individual, a family, or an organization. One such involves the phenomenon of a steady state or equilibrium referred to as homeostasis (Jackson, 1957). Essentially, the concept of homeostasis assumes that elements are mutually interdependent with some form of regulating device that preserves the steady state, rather like a thermostat. Therefore, the focal segment can tolerate only so much stress before it activates the control device that returns the system to a steady state. How well the system is able to readjust and how adaptive the regulating mechanism is are crucial in determining the health and longevity of the particular segment. A basic tenet of the concept of homeostasis is that the human being, the organization, and the environment do not remain static, but are constantly changing and constantly attempting to adapt to such changes.

Open systems theory applied to the analysis of the Vietnam veteran's situation invovles an examination of responses of his family, friends, community and country. How have these components of the veteran's system adapted or adjusted to the veteran to facilitate his return to a healthy balance?

Not very well, according to recent research data. There is a continuing rise in the number of veterans requesting psychological assistance and exhibiting maladaptive or dysfunctional patterns in various spheres. It is likely that 40 to 60 percent of the combat veterans of the Vietnam War have significant mental health problems (Wilson, 1980; President's Commission on Mental Health, 1976). Wilson (1978) called this an "epidemic," and predicted, in 1978, that it would peak in 1985. It is too soon to tell whether his prediction was accurate.

From a systems perspective then, we must conclude that it is not only the veteran who is suffering and adapting poorly; his family and his country are also feeling the impacts of his maladaptation. A delayed reaction and significant maladaptive responses to the Vietnam war have characterized all levels of society. We have yet to achieve a balance with respect to the war, the veteran, or his family.

That is not to say that we can't or won't return to a healthier state—the momentum is growing constantly toward resolving issues related to the war. A November, 1979, Louis Harris poll showed that 97 percent of the public thought that Vietnam veterans deserved respect (Harris, 1980). In 1971, 48 percent of those polled felt that Vietnam veterans were treated worse than veterans of other wars, whereas, in the 1979 study, this number had increased to 69 percent (Harris, 1980). While we once ignored or distorted the impact of the Vietnam War on our society, we now seem to be recognizing some of its repercussions and are attempting to resolve them. We perceive the problems more clearly now in the sense that we have identified the Vietnam situation as a problem. This, therapeutically, is a major advance.

The Harris poll suggests that we are moving toward a healthier stance by making a distinction between our feelings about the war, which remain negative, and our feelings about the veteran, which are becoming increasingly positive. This mood swing is further illustrated by the plethora of movies, books, and articles about the war and its veteran that began appearing in 1977. Unfortunately, while depicting the trauma of the war, many of these books, movies and articles continue a long-standing trend, portraying the veteran according to a brutal stereotype and reinforcing the social stigma that has followed the veteran too long.

The resurgence of interest and concern for the Vietnam veteran's plight has strained whatever balance he had been able to achieve in his life—which often involved a great deal of isolation. He cannot remain the same. Frequently reminded of the trauma, he is forced again to change, to adapt anew. Today, hundreds of thousands of veterans experience delayed stress symptoms as a consequence of the whole episode.

The symptoms most often connected with delayed stress reaction among Vietnam veterans involve a sense of alienation, bitterness, and emotional isolation. The veteran is wary and distrustful of the public's new-found concern for him. Because of the prolonged nature of his banishment, he has adopted maladaptive patterns of behavior that are difficult to change. And these behaviors, in turn, are deleterious to his family, his community, and our society. Many men and women veterans may never be able to cope very satisfactorily; they may never return to the mainstream, regardless of our more tolerant and accepting attitudes.

To remediate many of the problems, change in the larger system is necessary. Treatment of the veteran alone will not address the larger social problems. It is widely acknowledged by systems theorists that if one attempts change with only a small segment of a larger system, the system will act to balance itself by forcing that segment back into old, predictable patterns.

Systems theory does not prescribe that we intervene at a particular level, but it does suggest points of intervention where the greatest impact can be achieved and where the initiated changes can most likely be maintained. For most veterans, this impact is greatest at the family level—either with children or the couple unit alone.

Family therapy research has vividly demonstrated that treatment of identified patients is most effective when they are seen in the context of their immediate social environment because the members of that environment are usually also operating in a maladaptive fashion. If the veteran is unmarried and has no children, we may look to his family of origin—his parents and siblings—as the most visible system with which to work. Where he has neither, or is close to neither, it may be feasible to consider his friends or working environment as his social context. It is important that all these other systems be considered in working with the veteran.

However, the focus here is limited to the family (marital dyad) and specifically to the woman partner. If the family unit is the area of greatest impact, the woman partner is the one person, other than the veteran himself, who has been most affected. She has felt the brunt of the veteran's isolation.

What effects have the veteran's traumas had on his partner and on the relationship between them? What is the nature of her response and her feelings about her own behavior? More specifically, what are the implications for effective treatment and adaptive change? Before going into general issues regarding women in our society and the collective problems of women partners, I will describe our work in Denver with women partners of Vietnam veterans.

PART TWO: SUPPORT GROUPS: DESCRIPTION AND DISCUSSION

As requests for psychological assistance from women partners of Vietnam veterans increased, I felt pressured to take some action. I began by asking myself what was actually needed. Obviously, going directly to the women for help was a beginning. The Professional Psychology Center, University of Denver, in cooperation with the Denver Disabled American Veterans (DAV) Outreach Office, sponsored a Forum for Women Partners of Vietnam Veterans.

Forum for Women Partners of Vietnam Veterans

Women partners were invited to meet and talk about their experiences in relationships with Vietnam veterans: what problems they were having, how they coped with them, and whether or not we could find ways to alleviate the problems. It was, in effect, a method of assessing the needs of this population.

The two-hour meeting began with a brief overview of post-traumatic stress disorder (PTSD) and a presentation on some common dilemmas for women. The women then divided into small discussion groups, each facilitated by one of the co-leaders. After introductions, each group discussed three questions:

- What problems do you or other women face as partners of Vietnam veterans?
- What needs do you have?
- How might these needs be met?

The primary theme of the feedback was that the women felt good in knowing they were not alone, that others shared their problems and wanted to continue this kind of support. Yet some women were at opposite extremes: some felt their veteran partners had many problems, while others felt their partners had no problems at all. Additionally, they differed in their attitudes toward confronting the problems. Some expressed great anger toward their partners and were resentful that their own needs were not being met; others were concerned primarily with how they could be more understanding and helpful to the men. The latter were less inclined to discuss or focus on themselves, and were shocked by women who were angry at their partners.

Most women felt they had been nurturing, caring, and supportive, but that this had not been very successful in terms of the relationship, nor in terms of their own self-esteem and identity. Like the men, many felt helpless and demoralized.

Women came to the forum with very different needs and expectations. There were differences in age, marital status, and problems experienced. Other differences were related to the degree of focus on self, on the relationship, or on the man. Whether or not there were children was also an important differentiating factor.

There was no prescreening, but we later realized that it would have been helpful to have had some criteria for dividing women into more homogeneous discussion groups so that the less angry women would not have been alienated. Women whose partners were not in treatment were included, and we discovered that this was not a good idea because it led to even greater disparities within the groups. These women represented the majority of those who felt their partners had no problems.

More time would have been helpful. More educational material on PTSD could have been included, and more time for sharing allowed. A half- or full-day workshop would have given time for both an extended educational presentation and the small group sharing that the women found beneficial.

Most of the men were supportive of this meeting; in fact, an anonymous veteran left a large bouquet at the clinic just before we started the meeting. The following message was attached:

Dear Ladies,

There is a sadness in our hearts.

We've tried drugs and alcohol and kept it inside 'till we thought we would break in two.

The sadness is still there.

We want our fathers, mothers, brothers, sisters, wives, girlfriends to understand the sadness in our hearts—like seeing boys playing with toy M-16s and arguing over who killed who, when we are walking down the street and the people behind us are making fun of the way we walk, because we use a brace or crutches or maybe a cane.

Or maybe we go to a party and we see someone we remember from the war. Only we know it's not him because he did not come back from the war. And we remember how he died.

When we came back from the war, the only good Vietnam veteran was a dead one. Try to understand the sadness in our hearts, and help us to live with it.

At the close of the forum, each woman took one of the flowers home to give to her partner. A few of the more angry women were less inclined to make this gesture, but we felt a general agreement that this symbolic actrepresented the unity with which the couples might face a common problem—a problem not belonging exclusively to either of them that could best be confronted by both with a better understanding of one another.

Along with a letter thanking the DAV and the men in the group (one of whom was our anonymous donor), we attached the following poem, which conveys some of the dilemmas for both women and men in defining themselves and relating to one another:

For Every Woman

For every woman who is tired of acting weak when she knows she is strong,

There is a man who is tired of appearing strong when he feels vulnerable.

For every woman who is tired of acting dumb,

There is a man who is burdened with the constant expectations of "knowing everything."

For every woman who is tired of being called an "emotional female,"

There is a man who is denied the right to weep and be gentle.

For every woman who is tired of being a sex object,

There is a man who must worry about his potency.

For every woman who feels "tied down" by her children,

There is a man who is denied the full pleasures of shared parenthood.

For every woman who is denied meaningful employment with equal pay,

There is a man who must bear full financial responsibility for another human being.

For every woman who was not taught the intricacies of an automobile,

There is a man who was not taught the satisfactions of cooking.

For every woman who takes a step toward her own liberation,

There is a man who finds the way to freedom has been made a little easier.

(Author unknown)

Support Groups

The First Support Group

Since most women attending the forum thought it would be helpful to them to continue to meet, a support group was formed. Fewer women than had expressed interest in the group at the forum became involved in this support group. We have no particular explanation for this; however, it is fairly common in the process of group formation for some people to change their minds or attend only one or two sessions before dropping out.

It was a very heterogeneous group of women. Some women were there simply because their partners wanted them to be, and some came because they themselves wanted to be there. Most were married; some had children. Two women joined who had not attended the forum. At the outset, we decided the group would be time-limited, that we would meet weekly for one-and-one-half hours for seven weeks, and that there would be an option to recontract for additional sessions at the end of that time.

We began with introductions, an overview of PTSD, and a discussion of common problems and needs; we agreed that the focus should be on problems generated by living with veteran partners—how to cope with the situation and how to improve it. I would like to describe some of the women so the reader may get some feeling for women's concerns.

Sheila. Sheila, the most active participant at the first meeting, was very self-disclosing and described the pain she was feeling. Her husband was visiting his parents, and she was determined that he would not return to their home. He was, she said, an inveterate alcoholic who was often verbally, sometimes physically abusive. He was like a little boy she had thrown out time and time again only to allow his return after he'd done a great deal of pleading: each time he promised to be different and take more responsibility, and each time the relationship deteriorated rapidly. Sheila seemed to be at the end of her rope. She felt that his only salvation would be to learn how to manage on his own.

The group was somewhat taken aback by Sheila's seeming hardness, but there was also an undercurrent of sympathy, understanding, and admiration for her strength. Several women offered to be available following the planned confrontation.

Sheila did not attend this group again. When I contacted her after a few weeks, she said she had reconsidered her decision and she now wanted to put her energies into joint marital counseling. In retrospect, Sheila's decision to withdraw from the group was not so unusual. People who spill their guts to strangers at the outset are often embarrassed about it later. Sheila had not only done that, she had put herself on the line concerning her future behavior and had been unable to follow through with her plans.

Maria and Jennifer. Two other women did not return after the first session as well. Maria, a Chicana, seemed on the verge of bursting into tears during most of the session. She could not talk about her situation. Everyone was clearly concerned. I learned later from my husband, who was working with her husband, that they were in the process of separating. Living together had become unbearable even though they still loved one another. When I contacted Maria later, she said she thought the group was a "good thing," but still she did not return. Maria was in a crisis, and I believe she needed more individual attention.

Jennifer announced that she would not return at the first meeting. She mentioned that she had come simply because her partner wanted her to do so. But she said it was "his problem," and she did not see much point in becoming involved.

Dee. At the first group meeting, Dee talked without revealing much about her feelings. She alluded to being battered without saying so directly. Her problems with her partner included his drinking and rages.

During that week, Dee's husband had not come home or called all night. Her response on this and similar occasions was to mention it to him and simply let it go; he became abusive if she did more. The relationship had stabilized in this pattern, but the health of this couple was certainly questionable.

Throughout the first group, Dee seemed to think that this was the way it was and would always be. She expected no better. If anything, the sympathy she received for her partner's erratic behavior reinforced her tolerance of it. She enjoyed the attention she received when talking about her partner, but she could only talk about herself or her feelings in a joking, derogatory sense. In viewing Dee's history—her lack of intimate relationships and the turbulence that characterized her life—it is understandable that she could not conceive of deserving or being treated better. Her attendance was sporadic; she remained closed off from caring for others or being cared for by them.

Dee attended only one more session after missing one due to injuries incurred when falling down stairs after drinking. She avoided our calls and indirectly sent a message that she would not become involved in the second group. We were unable to break through Dee's defensive barriers. In retrospect, I think individual therapy would have been more appropriate for her.

Jean. Jean seemed a little more independent than the others. She felt that her partner was irresponsible and that he manipulated her with his delayed stress.

Although an active participant, Jean remained fairly aloof from the group. Although she rarely shared feelings, she once did talk about problems with her parents, saying she felt a lack of acceptance by them. However, she was extremely uncomfortable, and insisted that attention be diverted from her. She refused to talk about such personal concerns in later sessions, saying there was no point in thinking or talking about it. She did not continue in the second group, ostensibly because she and her partner would be quitting their jobs and going to Mexico. Jean had previously been in individual therapy for several years and had no inclination to return to therapy.

Karen. At the first group session, Karen noted that her husband also had a problem with alcohol and that she wanted to learn how to cope with the relationship better. At our third meeting with Karen, we were shocked to hear that her husband's mistress had also attended the forum and was even in the same discussion group as Karen. Without our knowledge, her husband had invited both women to attend the forum. Karen also revealed that she had decided to give her husband an ultimatum to stop seeing the other woman or move out. This was a surprise because Karen had seemed very timid, rather traditional, and very dependent. Much of this session was spent on this issue, and the other women supported Karen's assertiveness.

At the next session, attention immediately focused on Karen and what had happened to her during the past week. She had confronted her husband, and he had stayed home all week; however, he had not given her a verbal commitment that his affair would end. She was feeling good about the decision, its result, and herself. But she also felt somewhat overwhelmed by the possible consequences and the increased responsibilities she might have to assume. It was striking to observe that Karen did not show much emotion or feeling, and her verbal behavior was not appropriate to the seriousness of her situation.

Karen seemed to change more than anyone else in the first group. She went from feeling generally helpless and worthless to initiating some assertive actions. As her assertiveness became effective in the relationship, she gained some self-esteem. And, as she became stronger, she also grew angrier and less tolerant of her spouse. She confronted him much more, and the question of whether they would remain together became crucial for several months—this time at her instigation, not his. Karen was very committed to continuing the first group.

During the second group, Karen continued up and down in her relationship, but she was increasingly assertive, less helpless, and more positive about herself. She actually became something of a leader and certainly a supporter of other women who were more helpless. She was very excited about how she had changed; and, after many years of feeling beaten down, she was enthusiastic about what life held in store for her.

Incidentally, her husband terminated the affair he was having, accepted much more responsibility in the home, and is attracted to Karen's new fiestiness and energy. He has admitted to her that he likes her better now than when she was "his doormat," but he is also a little shaken since he can no longer take her for granted.

Joan. Joan was quite outspoken about her husband, whom she viewed as an irresponsible child to be tolerated simply because he was the father of her children. She had no expectations that he or the relationship would improve. She had become resigned to remaining in the marriage forever, despite the fact that it could hardly be called a marriage.

Joan talked more than anyone at the second session, again sounding very hardened and embittered. She was adamant that her husband would have to do the giving now. She said she would listen to him, but would otherwise make no effort to change. The more disconcerted the other women became about her attitude, the more rigidly she defended her position, openly labeling herself as a very hard woman. Joan clearly isolated herself from the others by portraying herself so negatively. We were concerned that she would not return to the group.

But Joan, like Karen, seemed to make many changes, perhaps more in attitude and opening herself up to others than in her actions. Immediately following the second session, there was a surprising transformation. She had made some positive overtures to her husband during the week, and he had responded in kind. Her whole manner and response to others was softer, and she received considerable positive feedback. While neither Joan nor the relationship was essentially different, it was a turning point for her. She showed a new hopefulness and a willingness to perceive her situation, and herself, more positively. Joan was also very committed to remaining with the second group when it formed.

Sheryl. Sheryl joined the first group at the fourth session. She was rather withdrawn for several sessions (understandable, since she entered midway), but she also appeared somewhat depressed and saw life and daily events simply as chores to be gotten through. Life was bland, joyless. Sheryl had been undergoing significant situational stress for almost a year, and she anticipated that the same problems would continue for another six months to a year. As Sheryl talked more and received support from the other women, she seemed to bloom. She became quite admired by the others for her insightfulness, responsiveness to them, and ability to handle difficult situations. Sheryl was just becoming comfortable with the first group as it ended; she continued with the next group.

Sheryl became a great asset to the group and seemed to gain a growing assurance of herself and the relationship with her partner. During one period in which she had become somewhat withdrawn, she was finally able to share some of her ambivalent feelings about her pregnancy. Subsequently, she shared these feelings with her husband.

Sheryl was the most responsive member of the group to the needs of the other women. If anything, she still had some difficulty bringing up issues she had not resolved. For example, she had had a child, her first, by her husband before they were married. She gave this child up for adoption. Since her marriage, she had one miscarriage. She did not share this information with the other women. Sheryl and Bruce have been married, divorced, and remarried to each other. The divorce occurred after they had been married for one year when Bruce suddenly and without explanation left the state and was away for a year. She perceived this as a turning point for them. Their relationship was much better when they finally got back together.

Lisa. Lisa, a new member to the second group, showed extreme learned helplessness. A housewife married to a veteran, she had two children from her previous marriage. She never voluntarily participated in group discussions. She did respond when questions were directed to her, but otherwise seemed very deficient in coping with and controlling her life.

Lisa had no friends and practically confined herself to the home for two years after working in a responsible position. She seemed to have only superficial contact with her environment and herself. She tolerated a dismal relationship with her partner, was utterly unable to cite any personal attributes other than cooking and cleaning, and could only describe herself as a "blah" person.

Certainly, we were concerned about how Lisa would survive in the group and were surprised when she remained. She had been in individual therapy for three years, finally giving that up when the therapist told her she could go no further until her partner also accepted treatment. Lisa seemed to have much anger and a strong will underlying the superficial facade she presented. It was encouraging to see her open up and move toward controlling her life in the third group. It seemed she just needed some unpressured time with the other women to feel secure enough to let down some of her emotional barriers.

The Second Support Group

The second support group began five weeks after the first ended. Four women continued from the first group, and two new members were added. This group differed from the first: we attempted more structure and direction. It was closed after the first meeting, and it was limited to eight weeks. Sessions were extended from one-and-one-half to two hours.

Members of the first group had requested that we focus on specific topics or issues during the second group; however, the only issues suggested were sexuality and the difficulties inherent in hearing war stories from the men. Again, we began with a discussion of PTSD symptoms, giving each woman an educational brochure in an attempt to allow new members to catch up with continuing members. We then moved rather quickly from the effects of PTSD on relationships to how the women felt about themselves. The latter topic involved discussion of how women take care of themselves and how they tend to devalue or ignore their own attributes and needs. One discussion did in fact center upon sexuality and war incidents as some of the women shared their stories and feelings about how sexual atrocities may have altered their partners' perception of sexual relations.

Obviously, these were short-term groups with very different women involved. In some cases, it was minimally helpful; in others, it was undoubtedly beneficial. Considering the significant problems that all of these women evidenced, psychotherapy, rather than simply a supportive atmosphere, seems a more appropriate treatment strategy. Yet I do not think any of these women would have accepted therapy. They joined the group ostensibly because of the men's problems and for the express purpose of sharing and support, not because of any admitted significant personal inadequacies. Those who left the group were probably less adequate and more needy of individual help than those who remained. Despite the fact that we have continued to call these groups "support groups for women," much more is obviously involved.

The general trend in the groups was to begin with an educational presentation of information relating to PTSD, after which women talked about the problems of their partners. This led into effects on the relationship, on the couple system, and, finally, on the women themselves. A major portion of group time was spent on problem solving. Toward the end, women were just beginning to acknowledge themselves and their own problems and needs. Some of the women only became able to contemplate and accept the idea of really changing some aspects of their lives when they realized that their own behavior contributed to dysfunctional relationships. In essence, the major objective of the women's groups rests here. To expect or push any radical change in a relationship when the partners are not involved together in the process of change is generally unrealistic, producing results that are, at best, unpredictable.

I had frequent informal communications with the leaders of the men's groups to assess and evaluate the dynamics of the groups and the couples. Most of the women came to the first support group because of pressure from their partners. However, this trend reversed. As the women derived personal benefit, becoming enthusiastic and personally committed to the group, the men became suspicious and hostile about what might be occurring. Some really seemed to expect an explosion or a women's revolution. They began to discourage their partners from continued involvement. For a period of several weeks, both the men and women expressed hostility about what they thought might be happening in the other group. There was, of course, no revolution, and the hostility subsided for the most part. In a dramatic outcome, this build-up and subsequent relief seemed to unblock some of the emotional barriers that separated the couples. Each partner began to perceive the other in a new light and with a new acknowledgment of his or her individuality.

Evaluation of the Groups

Below are some responses to parts of the written evaluations completed at the end of the second group:

Women Partners

1. Was the group experience beneficial to you? Why?

"Yes" was the unanimous answer. "It made me more aware of myself—better able to help with the delayed stress problems when I felt better about myself." "First to have information about delayed stress—then to have support and input from the other women." "Gave me the support I needed." "Verbalization helps make decisions and ideas more concrete—feedback on other ways of handling situations."

2. What was the worst feature of this group?

"The smoky room—the tape recorder." "Covering same ground for new members." "The silences, when no one was willing to talk." "No set forum—taping the group."

3. What was the best feature of this group?

"Trust and concern by other members." "The understanding and support gave me a boost that I really needed." "The leaders and the participants accepted each person at face value." "The small number of women, feeling of trust." "Rapport developed between the women."

4. Have you made any changes as a result of this experience?

"Yes, I had to learn to take a stand for myself." "I'm looking at my partner's attitudes and problems more objectively." "Yes, I'm less angry because of things I can't control."

In responding to other questions, women expressed a wish for a little more structure in the group, more intervention by the group leader, and that there be no taping or filming. However, they all enthusiastically asserted that they would recommend the group to others, and were about evenly divided on the question of mixing old and new members. We saw some problems in mixing old and new members. If more women had been involved, we probably would have begun an advanced group. Eight or ten weeks is a relatively short time span for a group whose members are so diverse and have such significant problems. The advantage in mixing old and new members is that old members can be more helpful to newer members, which speeds up the process of increasing awareness and tackling problems.

The groups helped the women identify their own needs and problems and define how their needs were or were not being met within their relationships. The focus of many of the women at the forum and even in the initial support group sessions had been on the men and their problems, rather than on themselves; as the support groups progressed, that focus shifted steadily.

A portion of each session was spent on active problem-solving. Women helped each other by sharing similar experiences and pointing out what type of action might be taken. Concrete plans of action were often made, and the women gained greater confidence and self-esteem. They were then able to bring this increased strength back into their relationships with their partners.

The first support group suffered from a lack of commitment from a number of the women, the late entry of others, and erratic attendance, all of which lead to some difficulties in the development of trust and sharing within the group. There was mutual understanding and agreement at the outset of the second group that all would attend regularly for eight weeks, and everyone made an effort to comply. Consequently, group solidarity and cohesiveness improved greatly.

The second group had a problem that resulted when the co-therapist and I attempted to guide members rather rapidly through identified phases. The first session focused mainly on discussion of and information about the delayed stress suffered by the veterans. The women moved quickly into discussing their relationships and themselves during the second meeting. Hence, we reinforced a focus on the women's personal problems and some general women's issues, including undervaluation of themselves and nonrecognition of their own needs. The new women were uncomfortable with such rapid movement toward centering on themselves; they insisted that we should discuss delayed stress and the problems of the men rather than themselves, whereas the older members were very ready to move into this phase.

This is one obvious disadvantage of mixing old and new members, and was clearly expressed in the evaluations. As discussed earlier, it would be ideal to offer beginning and advanced groups when enough women were interested. A larger number of women would also allow us to make the groups more homogeneous. Some women are in fairly stable relationships and have adequate social support systems, while others have neither and could benefit more from therapeutic support groups. The former would probably be satisfied with a more time-limited educational format in which the emphasis remained on the veteran and the relationship. A longer session, or perhaps two sessions similar to the forum, might accomplish this also. The forum is very workable and could be offered regularly given the need. It functions well to discriminate between those who simply want information and those who could benefit from a longer term involvement with other women in a similar situation. (A forum that would include men and members of the community is presented in Part Four, "General Considerations.")

I can only suggest guidelines for working with women partners of troubled Vietnam veterans. What will work best depends upon the particular environment, the kinds of clients, and the resources available.

Suggestions for future support groups of this type would include more prescreening to assess each woman's interest and focus, whether on herself or her partner. This prescreening should be done both at the initial forum and by personal interview. Such thorough prescreening would assist group leaders in forming more homogeneous groups, striking some balance between traditional and nontraditional women, and referring women who need other types of service to appropriate sources. When a woman is clearly dysfunctinal in many areas, has very precarious stability with her partner, or is no longer in a relationship with a troubled veteran, the type of groups we are conducting are probably inappropriate, and other modes of treatment should be considered.

The commitment to the group should be clearly spelled out during both the initial contact and the first session to improve attendance. Six to eight women seems to be the optimal number of members for each group if attendance is consistent. The time-limited nature of the group appears helpful initially in getting the women to agree to join. Initial focus on the men's stress-related problems and on the women's relationships with the men seems less threatening to the women than immediately focusing on their own needs.

The support groups serve three purposes. The first is a traditional objective of women's groups: raising self-esteem by acknowledging women's unique dilemma in our society while offering women the support of other women in defining and valuing themselves as individuals. The second follows on the first: with increased self-esteem and social support, the women learn to recognize how their own behavior may contribute to and help perpetuate dysfunction in their relationships. Third, with a positive self-concept and a realization of their own power to affect others, the women become ready to solve problems and to effect adaptive and lasting changes in the systems with which they interact. As women move into this third phase, and if their partners are similarly prepared, it may be appropriate to offer treatment to the couple or family system.

I firmly believe this process is facilitated only within an all-women's group, with only women serving as leaders. "Women as models," says Brodsky (1976), "are more convincing than male authoritarian leaders for whom the assertive role is a cultural expectation." This is a rather basic standard of feminist theory, based on the concept that bonding of women with other women is crucial to a woman's positive identification of herself. In other words, a woman who has difficulty in respecting other women will also have difficulty in valuing her own identity as a woman. As she acknowledges other women, she becomes able to acknowledge herself independently from men.

PART THREE: PROBLEMS OF WOMEN PARTNERS

I had many reservations as a woman about becoming involved in treatment efforts directed toward women who were identified through their close relationships with Vietnam veterans. A dilemma grows out of the fact that there is no common denominator among these women other than the war experiences of the men with whom they have relationships. Given that, how could the proposed women's support groups function without placing the women in an adjunctive position relative to the men? Would this develop into another women's auxiliary created out of and charged with the supportive functions of maintaining the position of men as being of greater importance and value than women? I did not want to play a part in reinforcing the supportive/nurturing roles to which women are traditionally conditioned.

Still, there were women in pain—women who had nowhere to turn to get the kind of understanding and assistance they needed. The following situation, not an uncommon one, illustrates my dilemma. The Denver DAV Vietnam Veterans Outreach Project was initially the only resource available locally for veterans suffering PTSD; it was also the only resource for their families. In fact, at the outset, the number of requests for assistance from family members and friends almost equaled requests from veterans. In response to one woman who was crying out for help, one well-meaning but unhelpful counselor told her she should be more patient and show greater compassion and understanding for her veteran husband.

However, this woman was on the verge of collapse. She had given and given and given and had nothing left, yet she was admonished to give more. There was no recognition that she, indeed, had her own problems. Following intervention through the women's group, she was able to see herself as central. Rather than focusing on her failures to help her husband, she was better able to take care of herself. Hence, she was better able to give support of a positive nature.

Her dilemma is one frequently found in a society tied closely to traditional sex-role definitions. Not all dilemmas are of such a life-and-death nature; however, the psychological repercussions can be extremely severe and permanently debilitating to the woman as well as her partner and the family system.

It is most difficult to discuss women in a sexist society in the context of what is perhaps the strongest bastion of "maleness"—the military system, to which women are rarely exposed and in which they, as both civilians and women, are distinctly second-class citizens. Compound the potential for dramatically different expectations with the traditional differences in sex-role socialization received by the men and women, and we have fertile soil for problems. W. D. Ehrhart (1978), a Vietnam veteran, expresses it well in his poem about a disappointing relationship with a woman he loved:

> *For a Sister of Mercy*
>
> *Those were unsettling times surely no time to pity a man trapped in a loaded barrel; there were too many fires burning, too many hammers waiting to fall; all those angry people in the streets, all those reasons why, those questions, and broken dreams.*
>
> *I did love you in spite of all my solitary explorations, that vast wound, some other life I could not share except in pain.*
>
> *You were kind. I am sorry I healed so slowly. There was no other way. I think of you often.*

Ehrhart (1978) writes:

> [there]...are real problems...however ill-defined and hard to disentangle from the web of influences which make us all—men and women—distinct individuals. But if I want my lover to be sensitive to and supportive of me, I in turn must teach myself to be sensitive to and supportive of her. Vietnam veterans, you know, aren't the only bunch that've gotten a bad rap to deal with.

Each partner in a relationship must attempt to understand how it feels to be in the other's shoes. Only then can we look more objectively at our interdependencies, the system of the couple and the family.

Sex-role Socialization of Women

At the risk of excluding many socialization factors that influence our development as men and women, I will discuss a few that seem central to women's conditioning and behavior, and to their unique conflicts. Illustrations of these effects on relationships, or on whatever system one is examining, will be presented later.

The major dilemma for most women can be characterized as the "Compassion Trap" (Adams, 1971) or "walking the tightrope" (Jens, 1979). The tightrope concept implies that the woman must maintain a precarious balance between supporting and not supporting another, always risking sacrificing her own needs or being labeled as selfish. Women are frequently punished in our society for acknowledging their own importance. To the extent that they have learned to be all-sacrificing for the needs of others, they have no self-respect and have, in effect, sacrificed their own identity. Such effects can be harmful for both the woman and man. The systems effect on the recipient of such total sacrifice may be unhealthy dependence and resentment.

This is one instance of the "double bind" (Jackson, 1967) that constricts women. The double-bind theory, like the tightrope concept, postulates that one is damned if she does and damned if she doesn't. It is a no-win situation of caring too much and over-protecting or caring too little, being selfish, and not fulfilling her socially defined role. A crucial aspect of the double bind theory is that one is not able to discuss the conflict with others. Such appears to be the case with most of the women partners who have not had the opportunity to share with others.

Women have been traditionally conditioned—that is, reinforced by the social culture—to be dependent, passive, noncompetitive, interpersonally oriented, sensitive, subjective, nurturant, unable to risk, and emotionally labile. On the other hand, men are taught to be independent, aggressive, competitive, task-oriented, self-disciplined, objective, courageous, unsentimental, rational, confident, and in emotional control.

Unfortunately, these latter terms are used to describe the mentally healthy individual. The terms that stereotypically describe women are, in fact, those used to describe pathological behavior in humans. Hence, we define mental health in terms of stereotypically male characteristics and mental illness in terms of "female" characteristics (Broverman *et al.,* 1970).

Jakubowski defines emotionally healthy individuals as those who believe "...that they can make an effective impact on the people in their environment" (1977, p.173). She suggests that women's lack of assertive behavior leads them to feel that they have no control over important events in their lives. Consequently, their behavior is characterized by learned helplessness.

According to Seligman (1975), learned helplessness is displayed when a person believes that the likelihood of a certain outcome occurring is the same regardless of whether or not the person responds in a given situation. The person operates on the belief that responding is futile. When such learning has taken place, the individual experiences great difficulty in discovering that his or her responses may be successful; therefore, learned helplessness becomes self-perpetuating.

This theory generally characterizes the way women have learned to view themselves in the world. Learned helplessness is also applicable to the veteran. The trauma of war produces a sense of loss of control that may influence the veteran's behavior later. (The feelings of learned helplessness among Vietnam veterans are described elsewhere in this book.) The woman may act to support her partner and be met by negative or inconsistent consequences that result from the veteran's own sense of lack of control or other manifestations of PTSD. Such an outcome contributes to her feeling of helplessness with regard to the veteran and may generalize to other systems with which she interacts.

When a pattern of ineffectual responding has occurred, the expectation of ineffectuality becomes a causal feature of the motivational, cognitive, and emotional deficits that accompany helplessness. Such a pattern is typified in the lives of women. While they may often exhibit behaviors that produce positive outcomes for men, the same behavior by women will frequently result in negative consequences for them.

If a woman has had a nontraditional upbringing or is consciously attempting to behave and define herself in terms of mental health (the male image), she is further castigated. When a woman and man display the same behaviors, he is likely to be considered aggressive, while she is considered bitchy; where he is thought of as honest, she is characterized as castrating; if he seen as courageous, she is viewed as impulsive; and on and on. The woman who has followed a traditional or "feminine" role set, such as a nonemployed wife and mother, is also subjected to demeaning descriptions and jokes. Bardwick and Douvan describe the effects: "In the absence of independent and objective achievements, girls and women know their worth only from other's responses, know their identities only from their relationships as daughters, girl friends, wives, or mothers...." (1971, p. 231).

To the extent that a woman attempts to combine professional and wife-mother roles, she commits herself to a position in which she must be a superwoman; and she invariably feels guilty about neglecting one or the other of her roles. The sex-role socialization process becomes apparent when women do attempt to break out of stereotypic feminine roles because there may be relatively little external support for acting assertively. It then becomes necessary to create a situation in which self-reinforcement can occur. Jakubowski-Spector reports that a "...major goal of assertive training is building a personal belief system which will help the client to support and justify her acting assertively" (1973, p.8). I think that such development is a primary objective within women's support groups.

Ironically, while society may now accept more varied roles for women than it does for men, there is also greater probability of ambivalence and identity confusion for women. Again, the woman is in a position of conflict-she is more likely punished no matter which direction she follows.

The outcomes of the double binds are devastating to many women. Some become extremely frustrated. Others lose their identity, if they had ever gained one. Still others hold low opinions of themselves and their worth relative to men. And many suffer all of these effects. Certainly, men experience conflicts of comparable seriousness, but men are not our focus here. Certainly, too, the points I have made are rather simplistic and perhaps exaggerated. Nonetheless, this necessarily brief outline of the conflicts faced by women generally is crucial to an understanding of the additional dilemma faced by the woman partner of a Vietnam veteran who is suffering PTSD. Within the couple system, each partner affects the other, and the combination of her dilemma and his traumas can negatively influence the dynamics and health of the relationship.

There is a trend away from the unidimensional stereotype that has traditionally placed men and women into slots that narrowly define them on the basis of gender. The inflexibility of sexual stereotypes is probably exaggerated in the media relative to real life. However, with the new uncertainties, our social system has become unbalanced, and the family structure must be redefined. Clearer criteria of femininity and masculinity are evolving that "...can be learned and can offer feelings of self-esteem to both sexes; where ...men are more nuturant than they were, while women are freer to participate professionally without endangering the male's esteem" (Bardwick and Douvan, 1971, p. 237).

New role freedom is an additional burden on the veteran and his partner when there has already been some difficulty in readjustment. Assessing the problems of women partners makes it easier to conceptualize the complexities and contradictions inherent in the situation of women with troubled Vietnam veterans as partners.

Commonalities—Shared Problems of Women Partners

A majority of the women we have seen in Denver are in relationships with men who experience more severe PTSD symptoms than does the average Vietnam veteran. Most report unstable or unsatisfactory relationships, a fact that seems attributable in part to war-related problems that adversely affect the men. Nearly all the women we see are concerned that their relationships may not be sustainable. Many are desperate, and some are either separated or very close to separating. Most of these women became involved with their partners since the men returned from active-duty military service. (It should be noted that 38 percent of the marriages of Vietnam veterans broke up within six months of their return from Southeast Asia [President's Commission on Mental Health, 1978]. The divorce rate for Vietnam veterans is higher than for the general population [Center for Policy Research, 1979], and clinical experience shows clearly that nonmarital relationships involving these veterans have the same trend toward instability.) Several of the Denver women have been previously married; many are married to veterans who have been divorced at least once. The majority of the veterans married now have children (either from their present marriage or from earlier marriages). And several of those who are not currently married have children from earlier marriages.

Women Partners

Many common themes run through the problems that the men have and the effects of those problems on the woman partners and the family systems. Those who are familiar with PTSD symptomatology will recognize the patterns. Although it has not been possible to specify which or how many of these concerns affect any one woman, those that seemed to be most universally shared within our sample are indicated below by an asterisk. Where the focus is on the specific problems of men as related by women, the following have been reported:

- He lacks self-esteem, suffers great insecurity, and feels worthless and helpless.*
- He is irresponsible in terms of holding a job, staying in school, and contributing to child care or household chores.*
- He exhibits erratic behavior without specific reason, such as rage reactions that alternate with remorse (Jekyll/Hyde syndrome).*
- There is heavy use of alcohol and drugs, as well as suicidal ideation.*
- He seems always to be in a crisis state, although the identified reasons may vary from week to week.
- He is extremely demanding, considering only his needs or feeling that his needs are more important than his partner's.
- He isolates himself from his partner, family, and others with a leave-me-alone attitude.
- He is unable to express or share his feelings.
- He is unable to handle frustrations or even to identify them.
- He seems unable to handle it when things are going well, feeling that he is unworthy.
- He is jealous of his partner's relationships and activities.

If we look at how the veteran affects the family system, we see the impact and the complications imposed by traditional sex-role stereotyping of men as well as women. Central issues are indicated below by an asterisk. Where the focus is directed to how the woman is affected by the man's problems, the responses include:

- She is overwhelmed by pressures and feelings of having assumed total responsibility, for instance, the strain of financial insecurity because of the man's job instability.*
- She experiences confusion about whether the problems are Vietnam-related and whether there will ever be any resolution of the man's conflict.*
- Both partners are building defensive barriers in the relationship and are unable to be supportive of one another.*
- She suffers from low self-esteem, is anxious, and feels a sense of hopelessness.*
- She feels guilty that she is somehow responsible for the man's rage reactions.
- She experiences many self-doubts generated by the emotional and job instability of the man; she is caught up in continually responding to crises, losing sight of her own needs or overall behavior patterns.
- She is afraid to say anything to him; and, in not knowing how to respond, she feels frustrated in her ability to help.
- She feels she is responsible for making it all better, having to mother or nurture the man, which can easily create greater resentment and irresponsibility on his part.

- Or she feels the converse—that it is all his problem—and refuses to be involved (seemingly a defensive position or survival stance when all else has been tried and failed).
- She feels that he has separated from her and their children with little sense of family and poor father-child relationships.
- She feels that support is not welcomed by the man, that she is being discounted.
- She is subject to emotional, verbal, and physical abuse.
- She is anguished by the man's frequent extramarital affairs.
- She feels dragged down by the man's negative attitudes.

After identifying problems of women partners, we have attempted to assess some of their needs. In most cases, these cannot be separated from the relationship per se. The dynamics between the woman partner and the veteran, the operating system, must be examined. Again, it is possible to conceive of how sex-role-related behavior has influenced the woman in terms of lowered self-esteem and lack of independent identity. Some of the expressed needs of the women in these circumstances include the following:

- To receive sharing and support from women experiencing similar problems, a process that lends strength to them in confronting problems and making changes.
- To gain more objective insight into what their problems are and how they can change their situations.
- To cope and solve problems.
- To have more opportunity to pursue their own goals and needs, to feel more independent.
- To develop greater skills and confidence in responding to the men.
- To have less friction, tension, responsibility, and some release from daily pressures.
- To have less ambiguity and inconsistency in their life situations.
- To have less negativity from the men.
- To have more mutual trust and honesty in the relationship.
- To be more appreciated by their partners.
- To experience greater financial and emotional security and stability.

It seems clear that women partners do in fact share some common problems. They generally report a feeling of isolation that is not just isolation from the veteran. In many cases, the woman and the family also seem isolated from society. They frequently admit that they have no one to talk to who can understand, including their parents.

Most of the women partners feel responsible for the veterans' inability to adjust satisfactorily. They feel they are also primarily responsible for the emotional and financial state of the family, as well as being the sole child care providers.

Their self-concept is frequently quite poor. They complain of guilt, anger, alienation, and mistrust—much as the veterans themselves complain of these feelings. It seems evident that many exhibit the same symptoms as the veteran.

There is evidence of physical battering among some of these couples; however, the women have been typically reticent to discuss it. We have gathered from the men and women in our therapy/support groups that battering has probably occurred in at least half of their relationships (see Agosta and McHugh, "Family Violence," this volume). Their experience, however, does not fit the usual battering pattern, which is characterized by two or three abusive incidents that are then continued in a cycle that is almost impossible to break (Jens, 1980). With the veteran couples, there seems to have been one or two incidents that were extremely frightening to both persons and that were not repeated. In fact, it is a common precipitant for one if not both partners to seek outside help. If it were not for this immediate movement toward recognizing problems, more couples would probably evidence the characteristic battering cycle; undoubtedly, many do.

Differences in Problems of Women Partners

Despite the fact that the women have in common their veteran partners who suffer from PTSD, the way this is expressed within the relationships or the family varies considerably. Life situations and individual characteristics are quite dissimilar, and each family operates differently.

The women have different needs and expectations. There are significant differences in age, marital status, and length of the relationship, as well as in the range and severity of problems confronting them. They may or may not have children from their current or previous marriages. Some of these women typify the "new woman" concept, valuing their personal independence and achievement and recognizing their own needs. Others fit the traditional pattern of women: they are concerned simply with being able to better understand and help their partners, not recognizing personal needs or self-identity issues.

Categorizing women as either traditional or nontraditional is clearly arbitrary. But for some purposes, when women appear closer to one or the other extreme, some continuity in their responses to their own situations exists. The more traditional women have centered their lives around their men and have made extreme sacrifices to hold their relationships together. They may now feel beaten down after having tried everything and failed. The earlier example of the woman who was suicidal, knew of no alternatives, and felt she had failed miserably typifies the reaction of these traditional women. Some of these women have considered separating or have even temporarily separated from their partners. But their own insecurities and lack of independent experience make this an almost impossible alternative. They do not have the wherewithal to live independently.

The response of the more nontraditional women has been to fight back, make impossible demands on the veteran, or walk out. If, despite her dissatisfaction, the woman had stayed in the relationship for various reasons, emotional barriers are often built between the partners. Therefore, the couples remain physically together but otherwise separated. Of course, labeling the women as traditional or nontraditional in order to point out general differences in their responses to similar situations necessarily excludes those who are not at such extremes.

At least two of the women with whom I have had sustained contact have fairly stable relationships with their partners. In these cases, the couples are following an escapist route, similar to the counter-culture revolution of the '60s and early '70s. They have together alienated themselves from the larger society and are otherwise undirected except that they want to get away from it all. Although there is stability in these relationships, markedly unhealthy dynamics are operating.

As I mentioned earlier, there are not only differences in value systems, but in the individual situations of these women. For example, Joan and Karen were both married shortly before their husbands were assigned to Vietnam, and each was about one month pregnant at the time. When the husbands returned from the war, their children were one year of age. While Karen's child was able to form an immediate attachment to his father, Joan's husband confronted almost the opposite response from his infant son. The child was initially terrified in his presence; he screamed, cried, and would tolerate no physical contact from the father. The husband responded by avoiding the child and maintaining as great a distance as possible from him. The father felt rejected and developed hostility toward his son. This hostility has characterized the father-son relationship ever since.

Let me further round out the picture of these two families to demonstrate how different the dynamics can be even though the problems in the relationship initially appeared to be similar. Joan had very little communication from her husband while he was in Vietnam. She had no way of knowing where he was or how he was doing for months at a time. When he returned after being away a year, she went to meet him at the airport. He had arrived there hours earlier and gone drinking with a buddy. She had no word from him until he came home drunk several hours later.

Joan expressed the uncertainties, the rejection, and the hurt she felt in her response; she became emotionally distant from her husband. She was one of ten children and had major responsibilities at a young age, and she currently manages to support her own family both financially and emotionally. During the year of her husband's absence, she learned even greater self-reliance. She is raising three children, has always supported the family with a full-time job that she likes, and has her own network of friends. Her husband has been in school during the entire period since his discharge from the service. He has not held a job or contributed to the support of the family, and he reports that he does not have a single friend. The limited interaction between Joan and her husband has a generally negative quality.

Karen also now has three children and has supported the family with a full-time job. Unlike Joan, she has neither wanted to work nor enjoyed it. Her husband has also been in school and worked sporadically. He has participated very little in child care or household responsibilities, demanding that Karen perform these duties because she is a woman. He has had several extramarital affairs and frequent drinking binges, and he seems oblivious to the effect this behavior has on Karen and the family. Karen does not have any real friends, except one sister with whom she can talk. When I first met her, she was what I would call a beaten down woman with a very low opinion of herself. Though Karen has done everything she can think of to help her husband and maintain peace within the family, he has responded by demanding more from her and abusing her more frequently. There is also an emotional gulf between them.

In the families of both Karen and Joan, rivalry between husbands and children for the woman's attention abounds, despite the fact that this is primarily negative attention-seeking and childish behavior on the part of the husbands. The husbands may exhibit overt behavior in this regard, such as complaining that the women are spending more time with the children than with them. Frequently, however, the behavior is more covert, as when the men abuse a child to gain their wives' attention. They may also become enraged over seemingly trivial matters, behavior that also focuses attention on them.

I would characterize Joan as a more nontraditional woman and Karen as more traditional. Joan would have little difficulty in caring for herself and her family without her husband, while such an alternative is very frightening to Karen. How do these women's attitudes affect their husbands? Why do these couples remain together when they seem so destructive to each other? What is the nature of the dependencies, interactions, and dynamics within these two families? Can the unhealthy patterns of these relationships be changed? How? Does it make sense to even attempt to remediate the problems, or should these people separate?

My last question is tough. I do not have an answer for it. Unfortunately, it is impossible to predict unequivocally what the effects on the system will be when an intervention is made and family members change (see Williams and Williams, this volume).

PART FOUR: GENERAL CONSIDERATIONS

Along with consideration of the individual and his or her family system, we must attend also to the larger system. The society is affected by the individual and his or her systems, and it, in turn, affects them. In a broader sense, a social phenomenon is occurring now in which many Vietnam veterans are destabilizing and showing delayed stress reactions. The increasing compassion for the veteran's ordeal, as well as the public's movement toward separating feelings about the war from feelings about the warrior are resurrecting old, unresolved issues and creating new ones. Such a climatic change means the veteran must again adapt. He cannot easily stay where he is even though he may have made a satisfactory adjustment from all appearances. Other veterans have been unable to reintegrate well and remain very unstable. They are now being pushed by society to recognize this, to question themselves; many must now acknowledge that they have suppressed some feeling regarding the trauma of the war and the hostile, negative reactions of society upon their return.

As a result, many partners are also experiencing new turmoil and sharing such symptoms with the veteran as helplessness, worthlessness, and isolation. In addition, women partners bring their own troubles, inadequacies, and needs into the relationships.

There is a definite need for aid to women partners of troubled Vietnam veterans and their families. As discussed earlier, the groups in Denver showed positive results and the women felt they had profitted from participating. After focusing initially on how they could help their veteran partners, the women later focused more on themselves. This seems to be a healthy direction: the situation has been reframed. This new focus involves acknowledgment of how their behavior contributes to dysfunctional patterns, and in some cases women must acknowledge that doing "good," by traditional social standards, may actually be counterproductive. Additionally, by being in the groups, they are exposed to others' experiences; therefore, new alternative behaviors that can facilitate change in their own relationships become available.

It appears that some women who have entered relationships with veterans since the war have brought with them their own unmet needs and felt inadequacies. One hurting person has found another similarly hurting person, and this factor alone has compounded the problems. When couples have remained together since before the veteran went to Vietnam, the traumatic changes the veteran has experienced due to the war have deleterious effects on the woman and the relationship.

As partners, the women and men in separate groups become more aware of themselves and begin to cope better, and they bring this strength back to their relationships. Both partners are then better able to form healthier patterns of relating to one another, as well as to their environment and other people. We are not reinforcing an unhealthy or overly dependent kind of relationship nor placing women in an adjunctive position to the men. On the contrary, we have a formal structure in Denver for working with couples and families.

It is time to look even beyond the system of the family to the community and society at large. We must also view the problem globally and intervene in the larger system: we need to give information to everyone. There would then be some sense of understanding and unity in awareness of the problem, as well as consensus on achieving greater stability and forward movement.

We believe community workshops, open forums, and better media representation can help educate and raise the awareness level of the society in general, particularly of those in the helping professions. Probably no more is possible or necessary for those not directly affected. But, for those who are directly affected, greater deficiencies exist for which education alone may not be sufficient. Our clients and potential clients need objective, outside, professional input to break their dysfunctional patterns. Guidance in breaking those patterns, in conjunction with a supportive, informed response from the suprasystem (our society) will facilitate positive personal growth in the veteran's family system.

Rather than following the format we used in the Forum for Women Partners, which isolated the sexes, it makes better sense to sponsor a workshop for veterans and their significant others. The initial phase could involve dissemination of information regarding the post-Vietnam era syndrome and delayed stress reactions in much more detail than we were able to provide at the forum.

It would seem appropriate to conduct such workshops on a quarterly basis, opening them to the public, particularly to persons who have been in contact with the Veterans Administration and DAV Vietnam Veteran Outreach Programs. It might be a good one-shot experience for some, regardless of whether they have expressed a desire for psychological services, because the workshop would be primarily an educational and sharing opportunity. For those desiring to go further, it would serve as the initial phase of a longer process. It would also provide us with more information regarding these people's needs and how we could best meet them within the already established framework of men's, women's, and couple's groups, family therapy, multi-modal treatment, and other modalities.

Certainly, the veterans of the Vietnam war have been left out in the cold. It is obvious that those involved with them share some of these burdens, are also isolated from the mainstream, and are indeed suffering. If the women can derive some security and strength from each other, they will be better equipped to help their mates and enhance their relationships. But let us not place these women in the impossible position of being "therapists" for their partners.

It is crucial that these women, their veteran partners, their families, and the general population, be provided with information about the delayed post-traumatic stress of the Vietnam veteran and be sensitized to the issues involved.

As concerned persons and as mental health professionals, we must recognize what the Vietnam war has done to the lives of hundreds of thousands of veterans. The pain and anguish it has caused have spread, damaging countless others who share the torn lives of these veterans. We who work in mental health must respond. We must join together—in our ideas and our efforts—to ameliorate this pain. We must effect positive change in the veteran system and in our own system as well.

REFERENCES

Adams, M. (1971). The compassion trap. In V. Gornick & B.K. Moran (Eds.), *Women in sexist society.* New York: Basic Books.

American Psychiatric Association. (1980). *Diagnostic and statistical manual of mental disorders* (3rd ed.). Washington, D.C.: American Psychiatric Press.

Bardwick, J.M., & Douvan, E. (1971). Ambivalence: The socialization of women. In V. Gornick & B.K. Moran (Eds.), *Women in sexist society.* New York: Basic Books.

Brodsky, A.M. (1976). The consciousness-raising groups as a model for therapy for women. In S. Cox (Ed.), *Female psychology: The emerging self.* Chicago: Science Research Associates.

Broverman, I.K., Broverman, D.M., Clarkson, S.E., Rosenkrantz, P.S., & Vogel, S.R. (1970). Sex role stereotypes and clinical judgements of mental health. *Journal of Consulting and Clinical Psychology, 34,* 1-7.

Center for Policy Research (1979). *The adjustment of Vietnam era veterans to civilian life.* New York: Center for Policy Research.

Chessler, P. (1972). *Women and madness.* New York: Avon Books.

Ehrhart, W.D. (1978, March). The long road home to intimacy. *WIN,* pp. 14-16.

Figley, C.R. (Ed.). (1978). *Stress disorders among Vietnam veterans.* New York: Brunner/Mazel.

Figley, C.R., & Sprenkle, D.H. (1978, July). Delayed stress response syndrome: Family therapy indications. *Journal of Marriage and Family Counseling.*

Harris, L., & Associates. (1980). Is America changing its attitutdes toward Vietnam vets? *DAV Magazine, 22* (1), 11.

Jackson, D.D. (1957). The question of family homeostasis. *Psychiatric Quarterly Supplement, 31,* 79-99.

Jackson, D.D. (1967). The eternal triangle. In Haley & Hoffman (Eds.), *Techniques of family therapy.* New York: Basic Books.

Johnson, B.S. (1976). Coming to grips with the problems of women: A review of the literature. *Social Work, 21,* 531.

Jakubowski, P.A. (1977). Assertive behavior and clinical problems of women. In R.E. Alberti (Ed.), *Assertiveness.* San Luis Obispo, CA: Impact Publishers.

Jakubowski-Spector, P.A. (1973). Facilitating the growth of women through assertiveness training. *The Counseling Psychologist, 4,* 75-86.

Jens, K. (1979, October). Personal communication.

Jens, K. (1980, May). Personal communication.

Minuchin, S. (1974). *Families and family therapy.* Cambridge: Harvard University Press.

Minuchin, S., Rosman, B.L., & Baker, L. (1978). *Psychosomatic families.* Cambridge: Harvard University Press.

President's Commission on Mental Health. (1978). *Mental health problems of Vietnam era veterans* (Vol. 3), pp. 1321-1328. Washington, D.C.: U.S. Government Printing Office.

Satir, V. (1967). *Conjoint family therapy.* Palo Alto: Science and Behavior Books Inc.

Seligman, M.E.P. (1975). *Helplessness.* New York: Scribners.

Wilson, J.P. (1978). *Identity, ideology and crisis: The Vietnam veterans in transition.* Unpublished monograph, Cleveland State University.

Wilson, J.P. (1980, May 21). *Towards an understanding of post-traumatic stress disorders among Vietnam veterans.* Testimony before U.S. Senate Subcommittee on Veterans' Affairs. Washington, D.C.

CHAPTER THIRTEEN

BUT YOU WEREN'T THERE*

Pat Hickman

I've got a lot to tell
I've been to the other side of Hell
Where people die for nothing and there's
A lot of pain and suffering
Where bullets either leave creases
Or blow you to pieces
Where blood flows like wine
And you're scared all the time

I don't mean to freak you out but
This is what war's really about
So if in the night you hear screaming
You'll know it's me..........dreaming

Where are they at now?
The ones who survived the Vietnam war
And were so close to death's dark door
That sent a lot of young men whose only sin
Was war.
When you called us we stepped forward
And risked all that we had
Of the combat experience you say
Was it really all that bad?

But to see in living color what
Comes out of the M-16 hit a human body
Bursting every seam
The war is over in history
But it never ended for me.

Nathan Marbly, 1981

*The title of this article is based on the poem reprinted above.

The combat veteran client has myriad symptoms and thought-provoking lifestyles that will fascinate any therapist. Nightmares, flashbacks, survivor guilt, suicidal ideations, and substance abuse are only a few of the problems that face the combat veteran.

The preferred treatment model for this special client population has always been therapy with a mental health provider who is also a veteran. Recently, however, Vietnam veteran professionals have recognized the need for the involvement of a female therapist to facilitate readjustment to society.

One must be familiar with some of the etiology of Vietnam veteran's problems with women. Many veterans find it difficult to become emotionally close, especially with women. Their intimate relationships suffer, struggle, and finally disintegrate. It is common to find Vietnam veterans who have been married twice, sometimes four times. The explanation is that symptom known as "emotional numbing." In combat, the veteran saw his friends cut down by gunfire, rockets, land mines, and snipers. He only had to lose a single "buddy" to experience grief, loss, and often guilt, but most veterans experienced many such losses. A popular coping mechanism becomes desensitizing oneself to the emotions that accompany these traumatic losses. This emotional desensitization technique for coping was learned in a stressful, life-threatening arena, and became deeply ingrained. Once this numbing is learned, it is generalized to other close relationships after the combat experience.

When the veteran returned to "the world," he attempted to lose himself in the mainstream and forget the war. He began to associate with women and try to lead a normal life. Yet, when he feels himself becoming "too close" to someone, the old learned behavior emerges. He pulls back, isolates, and withdraws from the emotional closeness. The fear of losing the person becomes too great to risk. It is not unusual for a veteran's spouse to claim that he has *no* feelings. She and the children can't get close to him, the emotional distance he creates drives a wedge into the relationship that sometimes cannot be overcome, leading to the eventual breakdown of the relationship. The woman spends a great deal of emotional energy trying to get near the veteran while his energy is directed toward keeping her away. The denial of his feelings can be devastating to his partner and to him (see C. Williams, "Women Partners," this volume). Inside, he desperately wants the emotional closeness of his family but sees the risks as too great to let go of his defenses. One veteran remarked that his wife constantly accused him of not caring about anything, not having any emotions or feelings, and yet he confessed that he cries every time he watches "Little House on the Prairie." The closeness of the T.V. family is what he wanted very much in his own family, yet he had no idea how to be a husband and father and the risks involved precluded his learning.

Another problem veterans experience is lack of trust. They mistrust government and its authorities as well as personal authority figures, and this is often generalized to women. To understand the genesis of this, we must understand how the military indoctrination "prepares" young men to go out and kill people identified as the enemy.

To accomplish this goal, the military employs certain psychological tactics. First, they dehumanize the "enemy," who become "gooks and dinks" rather than fellow human beings. The young soldier is also convinced that the enemy consists of soulless heathens, godless creatures that mutilate, destroy, and booby trap. Such sneaky, underhanded tactics could only be conceived by a brutal, sub-human culture. Now the anxious recruit is convinced the enemy is the worst possible sort of menace and must be destroyed.

The second part of indoctrination to kill involves some sort of motivator to evoke enough emotion to realistically accomplish the killing. The military chose, in some cases, to create anger by instilling the notion that their wives or girlfriends were "living it up" while the soldier and future "killer" was in a most dangerous situation. The women at home were depicted as harlots and hussies who couldn't wait for their men to leave so that they could sleep with the draft dodgers, hippies, and men who weren't "called to glory." The recruits were constantly reminded that their women were at home "fucking Jody" ("Jody" is a generic term for men who didn't go to war). With this kind of thought reform tactic, many Vietnam veterans became so doubtful of their women partners' faithfulness, and so concerned with their own plight that the anger, frustration, and sense of helplessness tended to build and build until they hit the battle. The enemy then becomes the outlet for all this pent-up emotion. Many veterans received Dear John letters, and 38 percent of those married before Vietnam were divorced within six months of their return.

Most soldiers lived a life without women. For the young combatant, female companionship was rare. Many veterans had sexual encounters with local women in foreign countries, frequented prostitutes, and began to formulate opinions that women were "bad" and not to be trusted. The Army ran houses of prostitution in Vietnam. Sex was rare, transient, artificial, almost always with prostitutes; there was no opportunity for warmth, intimacy, or sharing; nothing was sustained, and certainly there was no possibility of any meaningful relationship (see Sandecki, this volume). These lacks, the absence of tenderness, and the more general sexual deprivation, have had several important and unfortunate effects. One is that these men began to lose sight of the fact that women are human beings with whom experiences, thoughts, and feelings can be shared. Sex became physical lust. Another is the myth of masculinity—to be a man means "fighting and fucking." The military fosters this myth and the young men believed it.

The veteran brought these myths and behaviors home with him. The female partner cannot explain the change in her man. He may become very possessive and jealous. He does not allow his partner to go out alone. He may call home several times a day to check on her. She becomes a prisoner in her own home. Either the rest of her life is destroyed or she gets out of the relationship. The veteran doesn't understand. He assumes that he is showing her he cares about her, while in fact he is constantly pushing her away with his mistrust.

For the female therapist, these problems with women pose a challenge. And one's nonveteran status compounds that challenge. "What do you know? Why do you care? What's in it for you? Are you using us to write a thesis? To get your degree?" These questions are typical of those posed by many Vietnam veterans, and they are right. After all, "You *weren't* there."

The nonveteran therapist working with the veteran population is frequently challenged on his/her motives for doing this type of therapy. Cynicism and mistrust are not uncommon commodities.

Certain therapists possess the necessary attributes to work very effectively with the veteran population, and particular therapeutic approaches have produced positive results, while other approaches are dismal failures. It is my goal to share the approach and techniques that have served me well in this endeavor.

MAKING A CONNECTION

The Vietnam veteran population has difficulty trusting "outsiders." Feelings of resentment, possibly stemming from their self-identification as being used as political pawns, have built up for many years. This resentment is usually accompanied by anger/rage, depression, cynicism, and mistrust. Knowing this ahead of time prepares the therapist for the initial phase of treatment. The "testing phase" is usually characterized by questioning motives, testing knowledge, scrutinizing sincerity, and withholding of self, as well as other techniques that challenge the therapist.

It is helpful if the therapist has some *real* "connection" to the tragedy that surrounded the Vietnam war. This connection can be in the form of lost loved ones, writing to someone in Vietnam, being of the same generation, or in some way connecting herself to the veteran and the war as a whole.

Self-disclosure is an important tool for establishing a strong therapeutic alliance. The therapists must be comfortable sharing enough of themselves to make them real and sincere. Since I experienced the loss of my good friend and senior class president, as well as other friends and classmates, it is easy to share my own sadness, grief, and anger with the veteran to aid in establishing a relationship and model appropriate expressions of feelings. The prolonged "trauma pattern" both in war and at home (where they were greeted by protests and denigration) makes it difficult for a veteran to build a *trusting* therapeutic alliance.

The testing phase of the therapeutic alliance begins immediately with the veteran's questioning your motives for choosing to do this kind of work. As a former partner of a Vietnam veteran, I could certainly identify with what many of my clients were expressing. I was familiar with the jargon and knew a fair amount about what had occurred by listening to my former husband and his friends discuss their military experience. I was shocked to see that idealistic young boy I had married had been transformed into an angry, cynical man. Only someone strongly connected to Vietnam can use these experiences to provide the empathic self-disclosure that helps to lower barriers and build trust.

When challenged by a veteran about my motives, I have been able to gain his acceptance by connecting myself to Vietnam and showing him that I too was deeply wounded by that war so far away. (It should be remembered that there were also women who served in combat in Vietnam, and while the male gender is used here, it does not preclude appropriate consideration of the female veteran and her almost identical issues.) My life, too, had been drastically altered by a foreign conflict that also touched many of us left behind.

Most veterans strongly express the sentiment: "You weren't there, you can't *know* how I feel." But if the veteran can be led to better understand the concept of empathy, he can begin to let go of the idea that you can't help him. It has been helpful to me to use childbirth as an analogy. Most of the veterans with whom I've worked have been "hung up" on trying to make people "understand." When others are unable to "understand," the veterans become more frustrated, angry, and withdrawn. I encourage them to stop trying to force understanding on others and be more concerned with accepting that *no one* can understand how they feel. They are the only ones who have walked in those jungle boots. Even other Vietnam veterans cannot fully understand one man's feelings the way that man feels them.

The childbirth analogy is quite convincing. There is no way I can *make* any man understand the feelings that are associated with pregnancy and childbirth. No one can explain the feeling of a child growing inside your body. I cannot find words to describe the pain of labor and childbirth. No man can "understand" the woman's experience. He can be comforting, supportive, and appreciative of her suffering, but he cannot understand. But no one attempts to force that understanding as a prerequisite to fathering. Just as it would be unfair of me to suggest that because of this men cannot love children, nurture, and be good parents, so it is unfair of the veteran to reject me as a person who can be comforting, supportive, and appreciative of his trials and tribulations. This approach has been accepted and understood by my veteran clients without hesitation, and supports this budding therapeutic alliance. This is the beginning of being accepted and almost trusted.

The nonveteran therapist must be willing to be very patient with the veteran. Where veteran therapists may be allowed to get away with "pushing," the nonveteran therapist must slowly chip away at the emotional wall that surrounds and protects the client from intrusion that might lead to more pain. If the veteran doesn't let you in, you don't have any power to hurt him. Once the veteran has accepted the therapist, the treatment phase may begin.

TREATMENT ISSUES

Treatment involves looking for the stressors, ferreting out survivor guilt (see T. Williams, this volume), and listening to the veteran's stories. Quite clearly, one attribute possessed by a nonveteran therapist is objectivity. Vietnam veterans have been looking at their experiences through 18-year-old eyes. They distort the facts and continue to punish themselves for sins of omission, sins of commission, and anything else they can use to reinforce their own negative feelings. It becomes the therapist's task to help the veteran reconcile himself with his military experiences (see Jacob, this volume).

The corpsman who battled valiantly to save a shattered limb, instead of praising himself, chastised his ability by wondering what else he could have and should have done to ensure success. He remembers the ones he couldn't save and forgets the ones he did (see Shovar, this volume).

The ground troops who fought with all their hearts and minds still didn't win the war and lost a lot of buddies—seemingly for naught.

Faulty thinking plagues a large majority of Vietnam veterans, especially those who experience survivor guilt. When I suggest to the corpsman that it was certainly lucky he was available for the marine with the shattered limb, and isn't it great that he was there for the sergeant would surely have died if he weren't, it is evident that such thoughts had never occurred to him. Had the corpsman not been available, the limb would surely have been lost and possibly the life as well. This restructuring of the cognitive process can be quite beneficial to the veteran's self-esteem.

My goals with Vietnam veterans are to:

- Build self-esteem;
- Instill some pride with regard to their experience;
- Provide assertiveness training to help them deal with feelings in an open, honest, and appropriate manner;
- Alleviate guilt and responsibility; and
- Develop a more trusting attitude toward women.

As the therapeutic alliance deepens and strengthens, the veteran will begin to move from talking about the here and now to talking about Vietnam. The initial stories are usually fairly innocuous and still somewhat testing. An empathic, concerned response from the therapist can lead to more self-disclosure from the veteran.

While it is not necessary to memorize a map or a date book, it is helpful if the therapist has a chronological familiarity with the events surrounding the conflict in Vietnam. When a veteran gives you his years of service, you should know roughly what phase of the war that was. The Tet offensive, build-up, body counts, Phoenix, stand-down are all terms with which the therapist should be familiar to better know what this client might have experienced.

The treatment phase may include individual, group, and/or collateral therapy. It is helpful for the veteran to begin his therapeutic experience with individual treatment, become connected to someone, share initial stories, build trust, and open old memory banks with one person before moving into the more anxiety-producing arena of group therapy.

For many veterans, this is the first time they have talked about Vietnam with any other living human being. They are fearful of crying, fearful of rejection, fearful of reopening old wounds. Many discuss feelings of identity crisis. They express fears of "losing" a part of themselves during the therapeutic process. Their Vietnam experience, while painful, is still an integral part of their self-identification. Many hold on to their Vietnam history as if it were some valuable treasure with which they cannot part. Since self-esteem work is essential with most veterans, the process should begin as soon as possible in the therapeutic setting. I quite often recommend bibliotherapy as a possible esteem-building tool. Two books, *Feeling Good* (Burns, 1980) and *The Hazards of Being Male* (Goldberg, 1976), have helped veterans get in touch with their feelings.

If they can learn how to better identify and express their thoughts and feelings, they begin to feel better and more worthy as individuals. Once self-esteem begins to improve and trust is more established, one can begin to inquire about Vietnam.

If a veteran has difficulty verbalizing stories about Vietnam, some techniques may be employed to encourage the "opening up" process. Writing has proved to be a valuable tool with many of my clients. Some keep journals dealing with each day as it affected their feelings. Did they get angry that day? Why? How did they express that anger? What other emotions might have been "under" the anger? How did they talk to themselves about the way they handled the anger? If it was a good day, why? What were they saying to themselves about their feelings? How were they interacting with others?

Some of my veteran clients have used other talents that facilitate the therapeutic process. Song writing and poetry have been vehicles by which some have felt comfortable expressing their innermost feelings in a more socially acceptable manner. Through the exercise of writing, the veteran author also gains a heightened awareness of self.

As the veteran becomes more aware of his interactions with others, his response to stress, and his inner thoughts, he learns that he can be in control of his feelings and reactions to stressful events. For some reason, possibly because of military indoctrination or because they are male, or both, veterans find it extremely difficult to allow themselves to acknowledge emotions. Certainly on the battlefield, emotions were a luxury one could ill afford: your survival depended upon your being able to keep a cool head and make a calculated response. Since this behavior pattern was established in a life-threatening environment, it is incorporated in one's repertoire of behavior; in fact, it *becomes* one's behavior pattern. The veteran must use an incredible amount of psychic energy to keep up such a strong defense.

Writing in a journal serves as a yardstick that enables the veteran to become aware of himself as an emotional person. He is able to scrutinize his progress through the three-step process to change: awareness, risk, and trust. First, in order for one to change any behavior he must be *aware* of his use of the behavior in the past and present. Once he realizes how he responds to others, he can be helped to see alternatives to that behavior. Assertiveness training has been quite successful for me as a tool to facilitate clients' increasing their positive behaviors.

When awareness has been heightened, the veteran must be encouraged to begin taking *risks*. If he had always handled anxiety in passive-aggressive ways (i.e., drinking/drugging, displacement, outbursts, etc.), he could be encouraged to try to be more assertive: go to the person with whom you are angry and discuss it; walk away from a potentially volatile situation; express how you feel, instead of blaming the other person. If the client sees alternatives for behavior, some risk taking can begin.

It is best if the initial risks are small with a good guarantee of "pay off." While new behaviors don't *always* "pay off," the veteran can surely be advised that either way he will certainly feel better about himself. The therapy must be very supportive, encouraging, and resourceful during this phase. The process is facilitated by the therapist's willingness to become "over involved" with the client. This "over involvement" may take the form of a telephone call between therapy sessions just to "check" on the veteran. Positive reinforcement is vital to the veteran's successful readjustment into society.

Trust is the bottom line in this particular therapeutic approach. By becoming aware of his behavior and doing something positive to change it, the veteran begins to trust himself and his own new behaviors, and those new behaviors become strengthened and much easier to employ. As trusting oneself usually leads to trusting others, the therapist now becomes someone the veteran can trust.

When a veteran enters my office for the first time, I immediately begin the trust-building process. I aim to focus on the situation that precipitated the veteran's coming to treatment. Subtle "tie-ins" to Vietnam are very helpful to continue to remind the veteran that he is in treatment to address some specific issues from his Vietnam experience, allowing him to become comfortable with the idea that Vietnam may still be impacting his life. For example, if a veteran enters treatment as a result of marital discord, I may begin to explore his feelings about women, his first sexual experiences, sexual encounters in Vietnam, Dear John letters, etc. The motivation for this is twofold: first to see how he reacts to beginning to talk about Vietnam and second to see if he has changed (emotionally) since his Vietnam experience. As the veteran becomes comfortable with this process of "unpacking," I will assign the three-phase inventory examination. The three-phase inventory examination involves looking back at one's life in a systematic and structured way. The therapist can then employ cognitive restructuring techniques to enable the veteran to gain some objectivity.

It is important for the veteran to remember who he was before he became a part of the military. Many veterans feel that reliving Vietnam and letting go of any part of that will somehow change him, alter his personality, or that he will "lose" an important part of his identity. I believe that the core personality is still intact, just hidden from view, by the symptoms that accompany PTSD.

Phase I of the inventory addresses "Pre-Vietnam." I instruct the veteran to think back to junior high and high school. Who was he? What was important to him? Was he popular? Did he date? What kind of things would he die for? Goals? Values? Basically, this type of structured questioning helps the veteran to know what to look for when he goes back in time for self-examination. Were there problems in the family of origin? Did he use or abuse substances? What was fun? Who was influential in his life? I encourage the veteran that this will be fun and give him some examples of my own perception of myself during that period of my life. My self-disclosure consists mainly of my values during the '60s. When I give him examples from my own life, they tend to be sincere and yet not too revealing. For example, I may tell the veteran that my goal in college in the late '60s was a degree in theater and drama, but the turmoil and restlessness of that period interrupted my course. My goal was affected by my marriage to a Vietnam veteran in 1968: I changed to a career as a social worker. This kind of a disclosure connects me to Vietnam and also shows the veteran that life experiences influence many aspects of one's self, including personal goals. Suppose he looks back at himself and finds a popular, fun-loving, "semi-straight," all-American athlete, choir boy, etc. Today he is isolated, withdrawn, angry, cynical, and dependent upon chemicals to exist. If this occurs, we can then talk about how he has changed since he returned from Vietnam.

Phase II of the inventory deals with "Post-Vietnam." The same questions are posed as in Phase I and comparisons are drawn. We go through all of the areas together (intimacy, self-esteem, goals, etc.) and begin to talk about how he is different, the same, unsure, confused. Sorting out this information helps the veteran begin to put the effects of Vietnam in perspective.

Phase III of the inventory is "Vietnam." The same questions are posed and answered by the "combatant." What was important? Who was he? What were relationships like (and so on)? Survival was uppermost in the minds of the combatants. Doing a good job for home and country was valued. Women may have become "objects" as a result of the cultural barriers of language and values. As the veteran remembers what it was like to struggle for survival, fear for his very existence, and long for his familiar homeland, he begins to become aware of how the Vietnam experience has impacted many areas of his life. Awareness is the first step in the change process.

After he becomes comfortable with discussing how Vietnam may have altered his life, I begin to talk about PTSD. What it is, what it "looks like," why it happens, etc. We may discuss how other people (rape victims, hostages, survivors of major natural disasters, etc.) may also have PTSD (see Griffin; Agosta and McHugh, this volume). Normalizing symptoms is important, especially if the veteran sees himself as "crazy" or somehow very different from everyone else.

It is at this point that I give the veteran a list of symptoms of PTSD. If he has *ever* experienced any of these symptoms, I ask him to make a mark (-) by the symptom. If he still experiences these symptoms today, make the mark a plus (+). Now I have a wealth of information. I may find out that he had suffered sleep disturbances. When I ask how the sleep disturbances were vanquished, I find out substances were used for purposes of self-medication. I may find out that he still experiences emotional distancing from family and friends. Again, this opens avenues of discussion about the symptoms that have dissipated and the ones that endure. If all has gone well, the veteran is by now beginning to trust me. He is also beginning, perhaps for the first time, to entertain the notion that some of his current problems may be a result of what happened ten or twenty years ago during a battle on foreign soil.

Discussing symptoms and normalizing behaviors may help the veteran's self-esteem, especially if he views himself as crazy. This may be the moment to introduce the veteran into the group experience. The group helps reinforce the normalization of behavior, but a more important function is that it fosters socialization.

The selection of therapists for group is of primary importance. Two therapists are desirable for optimal group functioning and mutual support (Williams, 1980). If one therapist is a combat veteran, the other should be a nonveteran. The veteran therapist must expect and plan for inevitable role confusion in the group process. The nonveteran co-facilitator can be helpful in coming to his aid when this problem arises. I support having a woman as co-facilitator of the group. Since many of the participants have grave difficulty in relating to women, a sensitive female therapist can aid in their resocialization process and facilitate generalization of learning outside the group situation. Many of the participants in the group are struggling with intimate relationships; therefore, a woman can aid in their beginning to understand the female psyche.

For the veteran who has been very isolated and withdrawn, the group often becomes an important means of increasing his socialization skills. I encourage my veterans to reach out to each other when they are down, and instead of "bunkering up," drinking, or pacing the floor all night, call someone, go out for coffee together, or just sit and talk. If the veteran "lends" himself to the group, and uses group members in times of need, his chances of successful readjustment increase. Group members who are trying to maintain sobriety find this particularly helpful. In one of my vet groups, the majority of the members were working on staying sober. One member was thirteen years into sobriety, another was six years, and several others were just beginning to stay off the alcohol and drugs. The newer members "look up" to the members who had been able to have success with sobriety maintenance, and therefore tended to call one of them as one would call a sponsor in Alcoholics Anonymous. In the beginning of that group experience, many cups of coffee were shared through many long nights. Those who were having difficulty and reached out to other group members were rewarded positively by feelings of camaraderie and support. "Old" group members who had a fight with their spouse or a bout with depression also felt free to call someone just to talk it out. I have found that nothing makes a veteran feel better, feel more worthwhile and needed, than to be able to help a buddy in trouble.

On one occasion, a veteran came for a regular group meeting looking particularly down. He told the group how he had had a terrible week, he had fallen "off the wagon," his wife had threatened to leave him, a buddy at work had been seriously injured, etc. As his tale began to unfold, he talked about giving up; he said he had "tried everything" and nothing worked, and he was just plain tired of fighting. The group immediately was supportive and then began to confront their troubled brother. "Why didn't you call me?" was the resounding chorus from the group. One group member said that he was hurt and even angry that the veteran had not called him, especially since he had been helped through a difficult time by this very group member. This sentiment was echoed by other group members.

The old feelings of helplessness can be relieved somewhat in these groups. In Vietnam, the combatant was helpless to change or control his situation. People died and he couldn't help them; orders were given and he had to obey; his own government allowed the war to drag on and he couldn't do anything about it. Now, as much as twenty years after the fact, helping a buddy today somehow begins to make up for all the people and all the situations that couldn't be changed during the war.

Some long-term, meaningful relationships are begun in the group setting. It has been my experience that those veterans who use the group not only to work through issues of Vietnam, but also to begin to readjust to society through means of socialization, have the greatest success with their treatment. I have sometimes scheduled two veterans back to back for individual therapy so I could introduce them and encourage them to exchange phone numbers.

The therapist must also be willing to devote a tremendous amount of time to the veteran in these early stages of treatment. Sometimes I will call a veteran between sessions just to see how he's doing, to let him know I care about him, and to encourage him to get out and socialize. I call these "pep talks." Sometimes therapy in the early stages is strictly encouraging, supportive, positive reinforcement. One of my veteran clients once said he'd like to be able to put our therapy sessions in a bottle and carry it with him all week so he wouldn't forget or lose the good feeling he always had when he left the office. The veteran is now beginning to see that people do care about him, that a person who is not a fellow veteran can be loving, supportive, and concerned. If this person also happens to be a woman, some complications can arise.

The female nonveteran therapist must be prepared for and be able to handle some interesting testing maneuvers from the veteran population. The therapist must be able to deal with the "warrior stance." This means she must be prepared for the veteran to test her by means of intimidation or seduction. Intimidating behaviors may be graphic "war stories" told merely for the shock value. They may try to test your knowledge of Vietnam jargon by misstating something to see if you catch it. They may take a physical stance backed by anger and rage and tell you of "bad things" they have done. Whatever form this intimidation takes, the therapist must be able to take it. Language may be the simplest form of intimidation. Many Vietnam veterans use unique, inside jargon both to describe events and in normal conversation. There is also a heavy use of expletives and cursing in a rather graphic manner. If you are easily shocked, offended, or sensitive, this is not the population for you. Standing firm, not flinching, not reacting, not being intimidated, is the only way to get past that part of the testing phase. When he finds out you're not a fragile flower, those behaviors usually stop. If they are testing you and you pass the test, you can then proceed to the matter of therapy.

If the veteran chooses to use seductive behaviors for testing purposes, the female therapist must be able to deal with these as well. The veteran may "come on" to the therapist in many ways. He may compliment her on her appearance, compliment her body, strike seductive body postures, tell her of his sexual prowess and his sexual technique. This may be subtle or graphic in nature. Again, if the therapist is easily intimidated or is insecure with herself, she may not survive this part of the therapeutic process.

The seductive behavior may be the most difficult to tolerate. On one occasion, a veteran suggested that he could just take off his pants and "show me what he had right now." He stood up and began to unbuckle his belt. My reaction was to sit perfectly still, unflinching and matter of factly tell him that he didn't have anything I hadn't seen before, and if he proceeded to carry out his threat, I would be happy to call the police, and wouldn't that look good on his record since he worked primarily with children. He stood there glowering at me for a few seconds and then sat down. That seductive/intimidating type of behavior never occurred again, and we worked together successfully for almost a year. This example is somewhat extreme—seductive behavior is almost always much more subtle.

Some of my veteran clients "fall in love" with me. Some admit it, most don't, but this too can be used in a positive, therapeutic way. Since I am married and have three children, most of my clients see me as unavailable and leave it at that. However, some see that as a challenge and will attempt to pursue. It is very difficult to maintain a balance between your *sincere* efforts to show the veteran you care about him and yet not give him "come on" messages. I think touching is important, but reaching over and putting your hand on a veteran's shoulder may be interpreted in the wrong way. The best way to strike this balance is with an open, honest, and sincere approach. I also combine that with my "one of the guys" approach. This is easy for me since it is who I am. I have always enjoyed playing and watching sports events, so I can talk football with the best of them. I am not offended by "locker room humor," and can even contribute a joke or two myself, and perhaps because my father was a Marine combat veteran of World War II, I was socialized to be "one of the guys." My father took me hunting and fishing, we watched sports events together, and I learned all of the "words" at a very early age. All of this life experience has been instrumental in helping me work with this population with some degree of success.

If a veteran has not had a relationship in his life for many years, an inappropriate love attachment may form. This phenomenon is very serious, as it may preclude the veteran from developing a more realistic attachment in his life. If the client is fantasizing about a future with the therapist, he may make comparisons that no one person can meet, thus eliminating them as possible partners. The therapist must be able to set clear boundaries with the veteran and show him that this relationship cannot and will not materialize. I encourage my vets to talk to others or share their feelings with the group in hopes that they will become more oriented to reality. If he can see that he is avoiding an appropriate relationship by attaching to me, then the therapeutic process should produce positive results. The therapist may want to consider assigning homework involving social interactions with women, and then make his seeing you contingent upon completion of this homework.

The positive aspects of this type of therapeutic issue can be many. The veteran client may be experiencing feelings that have long been dormant. If so, he can learn how to identify feelings, appropriate expression of feelings, and healthy means of coping with them. This can then be generalized to other situations that may evoke strong emotions. The veteran can also learn more assertive behaviors by being open and honest with the therapist regarding his emotions. I tell my veterans that these are good feelings and they should not be uncomfortable or embarrassed by expressing them, although it proves to be difficult at first.

There may also be negative consequences if the vet is unable to see the inappropriateness of his attachment to the therapist. He may view this as another in a series of rejections. He may become depressed and withdrawn and fall back into an old dysfunctional pattern of behavior, and it may be an end to the therapeutic relationship. Another therapist may be able to help him work through his feelings or start over again. In either case, the therapist must stay "on top" of the situation and maintain objectivity. One pitfall worth mentioning is that of establishing a dependency. The veteran may be very vulnerable and the nurturing, supportive atmosphere of therapy could become too important. If you feel the veteran becoming dependent upon you, it is best to have a session regarding the status of therapeutic relationship. I explain I cannot *be* everything to him. He needs to establish a supportive social network for himself. I can help him begin to make contacts and encourage him to follow through, but I cannot *be* his support system. It is helpful to continue to remind the veteran client that our relationship is unique and therapeutic in nature and not meant to be permanent.

That doesn't mean that I no longer have any contact with veterans who have successfully completed treatment. I always give them an option to continue to contact me if a stressor arises at any point in the future. Many times, a phone call is sufficient to get through the crisis, but it may require one to three office visits. It is important for the veteran to know you will still be available to him if the need arises. This establishes some sense of security along with fostering increasing independence in the client.

Some characteristics of a good female therapist seem to be especially important. Experience with difficult populations is very helpful. These populations might include the chemically dependent, habitual criminals, juvenile delinquents, or any other that has a high rate of recidivism or an especially angry, volatile history. The female therapist must be confident and secure with her own sexuality. She must be able to be a woman and still be viewed as trustworthy and honest. She must be feminine without being fragile. She must be able to joke and laugh and yet still maintain sincerity and sensitivity. Finally, this woman may have some characteristics of "the Earth Mother" without being punitive or smothering.

In my practice, I also facilitate a partners group consisting of significant others. These may be girlfriends, wives, or friends of the Vietnam veterans. It is my belief that these women and friends need support, attention, and education with regard to their veteran partners. The groups allow the partners a safe arena to ventilate anger and frustration, and give them information about PTSD and why their particular partner's symptoms may still be present. It is my goal to help them see that on occasion they may contribute to breakdowns in communication by not understanding the nature of stress disorders. Significant others may encourage the veteran to talk, open up and share feelings, etc. The veteran interprets this as "pushing" and further withdraws from communicating. Some significant others may encourage the veteran to tell them about Vietnam, what he did and saw there. I discourage this practice. We discuss Vietnam in the partners group, and I tell them some "war stories" that I have heard over the years. I tell the partners not to ask. They may not really want to know. A particularly graphic example of this problem can be seen in what occurred with a client several years ago. The veteran had a difficult time with impulse control, rage, and substance abuse. His spouse had "pushed" him to talk for many years. One evening he became intoxicated, angry, and hostile. He finally gave vent to his stored-up anger and struck out. With his hunting knife, he demonstrated how to slit someone's throat using his children as models. He held them from behind, shouting and cursing that if she wanted to know what he did, he'd be glad to oblige her. Fortunately, no one was injured, but there was police intervention and the ordeal was quite disturbing for the spouse as well as the children. We discuss such things and see films in the women's group so they don't have to ask.

Some problems may arise when facilitating both veteran and partners groups. For example, the women may need someone to talk to, or a crisis flares and they naturally think to call me for help. Confidentiality must be maintained for both groups to foster and maintain trust. I tell both groups that we cannot discuss what goes on in either group, and we should not discuss, with our partners, specifics of what occurs in each respective group. "We talked about the differences between World War II and Vietnam," is acceptable. "Sue said John hasn't made love to her for months," is not acceptable and a violation of confidentiality.

I tell the partners that I care about them, I can give them support, a safe place to vent, and I will be there for them in the case of a crisis, but my first loyalty is to the veteran. The partners accept this approach, and it has not presented any problems to date.

The nonveteran therapist can be very helpful in other areas as well. Veterans tend to be curious about how civilians view them, what the civilians were doing while they were at war, how, if at all, the war affected them, and so on. The sensitive nonveteran therapist can be the bridge between an alienated veteran and mainstream society. Mistrusting civilians is common, and you can help the process of trust building with a strong therapeutic alliance. It is important that the veteran learn that others suffered, too.

For those of us who were contemporaries of Vietnam soldiers, it was terribly traumatic to be left behind at such a young age, to watch the T.V. screens nightly scanning for a familiar face, hoping to see him and fearing you might. There was an incredible sense of helplessness when the war escalated with the Tet offensive. We watched and mourned as our best and brightest came home in body bags or were maimed for life. It was painful to go to funerals of schoolmates who died before they were even of legal drinking age, who died before they ever got to vote, who couldn't be viewed because of the condition of the remains.

Particularly during the war, soldiers saw all hippies and protesters as enemies, traitors, or cowards. They did not get the message that it was possible to protest the war yet not protest the warrior. For every protester who spat upon a returning veteran, there was one who welcomed him back, yet most veterans did not see the positive, or perhaps the media chose to focus on the negative. For whatever reason, it is important that the nonveteran therapist be able to shake the veteran's hand, thank him for his sacrifices, and welcome him home, finally.

Female therapists also play a valuable role in helping the veteran become reacquainted with his own emotions. Many of my clients have told me that it is easier for them to share emotions with a woman than with another man. Since I have my own strong connections to Vietnam, I am sometimes moved to cry *with* a client. Sharing emotions with a client can aid in trust-building and model appropriate behavior. It does seem as if many veterans have not completed or even begun the grief process because they won't allow themselves to cry. Some fear the loss of manliness, others fear they won't ever stop crying. We can talk about grief versus depression, crying versus "masochism," and give vent to other emotions as well. Loving, supportive encouragement and extreme, unflagging patience are prerequisites for success for the nonveteran therapist.

I must be sounding like Mother Teresa with combat boots and an M16. The characteristics of the successful therapist are really no different from any other therapist with any other population. Joel Fischer (1978) speaks of "empathy, warmth and genuineness" (p. 189) as the vital characteristics of a good therapist. I would add patience, thick skin, and commitment. There is a payoff for working with the Vietnam veteran, and that is that most of them do get better. They can learn to trust, to feel, to cry, to socialize and to live life more fully—to "come home"—and that is reward enough for me.

I'd like to end this paper with another poem by Nathan Marbly.

Untitled

I've been called:
Baby killer, murderer, crazy man
But I risked my life for Uncle Sam
I went on missions to search and destroy
I even had to kill a fourteen-year-old boy!
There were no defined lines no front or
Rear, the enemy was everywhere.
I did what I was told, I followed
Orders. It never occurred to me to flee
To Canada's border. I don't want a hand-out
With the government you cannot fight
I just want to sleep at night.

I'm trying to put Vietnam behind me
But there are too many things that remind me.

The sound of a helicopter that
Glides through the air

In the park I watch the bushes
Cause I know that they're there

In my dreams I can see
Their bayonets shining bright
And I'm dodging green tracers
All through the night

How much longer can I stand this?
I never came home.

Nathan Marbly, 1980

APPENDIX 1.
DELAYED STRESS REACTION CHECKLIST

The major responses seen among veterans suffering PTSD have been compiled by pyschologists and psychiatrists working with the DAV Vietnam Vet Outreach Program. They are listed below. Most veterans show only a few of these responses. It should be remembered that PTSD among Vietnam veterans is not a mental illness; it *is* a reaction to the extreme stress these people suffered during and after the war in southeast Asia.

- Depression
- Sleep disturbances
- Tendency to react under stress with survival tactics
- Psychic or emotional numbing
- Emotional constriction
- Loss of interest in work and activities
- Survivor guilt
- Hyperalertness
- Fantasies of retaliation
- Avoidance of activities that arouse memories of traumas in war zone
- Suicidal feelings and thoughts
- Flashbacks to Vietnam
- Fantasies of destruction
- Cynicism and distrust of government and authority
- Alienation
- Concern with humanistic values overlayed by hedonism
- Negative self-image
- Memory impairment
- Anger
- Anxiety
- Hypersensitivity to justice
- Problems with intimate relationships
- Difficulty with authority figures
- Emotional distance from children, spouse & others
- Self-deceiving and self-punishing patterns of behavior such as an inability to talk about war experiences, fear of losing others, and a tendency to fits of rage

REFERENCES

Burns, D. (1980). *Feeling good: The new mood therapy.* New York: Morrow.

Fischer, J. (1978). *Effective casework practice: An eclectic approach.* New York: McGraw-Hill Book Company.

Goldberg, H. (1976). *The hazards of being male.* New York: New American Library.

CHAPTER FOURTEEN

GROUP THERAPY WITH VIETNAM VETERANS AND OTHER TRAUMA VICTIMS

J. Michael Jelinek

This chapter describes and outlines a working model of group therapy that the author and the editor of this book have utilized, adapted, and tried to refine since 1980. The model described is basically a short-term, closed group; it runs for 10 to 12 weeks, and once the group is formed, we try not to introduce new members until the scheduled sequence is completed. It is a structured group: specific goals and tasks are assigned throughout its term. Although the group model evolved from our work with Vietnam veterans, we are finding today that trauma victims (victims of industrial, occupational, and family tragedies) can benefit from and return to their premorbid personality state in a very rapid manner when a similar format is used. We find that groups must be trauma-specific. In combat groups, we have successfully included Korean and Israeli war veterans with Vietnam veterans.

Basically, the Vietnam veteran's therapy group is a peer group. It is a supportive, therapeutic milieu where the individual can present, explore, test, and resolve the emotional and cognitive aftereffects that stem from traumatic wartime experiences. Almost invariably, we have found that Vietnam veterans are conflicted around two key issues originating from their traumatic wartime experiences. First, the individual veteran is conflicted between his actual behaviors in combat and the idealized expectation he had of how he should have acted during combat. The second issue is somewhat opposite: it involves the veteran's conflict between things he didn't do during combat and the resultant feelings of guilt or shame he feels today. It is almost as if Vietnam veterans have polarized their belief system about wartime experiences in a manner that is similar to "damned if you did, damned if you didn't."

Unfortunately, veterans returning from Vietnam did not find an organized or sympathetic system that could help them with their conflicts. During the past ten years, veterans have been exposed to treatment modalities that have been helpful, detrimental, and confusing. Leaderless groups, rap groups, didactic groups, topic-centered groups, client-centered groups, free-floating groups, and Yalom-styled groups (1-2-3-4-5) have been tried. Trained therapists who work with Vietnam veterans will see many similarities between the model described in this paper and a traditional Yalom-styled psychotherapy group (Yalom, 1975). However, unlike a civilian or co-ed therapy group, the Vietnam veteran group can be extremely intense and demanding; self-destructive or explosive behavior is not uncommon. Therapists find the experience demanding, gut-wrenching, and exhausting.

Individual and group psychotherapy usually operates from the premise that change begins within the individual, a premise that is true for most of the clients with whom we come in contact. However, with Vietnam veterans and trauma victims, we find that it is necessary to look beyond the individual: external events are central and in some cases largely responsible for the individual's current difficulties. For example, a Vietnam veteran may be grappling with intense guilt stemming from his behavior during a firefight in combat (see T. Williams, this volume). The veteran may be so shamed by his behavior that he takes all responsibility for the outcome of action. In our Vietnam veteran groups, we look beyond the individual to external forces that had created the individual's traumatic experience—the military unit, the Vietcong, N.V.A., the military and political command structure, social norms, and peers. Recognizing and acknowledging that these forces played a major role in the trauma often helps veterans review their experiences in a less guilty and more rational manner. When veterans learn that they need not take total responsibility for the experience, we find that they have made a therapeutic breakthrough that allows the healing and reformulating process to begin. They can start to accept what has happened and live with themselves with less self-recrimination. We do not mean to imply that we help the veteran displace all responsibility for his actions onto external sources; rather we help him accept only that small portion for which he is truly responsible.

VIETNAM VETERAN GROUP DEVELOPMENT

I found the work of Jones and Bearly (1984) extremely interesting and helpful in describing and diagramming a working model of group development. Their most recent paper (1984) utilizes a group developmental matrix that nicely depicts two major dimensions of the group process and the different stages that occur in the therapy group. I will use their development matrix to describe the major steps and stages that occur in our Vietnam veteran therapy group (and many other psychotherapy groups). We can see two interactive yet separate dimensions: a social or interpersonal dimension and a task/functioning dimension. Many veterans have inadequate, maladaptive, or underutilized interpersonal relationship skills. The typical Vietnam veteran, in our experience, is a withdrawn, suspicious, anxious, somewhat angry and frustrated individual who could use reeducation in interpersonal relationship skills. In part, this is a result of their traumatic experiences, PTSD (American Psychiatric Association, 1980), inadequate social network systems, and sometimes pre-existing characterlogical symptomatology.

Interpersonal Dimension

The interpersonal dimension consists of five phases in our Vietnam veteran group: a dependency phase, a conflict/resistive phase, a sharing/working phase, a cohesive reformulating phase and, finally, an independent/growth-oriented phase. I will describe each of the phases according to our experiences with Vietnam veterans; behavioral and clinical examples will help to clarify the differences among these stages.

Dependent Phase

The beginning phase of group therapy for Vietnam veterans is a very critical time. We normally devote two weeks to this phase because it is a time when the veterans' anxiety, suspicions, and internal pain are intensified and, although they are looking for symptom relief, there is a strong tendency for them to withdraw or run from therapy. Most veterans have had minimal contact with formal group or individual psychotherapy, and are uninformed on group procedures and processes. Some are familiar with "rap" groups and believe this is what they will find in group therapy (for example, one of our veterans thought group involved telling war stories and then going drinking with the guys). During this phase, the therapists are very active in describing group format, rules, and the schedule, and in providing support for the veterans. We try to act as role models for the group by setting the pace and tone for interactions. For example, we might carry on a therapeutic conversation between the two leaders, and model for other group members how to ask questions, respond, or not respond.

The veteran usually has several issues to address, but is confused as to how, when, or with whom. We avoid opening traumatic issues during these first two sessions and focus instead on several curative factors described by Yalom (1975), which we have found to be particularly pertinent for Vietnam veteran groups. For example, they all want to believe that there is some chance of hope for them. They generally do not know how to get better, but they do know that their present life circumstances are somewhat unsatisfactory, unhappy, and unfulfilling. From the beginning, we make it clear that we believe that group therapy is the most effective modality for most Vietnam veterans. Occasionally, we have veterans who have been through other groups describe how group helped them. Many veterans are greatly relieved by the similarity of problems among other group members: often this is the first time they have talked about their experiences since Vietnam. In a group composed strictly of veterans, the veterans need not deal with one obstacle they feel so often—that others will never understand how they feel or what they did (see Hickman, this volume).

Socialization is another vital function of the group. Many veterans have been isolated or socially withdrawn, and they find it extremely pleasing to be in a group where they can interact and practice forgotten social skills.

These curative factors all work together to form an intensely cohesive group, one that is sometimes reminiscent of the closeness they felt with comrades-in-arms in combat. This is extremely helpful in getting the veterans involved and participating in group therapy, but is an issue that must be addressed towards the later stages of the group. During the first phase of the group, some veterans will say they intend to work on their problems, but will actively sabotage or delay the actual process to avoid dealing with the painful memories and emotions that can be overwhelming. As the group process begins, their symptoms might be intensified, and many feel like withdrawing and running. While the group members value this warmth and sense of camaraderie, they may resist the focused approach of the group and hamper the transition into the second stage.

Conflict Phase

The conflict of the second phase (which also lasts approximately two weeks) has to do with the ambivalence some group members feel about seriously addressing their own problems. The group members may experience difficulty with each other over differing points of view, concepts of their traumatic experience, or individual personality styles. Although the veterans value the warmth and acceptance of the group, many of them have remained isolated and have somewhat "rusty" interpersonal skills; actually having to work and communicate with other individuals can be stressful. Internal power struggles may occur within the group and confrontation may increase; some members may engage in detours or sidetracking maneuvers to attempt to keep the group from moving to the serious discussion of traumatic issues. One group member had a tendency to make jokes; this became a barometer that measured group tension: as tension mounted, this veteran would try to make more and more jokes to sidetrack and defuse or decrease the tension in the group.

Veterans report that they start to dream more, think more, and feel more about Vietnam during this phase. They frequently comment that they are feeling frightened of opening the door on the issues they thought they had locked away for many years, but also remark that they feel secure knowing they can turn to the group for support during this difficult time. A key message we try to impart concerns the reawakening of unpleasant memories and feelings from their traumatic experiences and their perception that they will lose control and perhaps hurt others or themselves. The group leaders should openly address this fear of uncovering unpleasant emotions and also try to reassure the veterans that although the feelings may be extremely frightening, they can be dealt with in a new manner without negative consequences. The conflict phase is a turning point where a norm is established that everyone can address forbidden topics or events that have been locked away for years.

Sharing/Working Phase

This phase can last from two to three weeks and is dependent upon the amount of trust and the number of different issues among individuals in the group. If there is a sense of comfort and trust within the group, there seems to be a smooth transition to working seriously on traumatic memories; members are willing to help others relive and reexperience the trauma; personal information is increasingly shared. During this phase, members definitely take more risks by disclosing information about their own traumatic experiences while appearing to await judgement from other group members.

For example, one veteran had a tendency to precede every recounting with a disclaimer that tended to discount his role in the traumatic experiences. He would begin by saying, "You probably all think I was a coward or a fool for doing this, but this is what I did...." When we pointed out this tendency, he reported that he greatly feared what others would think of him when he told them about his personal traumatic event.

We also find that individual group members take comfort in helping others relive and review past traumas. Blocking or sidetracking behaviors occasionally appear, but these can be decreased dramatically when a particularly traumatic event is processed with the entire group. Such events grasp everyone's attention, and can prove to be a cathartic experience in which they all vicariously relive their own traumas and ventilate some of their anger, fear, and frustration.

Cohesion Phase

The fourth interpersonal relations phase is perhaps the most productive and rewarding phase for the group. The group has a distinct sense of identity characterized by high levels of trust, camaraderie, tolerance, and an *esprit de corps* reminiscent of feelings they had in the service. The veterans begin to interact more freely and also begin to socialize away from the group with other veterans or new social networks. The group members are aware of individual differences and are tolerant of differences of opinion and coping strategies. This phase can be extended beyond two weeks because it feels good, and produces great relief.

Caution must be taken that actual group work—focusing upon and resolving the traumatic experience—is not forgotten and that the support group atmosphere is not allowed to dominate. This particular stage is characterized by the veterans' working very hard in group on psychological issues, and then socializing at another facility (a restaurant) where they practice interpersonal and social skills.

Independent Phase

The final interpersonal phase involves the termination of the group and the generalization of treatment results. Occasionally, some individuals are very reluctant to address the termination of the group. They desperately want to keep the sense of identity, cohesion, trust, and comfort provided by the group, and they fear the loss. For many of our veterans, the group experience has been the first social network they have enjoyed in almost twenty years, and this process (i.e., the group formation) needs to be clearly pointed out. Very frequently, we hear from our veterans that they can trust and socialize only with other Vietnam veterans. This has been reinforced, unfortunately, by some of their negative interactions with other social groups. They have a lot of difficulty believing that they can transfer the skills reawakened during the group to nonveteran social groups. Thus, we have the veterans describe positive interactions that have worked for them with new social acquaintances; any material that aids the generalization of social skills learned in group to the external world should be processed at every opportunity.

Sometimes members will try to bring up new material to work on in the group to avoid termination. Group leaders may point out these behaviors and address the loss issues each member might be feeling as the group ends. We try to have the group see that they came to the group experience with a rusty, unused tool (i.e., interpersonal relationship skills) and have created a new, finely adjusted and oiled mechanism that they can take out into the world. We point out the difficulty of the group process and how at times they felt like quitting or giving up; we help them acknowledge that similar things will happen in the outside world if they do not meet success with every attempt. Ideally, the veteran leaving group will have some sense of control and a sense that he can make new relationships, trust people, and live in the world of "normal people" as a "normal person." We hope the veteran also has learned new ways to cope with his internal anxiety or pain and that these new coping skills will give him a sense of independence and confidence that help make the transition from group more successful. Having a nonveteran, especially a woman, as co-leader facilitates this transition (see Hickman, this volume).

Task Functioning Dimension

The task functioning dimension addresses the job that we do in group. It consists of five stages in which the group leaders initially lead, demonstrate by role modeling, and provide a large amount of structure to group members; over time, the leaders withdraw and let group members develop their own leading styles. The real secret to running a Vietnam veteran group is to work yourself out of a job. By this I mean that you create a climate in the group so the veterans reawaken social skills, rediscover independence, work through their own problems, and take responsibility for their own lives. The five stages of the functioning dimension consist of an orientation phase, organization phase, a data flow phase, problem-solving phase, and a termination phase. The phases of this dimension roughly follow the same time sequence as the interpersonal dimension: most of these stages last approximately two weeks; occasionally they can go to three or four weeks, depending again on the individual state of group members and the issues that need to be addressed.

Orientation Phase

During this phase, the group leaders take a very active role and teach the group members about the procedures and format of the group. We discuss rules for the group during the first session, and try to keep them at a minimum. There are rules about confidentiality, coming to group substance-free, not destroying the furniture, giving permission so everyone can ask anyone any question they desire, and not complaining about the Veterans Administration. The leaders role-model behaviors that are necessary for the veterans to assimilate so they can work as a functioning unit. For example, group leaders may disclose their own traumatic experiences or coping strategies in a manner that makes the veteran feel safe—he can observe this interaction and perhaps feel comfortable enough to do so himself. The standards of the group, rules, tasks, and overall format are discussed in a didactic manner and provide the veteran with a sense of comfort in that there is some structure: if he begins to have discomforting feelings, he will not be allowed to get out of control. During this phase, we also have the group members agree, in either an oral or written contract, that they will attend the entire group cycle; if they want telephone numbers, we exchange them at this time.

Organization Phase

The group leaders delegate more authority to the group members in letting them make choices about the organization or direction and pace of the group. Decision-making rules, leadership roles, and problem-solving procedures are discussed. The veterans have a structure in which they provide the basic material, and the group leaders help channel that to therapeutic and working outcomes. For example, during the first and second groups, we may have a structured exercise during which we watch a videotape (such as "Wall of Tears," VietVet Video Productions) pertaining to the Vietnam war to help stimulate discussion. We find that such strategies quickly elicit information from other group members, and then we try to focus it toward therapeutic interactions and explorations. As the efficiency of these strategies increases and organization becomes more fixed, we find that group members increase personal disclosures. This second phase is a preparatory phase in the sense that it gets the veterans ready for the next stage where they will actively work on reliving, reformulating, and resolving past traumatic issues.

Data Flow Phase

During this phase, veterans begin to disclose more of their own personal traumatic difficulties. This can be a highly charged period because veterans are exchanging volatile recollections of their traumatic experiences. The data flow, if not channeled and monitored, can get out of hand. For example: while Joe was describing a particularly traumatic experience, we noticed other veterans backing away from the table and attempting to leave the room. When we pointed this out, they remarked that they were afraid that their issues would also surface and most definitely would overwhelm them. We reassured and reminded them that we could address their issues after we finished Joe's disclosure. During this phase, we hope to establish a norm where all veterans in the group can exchange beliefs, thoughts, or emotions that pertain to their traumatic experience.

Problem-Solving Phase

During this phase, the veterans exchange information about their traumatic experiences, and the group leaders try to use that information to help them find new ways of looking at the experiences. Cognitive restructuring can be a very important technique: we examine the veteran's basic thoughts and (perhaps erroneous) beliefs and either add to them, alter them, or subtract from them in such a way that the resultant perception is less distressing, more acceptable and comfortable. We actively use this process to help the veterans learn that there are other, less discomforting ways of viewing the problems. We also encourage other veterans to actively assist their fellows in testing past perceptions and forming new ones. We find that when a new belief is presented by the entire group, not just the leaders, the individual seems to grasp it, work with it, and accept it more easily. This phase can be the most productive and therapeutic time of the group because the members are actively working on testing and resolving past traumatic issues.

Termination Phase

This is the final phase of the group cycle. The leaders try to shut down the overall group and ensure that members are feeling secure about termination and will generalize the treatment results to the outside world. This phase could be sabotaged by veterans trying to introduce more material or remain in the problem-solving stage, or it can end successfully with the members moving to new social networks. The leaders should address loss issues well in advance of the termination phase, which in itself can last two to three weeks, to prepare the group for the resulting feelings of loss and sadness. Separation from a group can be very traumatic, and the leaders should monitor each individual veteran to see how he is making the transition. We strongly encourage all the veterans to call upon each other during this difficult time and to use their new skills to deal with feelings of loss, sadness, and grief.

STAGES OF GROUP DEVELOPMENT

The diagram in Figure 1 depicts the interaction of the interpersonal dimension and the task/functioning dimension that form the different stages of group development. The interpersonal and task/functioning dimensions must interact in a balanced manner throughout the course of the group to achieve the optimal results. If one dimension somehow overshadows or overpowers the other, the desired outcome of the group can be sidetracked or detoured—the results will be less than desired, and the group may lose its therapeutic value. During the first stage of group therapy, the interpersonal dimension of dependency and the task/functioning dimension of orientation should work together. While the veteran comes into the group feeling perhaps dependent and unknowledgeable about the process, the task dimension provides him with the structure, rules, framework and supportive atmosphere to enable him to continue the process. The duration for Stage I can vary from two to three weeks depending, again, on the individual veterans and the abilities of the group leaders to help unite the veterans in a working unit.

In Stage II, the interpersonal dimension (focusing upon conflict) should begin to interact with the task dimension phase of organization. As conflict begins to increase both within and among the group members, the leaders should provide an organized structure in which the individual members feel safe to ventilate unpleasant emotions and also be motivated to bring forth traumatic experiences. If the organizational aspects of the group are weak or nonexistent, the group members could become too embroiled over their conflicts, and they may try to regress to the more comforting beginning phase. On the other hand, if the leaders tend to be too structured and organized, the veterans may not take it upon themselves to risk sharing traumatic experiences and may feel comfortable remaining in a dependent mode.

During this stage, which can also last two to three weeks, the leaders should role model more intensely at the beginning and gradually taper off towards the end. The group members should get the idea that it is all right to mimic or imitate the leaders and bring forth pertinent material for group discussion. The two dimensions should work together in such a manner that the members know that it is okay for them to be greatly upset by internal conflicts, but the structure of the group is such that it will provide them with a means of expressing that unpleasant affect and also moving from it to a more healthy phase.

In Stage III, the sharing/working personal dimension should interact with the working task/function dimension. Group members should begin to share and work on traumatic issues, and the group leaders should facilitate this process. This is a very active, intense, and productive phase of the group that can be enhanced by the role that the leaders play in facilitating meaningful interactions. Generally, with a group that has reached this stage, the members are feeling secure with each other, they trust each other, and they are ready to roll up their sleeves and get to work on issues that have been troubling them for many years. As in the preceding stage, the leaders assume a more active role at the beginning of this stage and gradually taper off, reinforcing working behavior in other group members.

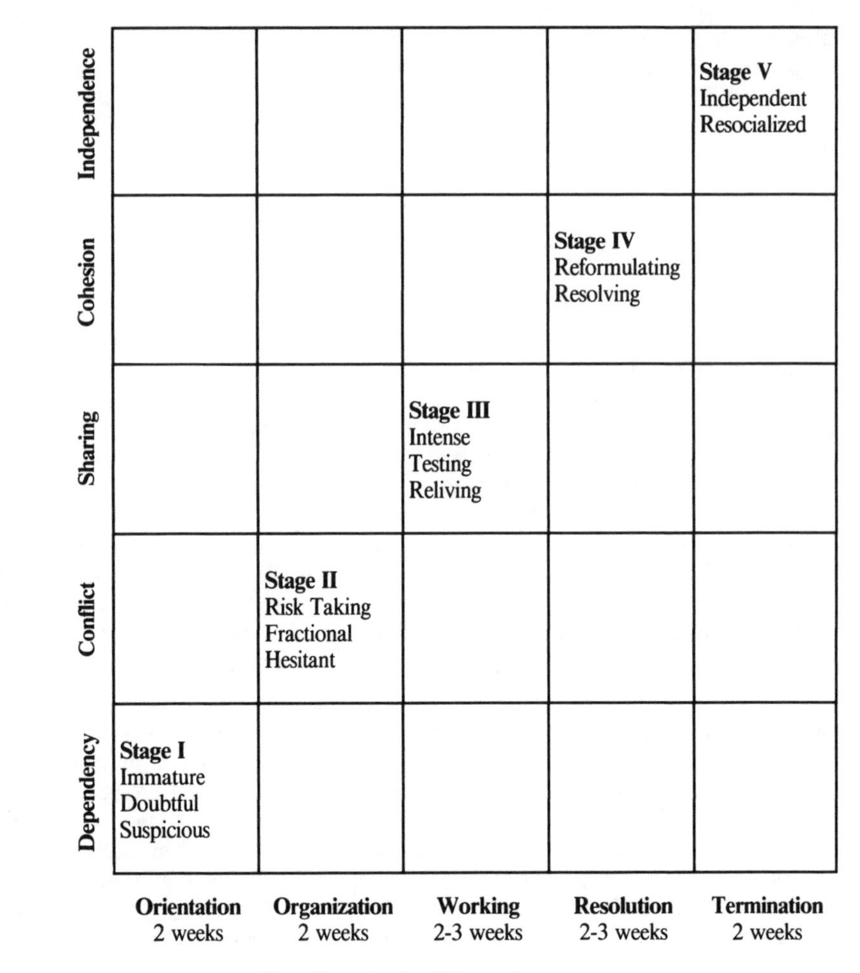

Figure 1. Group Development

In Stage IV, when the cohesive personal relations dimension interacts with the resolution task/functions dimension, the group is basically a functioning entity and the leaders are taking a less active role. The overall atmosphere of the group can be characterized as caring, sharing, and resolving issues that have been a source of distress in the past. We hope that group members have observed the procedures and working-through techniques employed in the earlier stages, and will be able to use these to work as a unit in dealing with their traumatic experiences. The group leaders may take a less active role in directing the discussions, but may be more active in making interpretations and clarifications on confusing issues. We sometimes get the sense that the group members dearly want to take charge and work on their problems, but they frequently look to the group leaders to provide clarification when they are either confused or stuck.

In the final stage, Stage V, the independence phase interacts with the termination phase, and the individual group members should be prepared to leave the group and move on, getting their lives together. The leaders do a lot of working during this stage helping to ensure that veterans do not set themselves up for failure in the future. For example, during one group, we reviewed expectations the veterans were forming for themselves to achieve in the outside world. Some of these expectations were outrageous or too optimistic, so we helped reframe them into more realistic goals that could be successfully achieved.

What is important to remember about the group development matrix in Figure 1 is that ideally the two dimensions come together in an equal and working fashion to enable the group to move through its progressive stages. Unfortunately, accidents sometimes occur and this smooth interaction is interrupted. Whenever a group tends to focus too much in one particular dimension at the expense of another, the logical evolution of the different stages can be inhibited or curtailed, and the group can actually in some cases regress to a less intense and safer stage. For example, a group that is overly oriented to the interpersonal phase will find it very warm, comforting, and supportive, but little therapeutic work will be accomplished to relive, test, and resolve past traumatic issues. In a sense, the veterans who are "stuck" in this supportive atmosphere may carry their pathology with them into the future. Conversely, a group may be so overly structured that even though it goes through the motions and follows the overall program, veterans may be denied the necessary elements from the interpersonal dimension that facilitate the sharing, grieving, and growing process.

A group leader might use this matrix to see whether and where the group has become sidetracked from therapeutic progress. As mentioned earlier, we normally run our groups over ten to twelve weeks, depending on the size (our groups have ranged in size from seven to ten), the degree of pathology within the members, and the type of issues they want to address. Normally, when a group cycle is completed, we have a break of one or two weeks and then begin basically the same group again. In the interim, we re-evaluate individuals to see whether they need to re-enter group for another session or leave the group and practice their therapeutic gains in the outside world without group support. As a result, we occasionally have had groups where "senior" veterans (e.g., veterans who have completed one group cycle) are mixed with "virgin" veterans who have had no therapy. Care must be taken in these groups to ensure that the senior group members don't try to sabotage or inhibit the process of opening traumatic issues. For these older, more therapy-wise veterans, there is sometimes a sense of discomfort at going back and reworking traumatic experiences that they felt they had already resolved. On the one hand, they may be pushing towards a more sharing, helpful, independent group, but on the other, they may be giving an unspoken message to new group members not to open and discuss traumatic experiences. Senior veterans mixed with virgin veterans may also try to act as therapists and speed the new group members through the stages before they are psychologically prepared to experience them. At such times, the group leaders must step in and process this phenomenon and encourage the new members to proceed at their own pace while attempting to have the senior leaders be more patient and helpful.

We have actually developed two different veteran groups over the years. We have our traditional group—we call it our combat group—for new members starting the therapeutic cycle; the issues deal with Vietnam traumas. The second group comprises veterans who have been through one or more group cycles. In this group, there is a "here-and-now" focus dealing with the difficulties surrounding generalizing therapeutic gains, resocialization, interpersonal relationship difficulties, and retaining employment. At times, the distinction between these two groups is very small, but group members report that it gives them a sense of progression to keep the two groups.

I hope this paper has given some ideas on the dimensions and stages of development that we observe in Vietnam veteran combat groups. This is certainly not the definitive text on doing group therapy; it was my intent only to describe some of the problems and solutions that we have evolved to help veterans deal with traumatic issues. Civilian trauma victims also may use a model very similar to this, and the actual time frame may be shorter. In our experience, we have found that the quicker we respond to a traumatic incident, the quicker we can help the individual through the grief/trauma cycle. Unfortunately, many Vietnam veterans have endured fifteen to twenty years between the traumatic incident and their start of therapy. During this extended period, many of the veterans have rigidly solidified defenses and coping styles that are neither very flexible nor amenable to much change.

Working with a Vietnam veteran group can be extremely stimulating, volatile, and rewarding. It is a constant source of pleasure for us to see a group of isolated, suspicious, withdrawn veterans join together and form a working, cohesive, functioning group where they can rediscover lost skills and incorporate new ones into a style that helps them move from past tragedies to future potentials. Many veterans ask us why should they even try a group when they have tried so many things. We normally respond that the only thing we know for sure is that what they have been doing hasn't worked so they might consider giving group therapy a chance.

REFERENCES

American Psychiatric Association. (1980). *Diagnostic and Statistical Manual of Mental Disorders (DSM-III).* 3rd ed., Washington, D.C.: American Psychiatric Press Inc.

Egendorf, A. (1975). Vietnam veteran rap groups and themes of postwar life. *Journal of Social Issues. 31*, 111-124.

Jones, J. E. (1973). A model of group development. In J. E. Jones J. W. Pfeiffer (Eds.), *The 1973 annual handbook for group facilitators.* San Diego, CA: University Associates.

Jones, J. E., & Bearley, W. L. (1984). Group development assessment, a working theory paper. San Diego, CA.

Scurfield, R., Corker, T., & Gongla, P. Three post-Vietnam "rap/therapy" groups: An analysis. *International Journal of Group Psychotherapy*, in press.

Sonnenberg, S. M., Blank, A. S., & Talbott, J. A. (Eds.). *Stress and recovery in Vietnam veterans.* Washington, D.C.: American Psychiatric Press Inc.

Walker, J. I. & Nash, J. L. (1981). Group therapy in the treatment of Vietnam combat veterans. *International Journal of Group Psychotherapy. Vol. 31*, 379-389.

Williams, T. (1979). *Psychological readjustment of Vietnam veterans.* Washington, DC: Disabled American Veterans.

Yalom, I. D. (1975). *The theory and practice of group psychotherapy.* 2nd Ed. New York: Basic Books.

CHAPTER FIFTEEN

FAMILY THERAPY FOR VIETNAM VETERANS

Candis M. Williams
Tom Williams

In the 1980s, extensive clinical research and attention has been focused on male Vietnam veterans, but very little attention has been given to their family members and close friends. The best information available (Silver, in press) indicates that more than 60 percent of male veterans have primary relationships with women. The inclusion of women partners and families is increasingly considered to be crucial to successful psychological treatment, as discussed by Figley (1978); C. Williams ("Women Partners," this volume); Scarano (1982); and Gruter (1981).

Unfortunately, the veteran's primary family system is still ignored by many clinicians. Even so, family systems sometimes reorganize without assistance, and accept the veteran's behaviors. However, there is resulting strain on all members.

When the primary family system has not been addressed, veterans revert to old behaviors and show an increase in stress disorder symptoms. Our clinical experience shows that veterans often get symptom relief from individual or group therapy, but that unless planned interventions are done with family systems, the possibility of permanent behavior change is reduced.

The purpose of this chapter is to acquaint mental health professionals with the usefulness of family systems theory in the assessment and treatment of Vietnam veterans' families, where the veteran shows a stress disorder due to combat experiences. We will first outline key characteristics of these families. Clinically, these families show differences when contrasted with families that do not have a member who has experienced extreme trauma. We will indicate the effects of systems and socialization on families, and particularly on women partners. We will also present guidelines for treatment in women partners' groups. Specific strategies of working with Vietnam veterans' families will be offered, and finally, we will describe a multimodal approach that integrates family therapy with other treatment modalities. Unfortunately, although somewhere between 7,000 and 10,000 women veterans served in Vietnam, we have not worked with their families, and therefore will not be referring to them.

Figley (1978) has written on families of veterans, and work by Silver (in press) is based on survey data of some 400 Vietnam veterans' families that received service through the Disabled American Veterans Outreach Centers. Silver's findings are not unexpected. He has found that the most powerful predictor of post-traumatic stress disorder is combat exposure, and second to that is impaired family functioning. These results fit with those found by Frye and Stockton (1982) in a survey of Vietnam veteran officers. In the latter study, the degree of ease in discussing Vietnam experiences with one's spouse best distinguished the symptom-free combat exposure group from the stress disorder-symptomatic group. Family functioning is apparently more highly significant than either developmental or personality factors. This research affirms what our own experience has indicated—that there is a strong correlation between PTSD and family dysfunction. The importance of family is further reinforced by findings from the Center for Policy Research (Egendorf *et al.*, 1981); these show that combat veterans who are doing well are in supportive relationships with women. Seemingly, then, marital support is a crucial factor in the successful adjustment of many veterans. How does PTSD affect the family? Let us look at some of the characteristics of these families.

CHARACTERISTICS OF IMPAIRED VETERAN FAMILIES

In clinical work (Scarano, 1982; C. Williams, "Women Partners," this volume) impaired veteran families show significant differences from other families. The following issues regularly appear and contribute to dysfunctional family patterns.

Veterans Viewed as "Identified Patients"

If one family member is identified as a "patient," as is often the case with veterans, then other family members expect the veteran alone to do all the changing. Family members usually do not understand how their own behavior can perpetuate dysfunctional patterns in family relationships. The veteran may need special attention, but frequently the family system or family substitute should also be targeted for intervention. The psychological unit is not just the individual; it is the individual in the larger social context. So long as veterans are identified as "patients," they can be maintained as scapegoats in the family or seen as the exclusive source of difficulty.

Post-Traumatic Stress Disorder

The pattern of PTSD symptoms is idiosyncratic—not all PTSD veterans suffer from the same symptoms. But certain primary symptoms—such as alienation, depression, and emotional numbing—will understandably isolate veterans from their families. Contemporary stresses often precipitate or exaggerate PTSD symptoms. The veteran as well as family members may avoid intimacy, because all seem to get hurt when they allow closeness or vulnerability.

Substance Abuse

Substance abuse, most frequently alcohol, has a negative effect on financial stability and family relationships (see Jelinek and Williams, this volume). Therapists should explore the possibility that partners may actually share in the substance abuse or may be acting as "enablers." Enabling partners may cover for veterans' abuses by making excuses for their behavior or by simply denying that there is any problem at all.

Violence and Rage

Cyclical outbursts of rage are characteristic of some war veterans. These may reinforce a fear of going crazy and of losing control of behavior. The rage may also induce fear and helplessness in family members who neither know when to expect it nor how to control it. Violence and battering occur too frequently. Although we have no national studies on battering, in a review of cases at the Vet Center in Fort Wayne, Indiana, about one-third of 600 men admitted to striking women partners or children. Not surprisingly, violent reactions are often associated with the use of alcohol.

Inappropriate Responses to Loss and Illness

One of the most painful and problematic features in Vietnam veterans' families is that the veteran often does not sympathize with illness or pain of family members, but rather becomes hostile and distant. Such a reaction may occur even though the veteran has strong underlying loving and empathic feelings and reactions. This may be part of the emotional numbing that is common to PTSD; it also impedes the veteran's ability to grieve for actual losses. Psychic survival in combat required cutting off feelings. The effect of this withdrawal is that significant others may feel hurt, rejected, unsupported, and sometimes angry and resentful about the veteran's inability to reciprocate for the care and support that they have provided.

Unspoken Rules

Frequently, there is an unspoken rule that veterans will not talk about their war experiences. They say that others, including wives or partners, could not understand. This has a kernel of truth: people can be horrified by the behaviors and experiences of soldiers in combat.

Horowitz believes that veterans need to share their feelings about what happened to them in Vietnam, but not necessarily the actual experiences. We find that giving veterans this reassurance when explaining family therapy makes it more likely that they will come into treatment. Part of the veterans' reluctance to talk about the war with their families is that they feel that the war happened a long time ago, and therefore should not disturb the family now. Such unspoken rules encourage veterans to repress their memories. But when ordinary life stresses come up, the memories return because the veterans have been unable to integrate their behavior during the war with their identity in peacetime. The "no-talking" rule keeps veterans emotionally isolated from significant others and perpetuates a tendency to see themselves as different or special (see Langer; Hickman, this volume).

Children Suffer

Clinicians are just beginning to assess the effects of PTSD on veterans' children. Children may act out family pathology with depression or with behavioral or school problems; they may seem immature. In many veteran families, mothers do most of the parenting. Veterans can be over-protective and over-demanding of their children. They may complain about being unable to be emotionally close to their children. This ambivalence may be a result of the veteran's having witnessed and/or having been involved in killing children in Vietnam. Whatever the etiology, there is frequently estrangement and emotional distance between fathers and children. Occasionally, veterans are able to express affectionate feelings toward their children while unable to do so with adult partners.

Mate Selection

Most veterans are in relationships that have developed since the war. Satir (1967) believes that, in marriage, one hurting person generally looks for and finds a similarly hurting person. Each partner has a low opinion of him or herself. Consequently, both are very needy and demand more from the other than is possible for any one individual to provide. Often, partners have superficial expectations of each other. When these expectations are not met, couples can become disappointed, resentful, and angry. Such relationships offer little satisfaction, support, or fulfillment.

Isolation, Mobility, and Alienation

For the past 15 years, clinicians and researchers have noted that some Vietnam veterans are alienated and isolated from others. Our observations reveal that this sometimes occurs for the whole family unit as well. We have noted that women partners frequently complain that veterans are jealous and do not tolerate their having social activities external to the family unit. In deference to the husband's pleas, these women cut their own ties also. Additionally, some veterans are uneasy staying in the same town or the same job and move frequently from one job to another and from one city or state to another. This keeps the family disrupted and maintains isolation.

Women as Mainstay

In troubled families of troubled veterans, women partners are often the primary financial and emotional support. They may be the major and most reliable breadwinners, and they may be almost totally responsible for child care and household chores. This leaves a rather uncertain role for the veteran and undercuts responsible functioning. Such patterns, especially when entrenched, may be seen by the clinician as due to passivity or infantile behavior in the veteran. However, chronic PTSD may lead to the same picture; differentiation of personality disorder from the stress disorder etiology is crucial (see Newman, this volume).

VETERANS AND THEIR FAMILIES

The veteran may be the identified patient, but the problems he or she experiences do not occur in isolation from other people. The problems occur and are perpetuated partly as a result of interactions with other people and with social, familial, vocational, political, and other systems in the environment. Negative patterns often develop over a number of years. Vietnam veterans who are dysfunctional due to stress disorder belong to primary support systems—families—that frequently are also dysfunctional. Usually, one cannot change one member of a family system and expect that other family members will simply fall into line. Assessment of long-term and systems effects is essential in the treatment of PTSD.

The success of any treatment of PTSD in combat veterans is problematic in the absence of educational or treatment efforts directed toward the various systems within which they live and that influence their behavior. Family systems operate with ritualized patterns of interaction and established roles. If one member attempts a change, the result is additional stress on other members. The latter are likely to respond according to previous patterns of behavior in an attempt to restore stability to the family system.

Many veterans feel that all that is needed is for the partners to understand what they are experiencing. The partner's understanding *is* necessary, but to the extent that it does not promote positive change in a maladaptive system, it is insufficient. Family members may be locked into negative habitual ways of responding to each other. According to reinforcement theory, the more one person gives in to the other's unhealthy patterns of functioning, the less chance there is that either can learn to relate in a healthy manner or effect positive change in the other's behavior. Total sacrifice by the woman is characteristic in dysfunctional combat veteran family systems, which do not afford personal autonomy to family members. Further, there is not the give-and-take or the flexibility that a family system requires to adapt to external stresses.

WOMEN PARTNERS

Unfortunately, a woman partner often thinks that her veteran partner's problematic behavior is her fault. As with men influenced by the male-oriented military system, women often seem to conform to culturally conditioned and stereotypical sex roles. To the extent that they have been affected by the stereotypes, women partners will have special problems that are different from, and more subtle than, the trauma of war for veterans. The concept of "walking the tightrope" (C. Williams, "Women Partners," this volume) identifies a dilemma for the woman partner who must try to maintain a precarious balance between supporting another person without sacrificing her own needs versus not supporting the veteran enough, thereby risking being labeled as selfish. These women, paired with a veteran who relates in a negative manner, are more likely to conform to cultural expectations that include a stance of total responsibility for the veteran. Such women feel compelled to always give a little more and to tolerate greater deviant behavior from the veteran. Thus, a negative cycle of the woman's being "responsible" and the veteran's being "irresponsible" is perpetuated.

Women partners have special problems of their own. Many have distanced themselves from others because of the veteran's problems and suffer from social isolation, so they also lack adequate social support systems. This adds pressure to primary relationships to supply all needs and increases the unhealthy dependence on the veteran partner, thus reducing the possibility of a healthy relationship.

Many women complain of helplessness and anxiety. This can be a result of the impossibility of satisfying the veteran's needs as well as his erratic and unpredictable behavior. Such women are often unable to control or effect any change in their husbands. The response to feelings of helplessness may be withdrawal or counterhostility.

Most women complain of anger; sometimes it is evidenced early on in treatment, but more often it surfaces later. The woman partner's anger may derive from many factors, including the veteran's hostility, lack of emotional responsiveness and caring, and inability to change. The woman's inability to produce change in the family, and her allowing her life to revolve around the veteran's demands and behaviors, also make her angry. Such problems for women partners result in a mixture of feelings of worthlessness, helplessness, withdrawal, and depression.

GUIDELINES FOR GROUPS WITH WOMEN PARTNERS

Women's groups are never viewed as a women's auxiliary. They should not be created for, nor should they be tasked with, the supportive function of maintaining or rescuing the veteran. Group treatment for women needs to validate the fact that women partners have their own problems and concerns that are worthy of attention and treatment.

Although most clinicians realize the importance of prescreening veterans who are invited to groups, women partners are often invited to groups simply because they happen to be in relationships with Vietnam veterans. Prescreening is indicated for all individuals for group therapy. Aside from personal dynamics, we have noted three special reasons for not referring certain women to a partners group:

1. Women who are severely dysfunctional in certain areas—for example, those who are suicidal—may need to have a different form of treatment.
2. Sometimes women who are in relationships with veterans who are extremely explosive and physically endangering should be offered family violence counseling.

3. We have found that some women who are currently not in a relationship with a veteran (because of a separation) may not fit in well with other women partners unless special care is taken to ensure that they are not perceived as models or misfits. The focus remains primarily on them, secondarily on their relationships.

Participants should agree to attend a specified number of meetings so that group cohesiveness is ensured and an atmosphere of trust and sharing is possible. Eight to twelve women is a good working number for a group. Ten to twenty weekly meetings, lasting from one-and-a-half to two hours, are usually the minimum required for accomplishing basic objectives. At the end of each sequence, women may choose to continue, but continued attendance should also be time-limited and goal-oriented. At least one of the group leaders should be a qualified mental health professional.

We believe that it is important for all group participants, including the leaders, to be women. As noted by Brodsky (1976), many women have limited opportunities to see other women in leadership positions and may tend to be inhibited and unassertive in the presence of men. This is not true of men's groups, where there are advantages to having women leaders. A male veteran leading a women's group usually subliminally reinforces a focus on the problems of the veteran. This serves to reinforce stereotyped cultural expectations that women are responsible for the welfare of veterans. In group treatment, women partners first need to be considered as individuals in their own right with their own needs, problems, and issues; this frequently should take precedence over work on the relationship with the veteran.

Leaders should have a solid clinical understanding of PTSD and know the psychological impact of the Vietnam war and its differences from other wars. Information should be provided to group members either in the form of a limited didactic presentation or handouts, with time allowed for discussion. This frequently prompts a positive discussion at home and interaction between veterans and women partners.

When both partners are concurrently in group treatment, there should be a continuing dialogue between the leaders of the men's and the women's groups, so that groups do not work at cross purposes and the problems of the various couples are kept in view. Both clients and therapists need to be aware of the necessity for this communication and informed of its content to the same degree.

Group Process Objectives

We see the group process as occurring in two phases, each with different objectives.

Phase I. Phase I is a time for sharing, support, and trust building. Women derive immense relief and strength from knowing they are not alone and that their problems are not unique. This phase includes discussion of issues of commitment, confidentiality, individual and group objectives, and the effects that change may have on their relationships. Information must be provided on PTSD and the effects on significant others. The women should be allowed to talk about their partners' symptoms, but should progress to discussing the functioning of their relationships and the effect that this may have on their own behavior.

Phase II. When group cohesiveness, support, and trust have been established, it is time for individual and group problem-solving and a positive behavioral change orientation. During phase II, it is best to avoid repetitious venting or scapegoating of male partners so that constructive work can take place. The women begin focusing on how they see themselves and what needs they have, such as social support systems. They need to establish and reinforce assertive behaviors directed toward meeting those needs.

Women, like men, often need to learn how to "act" rather than to just "react"; in other words, they need to take some initiative and control of their lives. As women in the group become fairly supportive of one another, they can begin to understand and be less defensive about how their own behaviors contribute to dysfunctional patterns of relating to their partners. It no longer becomes the men's problem alone, but their joint difficulty.

Successful work in an all-woman group produces increased self-esteem, feelings of personal autonomy, and development of outside support systems. When these occur, the woman partner gains greater capacity for action. When a woman partner begins to recognize that she cannot be responsible for the veteran, but that her own behavior does affect relationship interactions, it is time to consider whether marital or family therapy is desirable (if not already in process), or whether treatment may be discontinued.

SPECIFIC FAMILY TREATMENT STRATEGIES

The following strategies are directed at increasing cooperation between family members and enhancing certain life skills.

Removing the Veteran from the "Identified Patient" Role

The therapist should convey to family members that they must share responsibility for bringing about change. Problems should be described as systems problems by pointing out how members interact with one another and how interactions are constructive or destructive. Feelings that the veteran is abnormal because of reactions to Vietnam experiences should be explored and disallowed. The veteran is encouraged to talk with the family about Vietnam experiences, to the degree that this is tolerable to all parties.

Managing Rage Episodes

The family's methods of handling anger must be assessed. Rage episodes are sometimes brought on by substance (usually alcohol) abuse. Therefore, agreement to monitor substance abuse may be necessary. Next, the therapy should provide alternative strategies for coping with anger both for veterans and for other family members. The counselor or therapist should ask the veteran about episodes when he became violently angry. Usually, particular episodes can be recalled. Frequently, veterans are very afraid of a recurrence of violent episodes. Thus, they cope by withdrawing from any situation in which rage threatens. It is crucial that the veteran learn that he can control angry behavior through the experience of some success at control. Successive approximations to healthy, coping behavior may be necessary to learning to deal with anger. For example, veterans may progress from family violence, to putting holes in the wall, and eventually to jogging or other exercise as a coping response to stress.

Dealing with War Experiences

The therapist and family should attempt to determine whether unresolved issues from the past are interfering with the present. Most veterans have attempted to repress memories of Vietnam, to "put it behind them." But pain not worked through and suffering from PTSD do not diminish simply because they are ignored. To some extent, painful experiences need to be verbalized, cognitively restructured, and integrated into veterans' identities and self-image. This requires an understanding of the context of war and the atypical behaviors that war elicits.

Educating Families

Education is frequently a part of psychological treatment, but with this population it is particularly important. Veterans and family members often need help in relinquishing the view that the veteran is peculiar, different, or crazy. Education, including reading, will reinforce constructive change and action toward getting better control of symptoms, toward attaining greater intimacy, and toward the veteran's talking more about experiences and feelings with nonveterans.

Developing Mutual Support

The treatment should focus on partners' supporting each other and building a commitment. Since there may have been hurt and distrust in the relationship, it may be advisable to start by working on motivations for staying together before exploring the more explosive issues in the relationship. A suggested technique is Richard Stuart's "Caring Days" concept (1980).

Creating Communication Skills

Skills training is important for overcoming specific deficiencies. Communication exercises such as effective listening, giving feedback, self-expression, request-making, and assertiveness training may be important. Assignments and homework tasks may be required.

Negative interactions as well as positive interactions tend to have a high degree of reciprocity. Therefore, it may be necessary to separate veterans and women partners when domestic violence is probable. The intervention may involve letting family members or the marital dyad know that it is important not to ignore conflicts. The therapy then teaches the family how to actually contain and resolve conflicts. Stuart (1980) suggests some ways of teaching these skills.

It also may be important to teach couples new ways of telling each other when one is simply stressed and needs a nonjudgmental listener, as opposed to when one has a real disagreement with the other person.

Parent skill training is often required. An advantage of using this approach is that parents become united in the mutual effort of parenting. Consistency in parenting is crucial and may mean redefining roles and forming new alliances in support of one another.

Other skills concerning relationships and stress management techniques are often taught in a couple or family setting. These skills assist the family in developing alternative, positive coping strategies.

Clarifying Roles and Values

In Vietnam veterans' families, there is often overattachment to culturally stereotyped roles. In our society, tremendous role changes have occurred in the family during the past decade. Additionally, some veterans' experiences with war and the military system tended to burden stereotyped male-female roles. Obviously, a healthy relationship requires that neither spouse be unduly dependent on the other. The therapist must point out that family members need not necessarily agree with one another on issues, but each person does need to know how the other feels and be able to respect the opinions and positions of others. Essentially, effective treatment in the veterans' family system means helping veterans, women partners, and families break through learned helplessness, self-defeating patterns, and dysfunctional interactions that are likely to have developed over the years.

MULTIMODAL THERAPY: INTEGRATING FAMILY THERAPY WITH OTHER MODALITIES

Therapeutic intervention involves looking at the interactions within the family system. The treatment model usually advises veterans and partners to begin treatment in separate groups. Prior to this, individual therapy may be necessary. At such time as veterans and their partners join groups, couple or family interactions are not addressed per se, nor are radical changes in interactional patterns sought. Rather, the objective in groups is to take the pressure off the primary relationship by providing members with support systems external to the family.

This relieves pressure on the primary relationship: veterans and partners no longer feel as though they must have all of their needs met within the primary relationship. Groups allow members to experience the relief of finding out they are not alone and that other people share similar problems. This enhances self-respect, restores self-confidence, provides a feeling of strength, and prepares the individuals to recognize and verbalize feelings, acknowledge problems, and begin constructive problem solving.

Only when each partner gets to the point of accepting responsibility for both positive and negative aspects of their lives does the therapist open up the therapeutic system, encouraging a focus on the primary relationship; it is then time to move into marital or family therapy. There is sometimes an advantage to remaining in a support group even after family or couples therapy has begun. Separate groups should, however, remain time-limited, with the goal of developing other support systems.

When deciding on the appropriate treatment modality, one possibility is to use Minuchin's concepts of enmeshment and disengagement (Minuchin, 1974). If a couple is "enmeshed," greater individual autonomy is needed, and it probably makes sense to separate them into women partners' and veterans' groups. If the couple is very disengaged, then it may be best to bring them in for family or marital work so they can start learning to relate to each other better. Lazarus (1981) discusses pragmatic multimodal therapy.

Individual Counseling

The intake interview is usually the beginning of treatment. The intake often is the first opportunity for the veteran to talk about Vietnam and learn about PTSD. Crisis counseling is often required, and hospitalization or medication is occasionally indicated. The goal is to resolve any crisis, build trust in the therapist, and arrange for continuing treatment. Short-term individual counseling can be a precursor to group or family treatment. The spouse, if not the entire family, should always be encouraged to attend the intake interview.

Group Therapy

Veterans. Group work includes PTSD education, grief work, desensitization, cognitive restructuring, teaching interpersonal skills, developing support networks, problem solving, learning adaptive coping skills, stress management, conflict containment and resolution, reinterpretation and integration of experience, and discrimination of current life-style behaviors from war context behavior and personality. (See Williams, 1980, for a further discussion of group treatment of veterans.)

Women Partners. As discussed earlier and elsewhere in this volume, these groups focus on PTSD information, women's issues, building social support systems, assertiveness training, problem solving, and coping and life-planning skills. Such groups are most beneficial if the veteran is in treatment at the same time.

Multiple Couples Groups. These groups of reasonably healthy couples concentrate on development of social support systems, interpersonal and communication skills, conflict containment and resolution skills, parent training skills, and assistance in being mutually supportive.

Family or Marital Counseling. This treatment may include the children, if they are part of negative interactional patterns, or other relatives or significant people in the psychological unit. Obviously, the goal of such groups is not necessarily to ensure that the marital couple will remain together, but rather to reduce the possibility of undue suffering and the unpredictability of working with only one member of a family system.

Community Education and Outreach. Therapists can help create receptive community systems that facilitate rehabilitation for veterans and their families because they are no longer treated as outcasts. This may include providing literature on stress disorder and on available services. This is accomplished by offering community workshops, open houses, and professional presentations. All of these will help sensitize the community and enhance the possibility that veterans can feel at home again.

REFERENCES

Brodsky, A. (1976). The consciousness raising group as a model for therapy for women. In S. Cox (Ed.), *Female psychology: The emerging self.* Chicago: Science Research Associates.

Egendorf, A., Rothbart, G., Sloan, L., et al. (1981). *Legacies of Vietnam: Comparative adjustment of veterans and their peers.* Washington, D.C.: U.S. Government Printing Office.

Figley, C.R., Sprenkle, D. (1978). Delayed stress response syndrome: family therapy implications. *Journal of Marriage and Family Counseling, 6*:53-59.

Forgotten Warriors: America's Vietnam-era veterans. (1980, January). *Disabled American Veteran Magazine, 22*:8-17.

Frye, J.S., Stockton, R.A. (1982). Discriminant analysis of post-traumatic stress disorder among a group of Vietnam veterans. *American Journal of Psychiatry, 139:* 52-56.

Gruter, L. (1981). Families of a post-Vietnam stress syndrome. *The Family Therapist, 2*:16-17.

Lazarus, A.A. (1981). *The practice of a multi-modal therapy.* New York: McGraw Hill.

Minuchin, S. (1974). *Families and family therapy.* Cambridge: Harvard University Press.

Satir, V. (1967). *Conjoint family therapy.* Palo Alto, CA: Science and Behavioral Books.

Scarano, T.P. (1982, December). Family therapy: a viable approach for treating troubled Vietnam veterans. *The Family Therapist.*

Silver, S.M. (1985). The impact of post-traumatic stress disorder on families of Vietnam veterans. In C.R. Figley (Ed.). *Trauma and its wake.* New York:. Brunner/Mazel.

Stuart, R. (1980). *Helping couples change.* New York: Guilford Press.

Williams. T. (1980). Group treatment. *Post-traumatic stress disorder of the Vietnam veteran.* Cincinnati: Disabled American Veterans.

CHAPTER SIXTEEN

OUTWARD BOUND AS AN ADJUNCT TO THERAPY IN THE TREATMENT OF VIETNAM VETERANS

Bob Rheault

INTRODUCTION

The Outward Bound program for Vietnam veterans came about through a combination of events and because three vets were in the right place at the right time.

In 1975, the Outward Bound Center at Dartmouth, in collaboration with the Dartmouth Medical School, launched a small experimental mental health project. Mental health patients participated in traditional Outward Bound activities such as individual and group problem solving activities, ropes course, rockclimbing, hiking, orienteering, canoeing and cross-country skiing. The director of this program and staff from Outward Bound and the clinical facilities noted that the Outward Bound process was good for working with psychiatric patients for the following reasons:

- Tasks are inherently concrete, manageable, and solvable within a limited time period. Although the problems initially appear to be overwhelming, they prove to be solvable and geared for success.
- Mastery of skills and achievement of expedition objectives provide participants with a sense of accomplishment; this builds on strength and reinforces positive aspects.
- The supportive climate created by the instructor and the peer group, as well as the interaction generated by addressing specific tasks, allow conflicts, anxieties, and difficulties to be dealt with openly and examined in a straightforward manner.

The program—though small and experimental in scope—proved successful and enjoyed a modest expansion; but this was not a program for veterans. By coincidence, however, the director, Tom Stich, was a Vietnam veteran. Tom's program grew, and patients in different clinical settings were involved. One new group was from a Veterans Administration Hospital; and Willie R., a Vietnam vet, experienced an Outward Bound Program. When Willie was later admitted to the PTSD unit at the Northampton, Massachusetts facility, he was still excited about Outward Bound and sang its praises to Dick Sette, the unit director.

Dick Sette had a long history of working with vets, had started the PTSD unit, and was not afraid to try something new. He contracted Tom Stich, who in turn called me, and together we concocted the Outward Bound Program for Vietnam veterans in Dick Sette's tiny office early in 1983.

We were allowed to take patients out of the ward known as "7 Upper" for 96 hours—no longer; so we decided on a 6-day course with day 1 and day 6 at the hospital. Through the Hurricane Island Outward Bound School, we obtained enough scholarship money to pay for the first course; after that, we would have to raise our own funds—trying in the meantime to convince the VA that it was worthy of funding, and that this should become a regular part of the VA's treatment process. The first group of Vietnam veterans—all patients from the Northampton PTSD Unit—shouldered heavy packs and headed up into the White Mountains in May of 1983. Tom Stich and I, each with more than 10 years of Outward Bound experience and our own Vietnam memories, felt sure that we would build camaraderie, trust, self-confidence and pride. Outward Bound always seemed to do that, and it always seemed to lead to more open communications. The staff on "7 Upper" were going to "wait and see"; and the vets felt like they were "going out on a mission again."

THE OUTWARD BOUND CONCEPT

What is Outward Bound? Or what is an outfit like Outward Bound doing working in a therapeutic role with Vietnam veterans? Those are common questions and deserve an answer, for Outward Bound is little known and often misunderstood.

The program had its origins in the early 1940s in wartime England. It arose out of a need to instill spiritual tenacity and the will to survive in young British seamen. What began as a wartime school for survival has evolved into a worldwide organization that offers action-oriented programs for personal growth, service to others, and physical preparedness. Outward Bound takes people of all kinds away from their safe moorings of home, family, friends, and daily routine to cope with the unfamiliar, and uncomfortable, the difficult, and the adventurous, in search of an opportunity to understand, test, and demonstrate their own resources and leave behind self-imposed limits. The founder of Outward Bound, Dr. Kurt Hahn, sought to teach participants to persevere in the face of great difficulty while maintaining the highest standards of human cooperation and mutual service—an experience of "the moral equivalent of war." In Dr. Hahn's words: "The aim of education is to impel people in value-forming experience—[and] to ensure the survival of these qualities:

- an enterprising curiosity
- an undefeatable spirit
- tenacity in pursuit
- readiness for sensible self-denial
- and, above all, compassion."

The original program trained young men of Britain's merchant marine, preparing them for the rigors of wartime service and often for the ordeal of survival in a lifeboat in the North Atlantic. The concept proved successful under these difficult conditions and remained in operation after the war. Soon there were five Outward Bound schools in England, and the idea began to spread. In the 1950s, Josh Miner, a young teacher from the states, taught at Kurt Hahn's Gordonstown School and saw the potential of the idea. Upon returning home, he put together the first American Outward Bound School in Colorado in 1962, and helped set up the Outward Bound School that trained President Kennedy's new Peace Corps. Within four years, Outward Bound schools had opened in Minnesota, North Carolina, Maine, and Oregon. Courses are given in varied wilderness settings and range in duration from 3 to 30 days, but all include learning and then practicing the skills to function as a small group in planning and carrying out an expedition.

What sets Outward Bound apart, however, is that the goal is personal growth. The wilderness and the skills learned to deal with it are simply the vehicle for that growth. As time went on, it became apparent that the Outward Bound concept was applicable to a wide range of groups: young people, youth at risk, adults, educators, corporate executives and managers, women over 30, and alcoholics. It is therefore not surprising to find in the 1980s that Outward Bound is doing courses with Vietnam veterans.

As a matter of fact, the more we do the program, the more it seems that Outward Bound is especially applicable to this group. Many of the veterans experienced courage, brotherhood, determiniation, responsibility, and a real sense of power and competence when they were in combat. But the experience was invalidated, in their minds, by the outcome of the war and their reception upon returning home. Outward Bound gives them the opportunity to reexperience these strengths in themselves in a positive context.

THE PTSD PROGRAM

Of all the treatment techniques advocated for PTSD, group therapy seems the treatment of choice (see Jelinek, this volume). One of the resistances to individual therapy—"you don't understand what I've been through"—is neutralized when men are together who have had essentially the same experiences (see Hickman, this volume). Mistrust is much easier to handle in group situations; the therapist can help the group members gradually develop trust in each other, whereas in individual therapy the combat veteran is more likely to rebel against the therapist as an authority figure. Guilt is more easily dealt with as the individual in group therapy encounters others with the same feelings and watches as others gradually master their problems. The camaraderie found in group therapy decreases feelings of being isolated and scapegoated.

Rage, psychic numbing, alienation, intrusive/repetitive thoughts, and the inability to trust others are corrected as the individual finds meaning in his life's experiences through group work. It is as an adjunct to this process that Outward Bound can be most effective; for, in a sense, the Outward Bound course becomes an extended group therapy session—but with some significant differences.

The "rap session" around the campfire each night after a day of intense experience is likely to be more open, more dynamic, and more significant than other sessions in other settings. The course deliberately recalls similar wartime experiences. We carry heavy packs and again experience sore shoulders and rubbery legs. We work with maps and compasses and move out over unfamiliar territory, argue over the trail to take, or thrash through thick underbrush. We get tired, hot, sweaty, dirty, angry, and frustrated along the way; but we are able to exult and feel pride in the accomplishment of a difficult and challenging task. At night, we sleep on the ground, nurse sore muscles, and listen to strange noises in the woods. We cook over open fires or small gasoline stoves and draw water from streams, purifying it with iodine. We confront fear again on a sheer rock face while rockclimbing. We *need* each other to share the heavy loads, to help a vet who is hurting, to lend a hand across a dangerous or difficult spot on a trail, to make camp in the wild. The experiences duplicate everything except the shooting, wounding, and killing.

The courses we do with veterans do not differ greatly from Outward Bound courses anywhere. Depending on the region and the season, there are variations, but all courses include some kind of wilderness expedition involving route planning, hiking, camping, and usually a mountain peak as a final objective. In spring, summer, and fall we usually spend a day on a "ropes course" negotiating obstacles constructed out of logs, rope, and rough lumber strung high in the trees. Then we spend a day rockclimbing and rappelling—climbing up and descending near-vertical cliff faces with the safety back-up of rope and harness. In winter, we practice the additional skills of winter survival, winter camping, and snowshoeing, and the continual stress and challenge of dealing with the cold.

But what really sets these courses apart and makes them valuable for this particular group are the metaphors drawn from the experience, and the power that comes from real and intense action and interaction with others.

In the evening as we sit around a campfire and look back at the day, the incidents are recalled and lessons can be drawn that point the way for the future.

Frank C. recalls: "This morning on Blueberry Trail, when we were arguing about which trail to take, Doc and Pete didn't get involved; but later, when we found we'd humped a half mile down the wrong trail, they were the first to bitch about it." The lesson is obvious: Are you participating in the decisions that influence your life or are you just griping about what "they" decided for you?

John C. "damn near died" on the way up Mount Moosilauke, but somehow struggled on and stood proud at the top. "I was ready to quit a dozen times. My knee was really hurting and I was thinking, 'to hell with it,' but standing up there on top with you guys made me realize that I've got more guts than I thought, and your help and support made all the difference."

Dwight F. says of the mountain: "We made it to the top; we all did—one step at a time. If we could have seen how long and tough it was from the bottom, we'd have said, 'No way!'; but we did it—one step at a time. I reckon there's a lesson there for me."

In rockclimbing, participants are protected from the consequences of a fall by a partner on "belay" who holds the climber's safety rope and hence quite literally the climber's life in his hands. The oral contract between these two vets and the sometimes long periods when one must trust and the other be trusted are powerful experiences. Many have equated it to trusting a foxhole partner to stay awake and alert while others slept for an hour or two. After a scary fall on a steep stretch of rock, John called up to his belayer—who had held him and enabled him to regain his footing—"When I get up there, Butch, I'm going to kiss you!" And he did.

Backing off a cliff—even though one is supported by a rope, is an unnatural and frightening act, often equated with parachute jumping. Intellectually, you know its ok, but that does not eliminate the fear. Passing through the barrier is always a cause for elation and good feelings, hugs and backslapping. The lesson—not to allow fear to get in the way of taking necessary new steps—is learned in a powerful and memorable way.

Towards the end of the course, usually at the last night's rap session, the subject of closeness and camaraderie is on everyone's mind. Over and over again, we hear, "I haven't felt this close to anyone since Nam." The shared, tough experience of Outward Bound brings them close just as it did in Vietnam, but this time there are no wounds, no buddies lost, and no one to tell them that it was all for naught.

There is, of course, a carryover value to this feeling of closeness and mutual support; for these vets return to the hospital to complete their therapy. They have come to the field from the same therapy group and return together to continue the work. What has happened on the course can be a springboard for useful work back in the hospital. Outward Bound staff make sure that the clinical staff have the information.

What we are doing is surely only an adjunct to the weeks of therapy carried out in the PTSD unit. Even so, clinical staff who have worked with veterans and PTSD for many years and who work with and observe these men before and after Outward Bound are impressed:

> On returning from the Outward Bound experience, all the men without exception seemed profoundly moved. Many spoke in terms of renewed self-confidence, a feeling of having achieved something, and spontaneously observed that they hadn't felt like that since Vietnam. And many spoke of the sense of closeness to the other men, of being able to trust and rely on someone else for the first time since being in combat....Most of the participants experienced a marked relief from their numbed out state, which they subjectively found to be an event of major importance in their lives....

> We have observed that many of the men are far more accessible to meaningful psychotherapy thereafter, and we are of the opinion that this one dramatic experience of a crack in the armor they have built up over the years will continue to have a beneficial effect in the future for a significant number of participants.

Bruce Goderez, a psychiatrist in the PTSD unit at Northampton VAMC, made the above observation to us in a letter. His sentiments were echoed by Richard Pearlstein, a clinical psychologist in the same unit:

> The thread I see is a much-needed affirmation of self and an awakening of the sense of possibility that one can, in fact, change his life; he can do things he thought impossible. There is a liveliness and a reawakening of a capacity to genuinely struggle as opposed to going along with hospital routines in a vague hope that things will somehow get better. As a staff, we consider the contribution from Outward Bound to be the single most powerful tool in the program.

Dick Sette, who was director of the unit and who is a social worker, remarked:

> The men who actually go through the program develop a strong bond very rapidly which continues throughout the entire hospitalization and into outpatient treatment. This bonding helps shorten [the time spent on] clinical trust issues between men and staff, enhancing the therapeutic process on the unit.

William Boutelle, who is Northampton's Chief of Psychiatric Services, told us that:

> Both patients and staff of the PTSD unit believe that significant steps forward have been made by most participants in these courses. They have been able to build rapport more rapidly between themselves and staff. They often treat the therapeutic process with more sincerity and openness. Difficult issues emerge often more rapidly, and most importantly a special bond evolves which helps sustain these men not only through the program but also after completion.

By the end of 1985, Hurricane Island Outward Bound School had sent fifteen groups of veterans to the field. The program is an integral part of the therapy schedule for all but the most physically disabled patients in the Northamptom PTSD unit. And it works. No, it is not a magic trick, a quick fix, a replacement for other treatment. It is a powerful catalyst and expediter in the therapeutic process. We know this from the testimony of vets themselves and the staff who treat them.

So, where do we go from here? The obvious answer is to start Outward Bound programs as adjuncts to all of the thirteen PTSD units throughout the country. Northampton's program is well-known throughout the network of PTSD unit staffs who meet periodically to exchange experiences. Many directors are eager to begin doing the same thing. Outward Bound is a national organization with bases throughout the country; it is ready and able to replicate the Northampton model. The VA in Washington, D.C. is aware of the program, impressed with the results, and working towards a way to fund the courses.

Beyond these beginnings, all kinds of possibilities emerge: similar programs could be launched in collaboration with outpatient facilities. The concept does not have to be limited to Vietnam veterans or even to veterans or victims of PTSD. After all, the concept is simple and logical: action-based therapy works.

CHAPTER SEVENTEEN

SEXUAL ASSAULT VICTIMS: THE TRAUMA AND THE HEALING

Carolyn A. Agosta and Mary Loring McHugh

INTRODUCTION

This chapter focuses primarily on adult victims of sexual assault, with some discussion of childhood assaults and incest. Those who work with this population need to understand how strong an impact the ordeal had on these victims and their support systems. Please note that we will be using the pronoun "she" to refer to both female and male victims.

Before beginning, we would like to set forth some basic principles for working with victims. Victims of sexual assault, incest, and child abuse are people first, victims second. Oftentimes, they are frightened, confused, and unsure of themselves. They can become very dependent during treatment. They may be feeling very vulnerable as they approach a professional for help. As healers, therapists, volunteers, and counselors, we have the responsibility to respect the victim/survivor and her choices. She has the right to make her own choices. What that means is that we cannot and must not tell her what to do, even though we believe she may be further endangering herself.

We must maintain the highest level of ethical practices. If you have not recently read your professional code of ethics, read it now. If you are a crisis intervention worker or volunteer, we urge you to develop a "code of ethics" for yourselves. The National Association of Social Workers has developed an excellent "Code of Ethics." Some of the principles set forth by this code are: "The social worker's primary responsibility is to clients"; "The social worker should make every effort to foster self-determination on the part of clients."

Our role is to aid the victim/survivor in her healing process. Our role does not include investigation or fact gathering for police or district attorneys. We do have a responsibility to advocate in the criminal justice system to ensure that the individual rights of the victim are respected. *Even* the private practitioner has this responsibility. If we view this as a healing process for the person's entire being, our role becomes clearer.

The healer and the victim must be comfortable working with each other. If the healer/therapist gains information about the victim that she or he is uncomfortable with, it is the therapist's responsibility to refer that person elsewhere *immediately*. An example of this would be a heterosexual therapist who does not understand and accept that a person may choose homosexual relationships. Another example is a therapist who has biases, prejudices, or racist attitudes about a client and her culture. Not only must that therapist be able to "understand and accept," but also be able to aid that person in accepting themselves and *healing*. If you have any of these biases, refer immediately!

The final and perhaps most crucial point is that the person treating victims understand their own motives for doing so. If the primary reason is for personal gain, for personal healing, or because it is a popular issue, then the victim/survivor and society lose. Providers must have examined their own potential for victimization *and* aggression or violence. Thorough training and expert supervision will further prepare them to work with victims effectively.

SOCIETAL VIEWS AND ATTITUDES

When an individual is sexually assaulted, she deals with the experience and seeks to resolve it by way of attitudes and behaviors learned in early childhood. In this society, what one learns as a child will differ in very predictable ways depending on whether the child is male or female. In response to aggression, for example, one expects boys to be strong, tough, in control, and aggressive themselves. Anger is an acceptable emotion to them, it being one of the few feelings that men are encouraged to express. A man may externalize and see its confounding effects (sadness, loss, fear, fury) as existing outside himself. He may seek to resolve the conflict by retaliation or revenge. Male victims of child sexual assault and abuse are more likely to become perpetrators of violence in adolescence or adulthood due to this socialization.

Girls and women are more likely to internalize the trauma and its devastating effects. They are unaccustomed to dealing with aggression, and in response to it many women become less confident and more passive. They may experience lowered self-esteem and may, over time, develop a "victim mentality." This person sees herself as a victim: helpless, powerless, unable to change her situation. She can be controlled and changed by anyone whom she sees as more powerful than she is (which usually includes most people). As a result, she is more likely to remain in an abusive situation, for example, and be unable to see her alternatives. She may not actively protect herself if someone aggresses against her. She may, in fact, "set herself up" to endure more violence in the future. If all she has known is violence, she is only able to see herself as a victim. Despite the fact that she may be a successful business woman, she is powerless in personal relationships.

Further, women in our society are raised to be caretakers, healers, and the givers of comfort, not to protect and defend themselves. In fact, they depend on men for their safety and protection; first their fathers/brothers, later their husbands/male lovers. These women are not apt to develop skills or resources to keep themselves safe. They make themselves "safe" by denying the danger, for if they were to admit the danger exists, they would have to re-examine themselves, their vulnerability, and their relationships with the men they love. Such an examination threatens the norm, that unspoken agreement between men and women, such as: the man will materially provide for his wife and children and protect them from harm. The woman believes (or wants to believe) that "Now that I am married, I am safe and protected from awful things." This can be an awesome burden for a man to bear and one that cannot possibly be fulfilled.

"IT CAN'T HAPPEN TO ME"

To understand the response of a victimized woman, it is helpful to examine general attitudes about sexual assault. Self-defense and rape prevention instructors repeatedly hear that sexual assault does not happen to "women like us." Women often claim that they are married and their husbands will protect them, or that they do not put themselves in "that kind" of situation, so they are not in danger. "Teach those young girls who hang out in the park. Teach my daughter [sister, friend, niece, granddaughter.] "Women and men often believe that anyone who is sexually assaulted was "asking for it" in some way; that the victim brought it upon herself and was responsible for her own victimization. This false belief system ("it can't happen to me") is the way in which most women protect themselves, both from having to face the horror of sexual assault or the responsibility of learning prevention techniques.

The fact is that rapists feed this belief by blaming the victim to alleviate their own responsibility for the violence. The victim may accept this to reduce her own fear of future victimization and in order to minimize the impact of the trauma.

GENERAL RESPONSE TO SEXUAL ABUSE

The victim experiences the trauma and its disruptions in all areas of her life—physical, social, and psychological/emotional. Holding on to a dark and loathsome memory can wreak havoc on one's entire being. Denial and suppression of feelings may result in pelvic pain, pain during intercourse, and even migraines. In an effort to manage the emotional pain, individuals may abuse food and/or drugs and/or alcohol. Substance use/abuse and eating disorders become a way to regain control and numb the pain.

The victim often becomes more attentive to her surroundings and protective of her own personal space. She may become hyperalert: startle easily or burst into tears if frightened, even for "no apparent reason." Feeling constantly at risk and vulnerable to attack is physically taxing, and the stress of living that way often is seen in physical signs and symptoms.

Consider the impact of a sexual assault on one's social life and personal relationships. The stress is apparent in every personal interaction: whether with a stranger, acquaintance, co-worker, friend, or lover. The intimate relationship in her life is usually her first concern. Immediately following the sexual assault, the victim may experience a "honeymoon period" in which she is more active sexually than she was before the assault. She is minimizing the impact of the assault to "prove" to her partner that she has survived and is recovering. It is a strategy akin to "getting back on the horse." Both the woman and her partner want to restore a confidence in her sexuality. Women declare that what happened had nothing to do with sex or lovemaking.

The victim may report that she and her husband/partner share an intimacy that will overcome the violence she experienced. So determined is she to recover that part of her life that she often attempts to do so long before she is ready. Her partner is a strong ally in minimizing the effect and encourages the "getting back on the horse" approach. This is a very sensitive area of injury, one for which the real resolution is experienced much, much later. If she appears to be sexual initially, and then later shuts down, her male partner can become very confused and resentful. If she takes part in sexual activity before she is ready, the association may provoke a flashback. She might mistake her partner for the rapist. Her partner is apt to take this personally, feel rejected by her and perhaps become angry with her. Both of them are seeking simple answers, a quick healing process. It is difficult for either of them to believe that an event that lasted such a short time could have such an enduring impact.

The victim's family and friends are similarly surprised by the profound effects of the sexual assault. Initially, they provide understanding and support, but within several weeks, the violence their friend survived begins to sink in. They begin to realize that if this can happen to her, it can happen to them. So as not to acknowledge their potential for violent injury, they begin to examine her rape; how she responded, what she "should" have done, what they "would" have done. The victim will withdraw from them as her guilt and shame increase. Their self-concern and lack of understanding intensify her isolation. But the isolation began for the victim during her rape: she does not believe that anyone can possibly understand what she has experienced. She fears criticism, feels ostracized, and is terrified that the violence will occur again. Her embarrassment and isolation diminish the likelihood that she will ask for the support and help she desperately needs. Her energy is so depleted that goals that were once important no longer matter to her. Her trust in herself and the world have been seriously damaged if not destroyed.

Before the rape, she held a basic belief that she was a good person, that the world was essentially a good place, and that awful things do not happen to good people. Because of the rape, she is compelled to reevaluate herself or her world. Her first "explanation" blames herself: "Maybe I deserve this" or, "It is a punishment for something I did wrong." The rape was an experience unlike any she had ever imagined. If she ever had considered her potential for being raped, she always thought she would be able to get out of it. She did not have control then, now she wonders how many other situations in life she will be unable to manage. She questions her judgement, especially of men. Her fear of men may intensify as the reality of the sexual assault and its myriad ramifications begin to sink in. More often than not, the victim is acquainted with the attacker. At Ending Violence Effectively (EVE), the victim knew her assailant in about 98 percent of unreported cases. As was discussed earlier, in incest cases the assailant is usually a trusted member of the family. Small wonder that women/girls begin to doubt their judgement, especially of men.

The emotional/psychological impact of the assault creates a number of problems. The victim may experience sleep disturbances. She may have difficulty falling asleep; she may awaken at the time the rape occurred; she may have nightmares. If she was raped in her own bed, it is very likely that she will be unable to sleep there. Women have sold their furniture, moved from their homes, burned clothing, slept with a weapon, slept with a night light on, asked friends to stay with them or asked to stay with friends. These responses are not overreactions. In the mind of the victim, the rapist is omnipotent. She fears he may "slither" through the woodwork to get her. It is not unusual for a woman who has been victimized to enter her home, turn on all the lights, and check everywhere for someone hiding, waiting to attack her. Not only will she check the closets, under the bed, behind the doors, she may also check in the cupboards and the dishwasher! These behaviors are not unusual or necessarily indicative of another psychological disorder: they are a common reaction to sexual assault.

Incest victims are less likely to participate in these kinds of rituals. Their helplessness and powerlessness are more deep-seated and permeate their choices and decisions in all aspects of their lives. For an incest victim, the ritual of searching her home for intruders is too simple. The perpetrator is a part of her. When he is no longer around, she may create an atmosphere of control over all aspects of her life or the opposite may occur. She may demonstrate total helplessness and lack of control over the simplest decisions.

Another common manifestation of psychological trauma is the "flashback." Flashbacks occur with some frequency for sexual assault victims. These are waking memories of the violence, wherein the victim is unable to distinguish what is real: she sees before her the scene she is recalling. It has all the makings of a psychotic break; however, it is short-term, temporary, and memories evoked are of the specific trauma (see Newman, this volume). Reliving the event can be a way of rejoining oneself at the scene of the violence and recovering the feelings that were unsafe to express at the time. Facilitating the victim through the flashback may be very beneficial, or it may be contraindicated. Two examples follow.

Ann was in group therapy and had been since weeks after her assault. It had been five months since her rape. Ann told her group that the rape was so violent that simply talking about it would cause her to die. Ann was encouraged to "go through her rape." This is a technique in which the victim chooses to remember, describe in detail, and re-experience (to a certain degree) the traumatic event (see T. Williams, this volume). Ann was terrified and unwilling to remember her horror that vividly.

Two days later, Ann joined six other EVE clients for a three-day wilderness therapy course.

This experience provides an opportunity for one to challenge herself physically and emotionally, and test the limits and restrictions she may have imposed on herself (see Rheault, this volume) The following are two very different examples of the impact of flashbacks and their use in treatment.

Ann had just climbed a 30-foot rock face, her first experience with climbing. She was sitting on a rock, her head in her hands. She had complained of a headache earlier, and nothing had worked to relieve it. Her therapist asked her when she had experienced that before, and she immediately flashed back to her rape. She was in the rapist's truck, struggling. Her therapist was an invisible observer, "watching the violence" as Ann described what was happening. He had brutally beaten her, using his fists and a hammer. Ann was choking on the blood and wanted to vomit. She was unable to distinguish reality; she feared that if she vomited, he would surely kill her. The therapist encouraged Ann to vomit, but she refused. After much hesitation, Ann finally let go and vomited. Her headache was gone instantly, and she experienced enormous relief immediately. Fear of death at the climbing wall may have resonated with an earlier identical fear. Allowing herself to re-experience the fear and survive opened the way for further risk-taking and healing.

Sue was an incest victim. Her stepfather assaulted her through most of her childhood. During a therapy session while talking about the rapes she had experienced, she had a flashback. Her eyes rolled back in her head, she began to thrash around on the floor. She had "left" the therapist's office. She was reliving her childhood violence. These occurred several times during the course of treatment. Each time she would be exhausted, but experience no relief. She would become flooded, then drained. Therefore, it provided her no material to be used in her therapy. The only piece that Sue was able to draw from the flashbacks was her rage with her mother for not protecting her. While it had the appearance of a seizure, it was a reaction to a very potent emotion. She was able to communicate with her therapist, but had little or no memory of the flashback. The goal of her treatment was to reduce the frequency of the flashbacks, integrate what she did remember, and find relief from her feelings of guilt and responsibility.

STAGES OF RECOVERY

In aiding a person through her healing process, it is important to begin where she is and to understand her world. To have knowledge of the specific trauma is important, but to have information about the individual's interpretation of that trauma is essential. The healers/therapists must ask the questions that will aid in their own appreciation of the victim's world. For example, if she is a woman of color and the healer is anglo, the healer must ask what it is like to have grown up in her world. The same is true for a healer of one sex and a victim of another. If the healer does not ask the questions, the healer will be limited in understanding and appreciation of the victim's experience. The stages are meant only as a "guide" for treatment. Some individuals have reported that they went through all of the stages in two weeks. Generally, it will take about eight months to move through all six stages. Some will linger longer in one stage than another, depending on their view of the world and the messages which they learned during childhood. The goal is to assist the person in her healing. We see the individual as moving through a three-step process. First, she identifies herself as a victim: "I am a victim of sexual assault." Second, she acknowledges that the healing has begun by stating: "I am a survivor. I made it through a terrifying, life-threatening experience." Third, the healing is moving toward completion. It is not enough to have "survived," she wants more: "I was a victim. I survived the experience. Now I am a stronger, healthier person than I ever was." She begins to take more responsibility for her safety, her awareness and her healing. This is an exciting time for both the person who was victimized and the healer!

In the course of treatment for sexual assault victims, six therapeutic stages have been identified. At EVE, the majority of victims treated have been found to experience varying degrees of these stages. As each stage is presented, the treatment approach will be identified as well. Remember that these are only to be used as guidelines.

Stage One: Denial

Denial begins during the ordeal of the sexual assault in the form "this isn't really happening to me." In the more than 2,000 interviews conducted at EVE, sexual assault victims consistently describe themselves during the assault as if they were watching themselves from a distance of three or four feet. The victim dissociates herself from the violence because she is horrified, terrorized, and humiliated by it. It is her coping mechanism, the way in which she protects herself. Virtually all the clients at EVE describe the assault experience in a similar manner. Once the assault is over, they look back at it from the distance they imposed in an attempt to convince themselves that it did not really happen: "That was a horrible nightmare." The denial that began with "It *can't* happen to me," (as described earlier in this chapter) continues with, "This *isn't* really happening to me" and ends with, "This *didn't* happen to me."

In her effort to recover control over herself and her environment, she may describe the assault as if it happened to someone else. Her descriptions of brutal or humiliating acts may be devoid of emotion. She may omit significant details or she may question whether events really happened to her. This is especially true of incest victims who have repeatedly dissociated during the violence. In incest, the abuse is rarely a one-time event, but rather a series of assaults over a period of months or years, often beginning at a very young age. The tendency to dissociate is more profound in the incest survivor. Matters are further complicated for these victims, since the perpetrator is usually a trusted family member upon whom she is very dependent. This betrayal of trust causes more confusion for the victim. She is overwhelmed and flooded with emotions. To maintain control over herself, she shuts down further.

Denial is also manifested by the victim's minimizing the violence. She may say, "Yes, this did happen, but it wasn't really that bad. It's over now and time for me to get on with my life." The process of making light of the trauma is a way for her to avoid facing it or acknowledging the damage it caused her.

This first stage is then characterized by denial, intellectualizing, and minimizing the violence or its impact. Her report to the police may be incomplete, disorganized, or inaccurate. Remember that she experienced the rape from a distance, not as if it happened to her. She may not remember what the rapist looked like or the chronology of events. It is no wonder that police departments report that as high as twelve percent of their cases of rape are "unfounded."

During this stage, it is important that, as her healer/therapist, you encourage her to talk about what happened, in detail. As she experiences a safe place to discuss her rape, she begins to feel the emotions of that violent encounter, then she may begin to recover her memory. She allows herself to speak the horrible words that lend reality to her nightmare. As this occurs, her fear level will heighten, she will become more in touch with her pain, and she will experience relief; she will understand that there is a reason for this confusion/disorientation.

Stage Two: Catharsis

At this point, she begins to experience some catharsis. It can be a tremendous relief for her to begin to identify and clarify her emotions and for her to receive validation for those emotions. She is experiencing some relief from her initial symptoms. Further, she will most likely have additional information for the police. As her healer, it will be important to be her advocate as well, aiding the criminal justice system in understanding the victim. The police will not necessarily understand why two weeks or two months following the assault she has more information than she did immediately after the violence.

During this stage, it is crucial for her to talk *in detail* about the rape. Pay close attention to detail: are there parts she is omitting? This may be happening because it is too painful to discuss or she fears your judgement of her. For example, one of our clients reported that a man had grabbed her off the street, took her to his apartment, told her to take off her clothes and lie on the floor. She did so. He then removed his clothes and laid on the floor beside her. Then he told her to leave. Initially, her therapist assumed a rape had not taken place. The therapist explored further and asked the woman to slow down as she described the encounter. By this process, it was discovered that penetration had indeed occurred. The woman was too ashamed and afraid to say the words out loud. It was the victim's first time seeing a man nude; consequently, as soon as he undressed, she "went away." The point that she could emotionally return to the violence was the point at which she felt "safe": when he told her to dress and leave.

Questions were asked of this woman to help her "slow down" the process. She could not control what was happening during the violence; however, she can slow down the way in which she reexperiences it during treatment. Some questions included: "How were you feeling when you took your clothes off? When he took his clothes off? Where did you look when he was undressing?" If she is not responding with feelings, assist her in identifying them: "That sounds scary. Were you afraid?"

The goal of this stage is to assist her in discussing what happened and in recalling as much detail as she is able to handle. She has the right to say "Stop" when she needs to do so. Remember that she must have the control of her own process; you are there only to facilitate that process and to create as safe an atmosphere as possible.

Stage Three: Guilt

The third stage is the "point of guilt": she feels responsible for what happened to her. It is an inadequate coping mechanism, one that one-hundred percent of the women interviewed at EVE have reported experiencing. Blaming herself is a way for her to feel power and control over what happened to her. It is safer and easier for her to deal with her guilt than to deal with the fact that she had no control over the violence or with the fear that it could happen again.

Group therapy is a very powerful setting for confronting one's own guilt. The victim hears other women blaming themselves and is able to see their faulty analysis. Once she begins to let others "off the hook," she will soon relate it back to herself. For example, Barb had recently been raped. She was feeling guilty for having left her second story window open, "allowing" the rapist to enter through that window. Jean had been raped several months ago on a date. Barb was belittling herself for having left her window open. Jean interrupted stating that if Barb was responsible for her rape, then Jean was even more so, since she had chosen to date her rapist. Barb spoke up, refuting Jean's statements of self blame. Jean, who had been trying to make a point with Barb, asked, "What about you?" Barb had a sheepish look as she began to nod in recognition.

During this third stage, it is important to aid her in understanding her guilt and for her to begin to let go of that feeling. Group therapy is a very powerful support for her through this process. Again, you are only a facilitator for that process. Validate her feelings, understand the importance of her guilt, and leave the control in her hands.

Stage Four: Loss of Control

Once the victim has dealt with *most* of her feelings of guilt, she is faced with the fact that she had *absolutely no control* over what happened to her. As this occurs, she begins to move into the fourth stage of her process, the loss of control. This is the point at which her tears *really begin*. She is able to identify her losses and face the pain and sadness. Many will say, "I am afraid that if I start to cry, I will never stop." Her support system is more important now than ever; she needs all the nurturing she can find. Again, group therapy is going to be an essential component to her healing. She is recognizing that an episode of a few minutes (or hours) has had an impact on her that will last the rest of her life. She is also able to acknowledge that she is beginning to heal and to feel less "crazy." Imagine yourself the victim of a hideous crime, believing that you had brought it upon yourself; that can be "crazy-making!" It can be vital to encourage her grieving and urge the group members to provide comfort and support to each other.

During this stage, pain and losses are being grieved, guilt feelings are being resolved and new questions are arising. As she stops criticizing herself, she begins to examine her view of the world. Now she sees that the information she had about the world was inaccurate. The world has become a dangerous place where arbitrary acts of violence do occur. She looks skeptically at men and wonders who else in her life has the potential for violence. She feels less secure in all of her relationships, especially with men.

Stage Five: Anger and Rage

As she realizes that she was not prepared for or protected from the violence, she becomes outraged. Anger is stage five in the healing process. She asks: "Why didn't someone tell me about this? Why wasn't I taught self-defense in gym class, instead of the stupid games we played? This isn't fair!" She is furious with her husband; why did he not protect her, the way husbands are supposed to protect their wives? He cannot do enough to relieve her anger and frustration. She may be angry at the system for not catching the rapist. Or, if he is caught, for not getting the trial over fast enough, or not sentencing him to the full extent of the law. She is angry with her therapist for not telling her what to do, or for telling her what to do, or for not preparing her enough. She is angry at everyone for not feeling the pain she feels. She is angry at her boss for thinking she or he can tell her what to do! She is angry at her children for being so demanding, for needing her. She is angry at her parents for wanting to control her time, know her whereabouts. Everyone gets a piece of her anger, except the person who deserves it, the rapist. He is the "least safe" target for her rage. He is still too powerful, she is still too afraid.

It is essential for her to receive help in directing her rage. It is healthy rage and puts her in touch with her strength and power. It needs to be coaxed and encouraged, as well as appropriately directed. There are a variety of ways to facilitate this. One is to encourage her to take a self-defense class, designed specifically for women, by women, preferably taught by women. This can help her connect in a very powerful way with her strength and provide pragmatic tools for protecting herself and reducing her vulnerability. Another very effective method, mentioned earlier, is wilderness therapy. There she is able to use her rageful energy to challenge herself physically and emotionally while taking steps to overcome her fear. Both self-defense and wilderness therapy are essential adjuncts to treatment at EVE (see Rheault, this volume).

There is another tool that can be powerful and clearly direct anger. One of EVE's clients discovered it inadvertently. Upon learning that her *three* rapists only received 180-day sentences, the victim became outraged. She decided to call a press conference to let the "world" know about the injustice of the criminal "justice" system. The media were there *en masse;* over 100 women and representatives of ten agencies attended. It was the beginning of a court watch for that particular judge. His behavior changed as he began handing out more stringent sentences, especially in rape cases. She was given clear direction and an outlet for her rage. She experienced immediate relief as a result of her actions.

More and more victimized people are engaging private attorneys to file cases in civil court. These proceedings may be against the rapist or a negligent third party, such as an apartment complex owner, hotels, shopping malls, parking garages, and many others. This may serve as another way for her pain to be acknowledged and validated. It can also be a satisfying way for her to direct her anger. If businesses and their owners are forced to pay substantial sums for damages, they are more likely to improve their security. Effecting social change can be a very powerful healing agent!

As with any other suggestions or recommendations of this kind, it is always important to ask, "Whose needs are being met?" In other words, as her therapist, ask yourself, "Why am I using this technique? Who is served by this suggestion?" The healer can inform the victim of her legal options without suggesting a course of action. It is critically important to the sexual assault survivor that these decisions are her own, that as much as possible, she control the process.

This fifth stage is marked by rageful feelings. She will need assistance in healthy directions for these feelings. As her therapist, you will be experiencing some of her anger. Do not become defensive about it. Acknowledge her anger and help her focus it on the rapist. Remember that he is the least safe for her anger, so she needs to control when and how this happens.

Sixth Stage: Integration and Acceptance

As she moves towards the end of this stage, a calmness begins to be noticed. She begins to feel more comfortable, more *in* control, and less need *to* control. In the sixth stage, she integrates and accepts the experience. She has learned to manage her fear, to use it to move to anger, then into action. Her anger is less reckless, more clearly directed. She is feeling far less controlled by the rape. She can think about it, remember it, and not become frightened or feel helpless as a result. What has happened is that she has taken a horrible, violent, painful experience and turned it around to make herself more powerful, stronger, and self-reliant. This process does not end when the therapy ends. Many of EVE's clients have become involved in the victim movement following termination from treatment. They have joined service organizations, told their stories publicly, volunteered for the rape hot line, trained police officers, and so on. Some have trained to become self-defense instructors. Virtually all of the instructors of the Self-Protection Instruction Team, Colorado, have been victims of violence; most were clients of EVE.

TERMINATION

Leaving therapy can be a very painful experience, especially for the person victimized as a child. It is important that termination be thorough. Help the individual identify what she has gained while in treatment. She needs to be aware of the important role her group and her therapist/healer have played. The group needs time to say "goodbye" to the person leaving; she, in turn, needs the opportunity to do the same. Having time to express the mixture of emotions about the loss of that person, and her loss of that important group will be pivotal to her being able to let go. The healer will need to acknowledge her/his feelings about the person leaving group. At EVE, one-fourth to one-third of the time in treatment is devoted to termination.

SERVICES FOR FAMILY MEMBERS

The family is a very important part of the victim's support system and therefore needs to be included in treatment. In addition, family members of the sexual assault victim have also been injured by her victimization. As was mentioned earlier in this chapter, husbands or intimate partners experience helplessness, anger, and sadness because of their partner's rape. Oftentimes, they need help identifying the feelings and learning to express them in healthy ways.

This kind of trauma introduces tremendous stress in an intimate relationship. It may be important to the couple to address the issues together, as a couple, or as a family. If the partner and/or children perceive themselves as victims, they must be provided an opportunity to let go of their pain. Ask them how they learned about what happened and how they felt at the time. You may hear as severe a level of trauma experienced by loved ones as is described by the victim herself. Siblings may even appear *more* traumatized than the victim herself!

Some victims will resist including family members and some family members will not wish to take part. At least involve them in one session, early on in the victim's treatment, to help them understand her experience and what to expect in the coming months/years. A little guidance and permission may enable them to talk with her, ask her questions about what happened, support her, and receive support for themselves.

The experience of couples following an assault varies. One possible response, however rare, is for a couple to exchange support and "take turns" in each role: needy and supportive. Another response for the partner is to feel responsible for what happened and have the need to control the behavior and actions of the victim. That partner is feeling victimized and helpless, too. Let them know that there is a place for them to talk, ask questions and be heard, that they do not have to go through this alone.

Parents of victims experience the same confusion and feelings of inadequacy that confound partners of victims, but with an even heavier burden of guilt. Parents are often tortured by self-blame and punish themselves for not having protected their child. The mother and father of a very young victim are horrified by the violence and its effects on their adorable toddler who is suddenly hostile or withdrawn. Perpetrators of child sexual assaults are usually close acquaintances of the child and the family: another family member, neighbor, babysitter, etc. When they learn of the victimization, parents believe that they "should" have known, "should" have been able to predict or anticipate such behavior though they had no clues, no reasons to suspect wrongdoing. Parents are likely to be the parties who put their child in contact with the perpetrator because parents are responsible for all decisions affecting the child and his or her well-being. So when Mom chooses a babysitter who later molests her child, Mom feels it is all her " fault." Furthermore, when molestation or sexual assaults occur during critical phases of early child development, the impact and long-term effects are very difficult to predict. Parents know that. They fear their four-year-old will be scarred for life by this injury.

While therapists/healers must not make guarantees or feed false hopes or expectations, they must provide the reassurances that will give this family maximum opportunity to heal and recover together. The parents' guilt acts as a barrier to recovery in much the same way as does the victim's guilt. In the context of the family, guilt wells up for Mom when her child acts out aggressively with a playmate or younger sibling. Mother is less able to comfort the frightened or angry child when she is flooded by feelings of guilt and remorse. She experiences tremendous regrets for her choice so much so that she feels ill-equipped to deal with its consequences. As a result, she may not be able to make the adjustments necessary to cope with her child's distress.

Parents must, therefore, provide the child with additional resources. The child's therapist becomes a trusted parent figure who (much to the child's surprise and relief) remains calm when he or she hears about the "bad" touching. Parents must also provide themselves with resources. In a substantial number of cases at EVE, it has been discovered in evaluation sessions that a parent of a victim is herself a victim of childhood sexual abuse. This may have the effect of further diminishing the parent's capacity to respond effectively to her needy child, because Mom is flooded with memories of her own pain and confusion and identifies very closely with the child and his or her distress.

At EVE, we require that parents take part in a parents support/education group if they have a child in treatment. The focus of the parent's group is to provide resources, support, and information to parents whose families are in crisis due to a sexual assault. The disruption in the family is likely to be profound. Mandatory reporting requirements in the state of Colorado make criminal prosecution likely, so courtroom advocacy is usually a component of the therapist's work with the family. The perpetrator is often a close family member, so essential interventions to protect the victim will disrupt the entire family. These parents will need information and support as they seek to organize their own feelings and deal with their child's distress and the disruption in the family.

The mother and father of an adolescent who has been molested or sexually assaulted are often terribly confused. Society blames the victims, their son or daughter, for bringing the violence on themselves. The majority of all sexual assaults upon children are perpetrated by someone known to them. For teenagers, the opportune occasion is often a date. In one family session, a father accused his teenage daughter of "asking for it" by the way she dressed. Another father once remarked, "Well, she had to learn about sex sometime." These remarks arise out of the fathers' needs to minimize the violence and deny its effects on their teenage daughters.

Sometimes parents are so overwhelmed they are reluctant to involve themselves in treatment. They don't trust themselves to say and do the right things for their child. Their guilt and feelings of inadequacy move them to depend too heavily on "the professional" for the child's recovery. These parents need support and validation for being caring and concerned and for seeking help. A parents' support group can be a non-threatening introduction to the issues. Films, lectures, recommended readings, and open discussions of mutual problems are all important. Parents will be relieved to know they are not alone and their child's responses to the violence, as well as their own, are not unusual. Occasional family sessions are important to bring all members together to discuss openly what has happened and to reduce the isolation of individual family members. Male siblings oftentimes feel left out. Despite the fact that a brother claims lack of interest, he does become involved when invited to do so, and he does have feelings about what happened to his sister. Facilitating his expression of those feelings is important.

Including family members in treatment is important for the recovery of the person victimized, as well as the entire family. This is especially true for children who have been victims. The relief of the other family members is evident in their own commitment to therapy and the commitment of the victim to complete the treatment process. Healing is essential for the whole family.

SUMMARY

In closing, it is essential that the healer/therapist start where the person is now. It is important to ask questions to gain an understanding of her experience and her world. Identify all victimizations throughout her life by asking open-ended questions. If you are a male therapist treating a female client, an anglo person treating a person of color, a heterosexual therapist treating a homosexual client, or the reverse of any of these combinations, discuss these issues openly with the client. Be clear, direct, and honest.

Last, remember that you are dealing with a human being. Please be sensitive, caring, and respectful.

BIBLIOGRAPHY

Bart, P. B., & O'Brien, P. H. (1985). *Stopping rape.* Imsford, New York: Pergamon Press.

Brownmiller, Susan. (1975). *Against our will: Men, women and rape.* New York: Simon & Schuster.

Denver Anti-Crime Council (1984). "Resist If You Can: Prevention of Sexual Assault." Denver, Colorado. Copies available through Ending Violence Effectively, Denver, Colorado.

Hilberman, Elaine (1976). *The rape victim.* Washington, D.C: American Psychiatric Press.

Medea, A., & Thompson, K. (1974). *Against rape.* New York: Farrar, Straus and Giroux, Inc.

Ryan, William (1976). *Blaming the victim.* New York: Vintage Books.

CHAPTER EIGHTEEN

FAMILY VIOLENCE

Carolyn Agosta
Mary McHugh

INTRODUCTION

A man's right to hit his wife has been condoned throughout history as an acceptable disciplinary measure. English law permitted a man to beat his wife with a stick so long as it was no thicker than his thumb.

"A woman, a spaniel and a walnut tree, the more they are beaten, the better they be." A man was seen as responsible for his wife's behavior, as if it were his own. Therefore, if she committed an "offensive" act, she could expect to be punished. The "offense" might be any act or behavior that her husband and/or his male friends determined to be inappropriate.

Being beaten is still seen as a normal part of a woman's life in many segments of our society. Unfortunately, the probability goes up for women whose partners suffer from PTSD. Many still believe that a man has the right to control his property—his wife and children—as long as this is done behind closed doors and no serious physical damage occurs. Based on the judgements it renders, our own criminal justice system implicitly upholds this belief. Traditional sex roles reinforce the "right to violence." Man has the authority, woman is "his property." She is raised to be passive, submissive and helpless. His role is just the opposite: to be strong, aggressive and in control. As a boy, he is taught to be tough and to be in control. He soon learns that girls are to be "protected" and controlled; that he is more powerful and has more rights than they do. He learns that what he wants and needs is more important than what girls want, and that his decisions are right.

Girls, on the other hand, get the opposite message: they are encouraged to be quiet, to get along with playmates, to help mother in the kitchen, and keep themselves and their clothes neat and clean. In a Denver preschool, a group of two-and-one-half year old girls complained to their teacher that there were not any boys to play with them. When the teacher asked why they needed boys, the girls said they were playing hospital and needed a doctor. They had learned at the precious age of two-and-one-half years that their role was "helper." They did not believe that women could be in charge.

The resulting female behavior is learned helplessness. She cannot take care of herself; therefore, she must depend upon a man for her survival. She learns to be passive and helpless. The resulting male behavior is superiority and dominance over women. Some men learn that violence is an acceptable means of asserting their authority over women.

It is not surprising, then, that the experience of the staff at Ending Violence Effectively (EVE) and many other agencies indicates that women who have been battered over a long period of time are a difficult victim population to treat. Part of the reason for this may be that it is the population we as a profession know the least about treating. Another reason may be that we feel so protective of these women and are more apt to "rescue" them than to provide good treatment. Across the country, battered women are ignored and unsupported. Their treatment facilities are the least likely to be funded. There are still those who believe that shelters are "lesbian training grounds": shelter staff are allegedly "luring" battered women away from the family and "teaching" them how to be homosexuals.

Despite the obstacles, excellent services are being provided. The more therapists learn, the more they realize they need to learn. This chapter is an attempt to impart some of that information.

Family violence may often be both a symptom and a cause of PTSD. That is, in situations where one member of the family has been exposed to extensive stress or suffered trauma, the violence may be one manifestation of the rage and depression that have grown since the original trauma. For those who are the victims of this violence, the violent event may be setting the stage for the later eruption of symptoms of PTSD.

EARLY WARNING SIGNS OF VIOLENCE IN A RELATIONSHIP

Traditional sex roles are generally seen as very positive in this society. Society endorses and maintains the inequity between the sexes. Tradition dictates that a man be "king of his castle," that "what he says goes," that he "wears the pants" and is "head of his household." Combine those beliefs with a mentality in some circles that women are not only inferior but evil—"bitches," "cunts," "whores"—and there is a potential for violence.

Someone who harbors these attitudes and who is also sexually coercive has an even greater potential for volatility. If he assumes sex is his "right" as part of this relationship, or his "right" when he is feeling out of control in other areas of his life, he is not likely to give much consideration to his partner's desires or needs—rights are to be taken, not requested. The woman thus loses her individuality and humanness and becomes an object for his use.

And if we add a violent temper to the above traits, the chances increase that the man will be dangerous in an intimate relationship. He may begin to be verbally abusive and refer to his partner in derogatory terms that objectify her. He may cuss at the neighbors' children for getting in *his* way, throwing trash on *his* lawn, or for "being children." He may kick the dog or veer to hit the squirrel in the street. His inhibitions are often lowered if he is using drugs or alcohol. He may be physically violent by punching the wall, throwing and breaking things, or breaking something of hers. She senses the danger but denies that the abuses are directed at her. She is afraid of his behavior but she may not identify it as a fear of him.

Four conditions have been identified here: traditional sex roles, sexual coercion, derogation of women, and a violent temper. These conditions become more predictive of violence as a man becomes more involved in a relationship and becomes increasingly possessive. It happens very subtly as he resents and undermines the parts of his partner's life that are outside his control. If she is spending time with women friends, he may say, "Sweetheart, I love you so much and want to be with you so much. Stay home with me instead of going out." She is flattered by this and may stay home. Or the other extreme may be that he will say, "You're going out with that bitch, Susan? I don't know why you hang out with that stupid broad." This implies that she is better than her friend in his eyes and that if she wants to "keep" him, she had better give up her friend. Slowly, she lets go of more and more friendships until one day she realizes that although she has him, she is essentially alone.

While many men and women see these situations as "classically romantic," they make for a volatile and dangerous situation in an intimate relationship.

The relationship is characterized by isolation. The woman becomes less involved in other activities and begins to feel like a prisoner in her own home. He becomes increasingly controlling and demanding. It appears that the harder she tries, the less she does "right." Her identity is centered around her role as wife and mother. This has been reinforced by the childhood socialization that encouraged her to be selfless, to give to others first. She sees her needs as less important than those of her partner and children. Because she is so identified with her home, her partner soon discovers that criticisms of her performance of household "duties" are particularly potent.

Ann was a housewife with no other job; her husband worked outside of the home. He had been complaining that she was a terrible housekeeper. When he left for work one morning, he told her that the house "had better be spotless" by the time he got home. She spent the day scrubbing the floors, dusting, washing, and was very proud of the thorough cleaning she had given their home. When Joe came home, he walked in the door, ran his fingers along the top of the door frame, found dust, and beat her so brutally that she was hospitalized. He had not said one word to her. He used her actions as his excuse for violence.

Jane's husband complained that she never did anything for him, that she was self-centered, and on her own timetable. He had been beating her for years for this "reason." When he left for work one morning, he told her he wanted steak, medium rare, for dinner that night. He would be home at six o'clock, and "dinner had better be ready." Just before six she put the steaks on to cook. Ed came home at 7:30 and beat her because the steaks were overcooked.

Because their reality was so distorted, neither Ann nor Jane could see the double bind they were in. They still loved their husbands and believed that they themselves had to change. They truly believed that they were responsible for their husbands' behaviors.

The relationship becomes symbiotic, that is, there is an intense interdependence. The two people are merged, unable to separate themselves from each other. There is a fear that they will literally die without the other. There have been cases in which a wife has left the relationship and the husband has experienced such tremendous pain that he kills her (and often the children) then commits suicide. So strong was his unhealthy "need" for her that he felt tremendously helpless and out of control. He saw no future, no options because the two of them had been one in his eyes.

But wives, too, have a tremendous feeling of dependence upon their husbands, although their reasons are very different. They grew up learning that women are dependent upon men for their livelihood. While this is slowly changing, it is still a prominent belief among most in our society, and there can be no doubt that men are still in control economically. Moreover, women have heard from their husbands that they are ugly, responsible for his rage, and have no chance for finding another man. They are ashamed of the violence, and believe that it is their fault a beating occurs. They cover up the truth with lies to explain the black eye or bruises; they may have begun to fear for their lives or the lives of their children.

As the violence continues, the wife's affect becomes more and more flat; she numbs herself to the pain. She shuts down emotionally each time she is beaten and will gradually shut off all emotions in an effort to deaden the pain. Her reality becomes distorted. A woman who had been hospitalized several times due tc her husband's beatings reported to a counselor that the last few beatings were not "bad" and that she was only left with a few bruises. Her eye was black and blue and swollen, chunks of hair had been yanked out of her head as he threw her back and forth across the room from one wall to the other. She estimated that the beating had lasted one hour. Most of her body was bruised; however, since she was not in the hospital, it was "not bad."

The battered woman lives on the edge of terror, confusion, and shame. She becomes survival-oriented, trying to anticipate his every violent outburst, either to bring it on sooner in order to get it over or, if possible, to avoid it completely. She believes his reasons for the abuse: that they are her fault, her responsibility. She believes that if she changes, he will change. She believes that she loves him and continues to hope that the beatings will stop.

WHY THE VICTIM STAYS

Lenore Walker, through her research with battered women, has developed a three-phase cycle of violence that seems to occur in most, but not all, battering relationships. This way of discussing the problem can aid therapists and others in understanding the violence and why the victim stays.

The cycle begins with "tension building." Tension builds as the man becomes angry more easily. He may be more jealous. He yells more, is more verbally abusive and may slap the woman or the children. If he abuses drugs or alcohol, he will do so even more during this phase. She attempts to pacify him; to keep the peace and to manipulate him in an effort to reduce the mounting tension.

The acute battering incident is phase two of the cycle. This is the point of highest tension. The abusive language and possessiveness become brutal to such a point that she can no longer tolerate her fear, anxiety, and confusion. She becomes overwhelmed and may want to get the inevitable over with, so she "provokes" him; she pushes his buttons. It is important to realize that she manipulates the situation unconsciously; it is usually in response to her terror and anxiety, which has reached intolerable proportions. Perhaps she relieves her helplessness by "controlling" to some extent the timing of the violence. He will beat her. He will vent his rage on her body, heedless of her injuries and pain. She has dissociated from her body. This unconscious mechanism of survival enables her to live through the assault. She protects herself physically as best as she can and waits for the beating to end.

The final phase is the "loving, contrite" stage. This is the stage that "hooks" her back into the relationship—her needs for tenderness and caring seem to have been met. If a woman leaves the relationship, it usually will be during stages one or two. Once she has moved into stage three, it is less likely that she will leave. This stage is marked, as the name indicates, by loving remorsefulness on the part of the batterer. He convinces both himself and his partner that he is sorry for what he did, that he will change his behavior, and even that he will seek help. He may beg her forgiveness or may lavish her with flowers and gifts, take her to dinner, etc. She wants to believe him, and often does. She lets herself rebond with him. They become a "loving, intimate" couple. Their sexual relations during this time are "the best," and very fulfilling according to her reports. She convinces herself that his violence was temporary and contrives excuses for his behavior. This is the man she fell in love with and married, the "other man" is gone and was simply a product of stress, financial concerns, trouble at work.

The fact of the matter is that the violence will continue. The cycle will repeat itself. The beatings will most likely increase in severity and frequency.

Understanding the cycle of violence helps one to understand more clearly why she stays, and other factors also strongly influence her decision. While a battered woman has many strengths, self esteem and the will to change are not among them. She believes the messages that indicate that he has changed and/or that it is she who needs to change. Outside forces encourage her to remain. The prevailing attitude of family, church, friends, and neighbors suggests, "You have made your bed, now you must lie in it," or, "The children need a father." She hears from her minister, priest, or rabbi that she must be a good wife and mother, that God does not give her more than she can handle; that if she is good, her husband will not hit her, or that he is under a great deal of stress and cannot help what he is doing. Her family either echoes these sentiments or is afraid to support her for fear of the danger to themselves. If she was a victim of abuse in her childhood, or witnessed her father abusing her mother, she assumes that "this is the way things are."

The agencies to which she turns are little help in solving the problem; they tend to give it back to her. Police intervention is usually less than adequate. Officers have reported returning to the same home five or six times during a month or week, even in one night. They seem to lack understanding about the volatile situation in which they have left the couple and tend to minimize the danger. Even though in most jurisdictions the officer could make an arrest, he does not. The victim rarely receives the aid and protection she so desperately needs.

We know of a situation in which a woman and her small child left her husband, a wealthy but extremely abusive man. She had tried to leave him several times before, but each time he dragged her back. She felt that to get away she had to leave the state. She was staying in a shelter in a large town and had gone to the store with her child. As they were driving down a main street, her husband spotted her and tried to drive her off the road. Much to the woman's relief, the police were close by. They grabbed the man who was yelling, "Wait, she's my wife." The police asked her if this was true. She said yes. Then the husband began to explain how she had left him, that he was wealthy, and that he wanted her back. The woman said "But he beats me!" One of the officers turned to the child asking "Does Daddy hit Mommy?" The child said, "Yes." The husband said that he had changed and was leading a good Christian life now. The officer turned to the woman and said, "It doesn't sound like it's so bad." The husband was not ticketed for reckless driving. The wife was able to persuade the officers to keep her husband there while she got away.

The judicial system, including district attorneys, often take cases of family violence very lightly: rarely is the husband court-ordered into treatment; he often gets off with probation. (Note that this is beginning to change in many major cities, Denver and Minneapolis being only two of them. Arrests, jailings, and court-ordered treatment have become part of standard operations.)

Economic factors also keep the woman in the home. She may have no access to cash or credit cards and no property in her name. She may be a homemaker with few marketable skills. She may be a professional, but he controls all the money. She will not qualify for welfare until she moves out, yet she cannot move out without being assured of food and shelter. Friends and family may be reluctant to take her in or loan her money: they too may fear him.

The more frightening her situation becomes, the more overwhelmed, depressed, and helpless the woman feels. She may resign herself to the futility of her situation. She sees no way out, believes she has no power to change the situation, and, over time, becomes completely isolated.

Certain factors, however, do seem to change the status quo and influence the woman to leave the violent relationship:

- He begins to abuse the children;
- She fears he will kill her or she will kill him;
- She abandons all hope for change;
- She learns of other women in the same or similar situations and finds a safe place to go.

Assumptions of the Therapist/Counselor

It is important to assume that the violence occurred and was traumatic. If anything, the victim is minimizing both the violence and its impact. Keep in mind the societal and personal influences that encourage her to stay in the relationship. It is understandable that she minimizes or denies the violence when she has or perceives no alternatives.

While the battered woman is in crisis, she will probably be unable to deal effectively with her victimization. She feels so overwhelmed and confused by the changes she is making that it will be important to help her quickly feel some elements of control over her life. She will also be in terror of the batterer who is omnipotent in her eyes. She doesn't feel safe, even in the shelter or the therapist's office. Helping her to feel some relief at this point is essential.

In continuing to examine your assumptions as a therapist, you need to bear in mind that any woman is a potential victim; her choice of a man was not a choice of his violent behavior. Neither did she "deserve it" or "ask for it." She does not have to do something "wrong" to be beaten. Despite the fact that she often blames herself, *he* is responsible for *his* violence. Most victims of battering experience this guilt, feel responsible for the man's violence, feel at fault. While they share in the responsibility for the relationship's not working, they do not share in the responsibility for his violence. The woman is probably getting mixed messages from family, friends, and the system. While they may be well-meaning, they do not provide support for her in this crisis. The messages vary from one extreme to the other: "If you were a good wife and mother, he wouldn't beat you." "Just leave the jerk, then we'll help you." "If you're staying, you must like it."

In addition to external pressures, her love for and loyalty to her husband influence her to stay and hope he will change. Further, she is terrified of the threat he poses to her and her children: he has carried out threats in the past, he can do it again. When he says, "I'll take the children and you'll never see them again" (a typical batterer's threat), she believes him and sees no way in which the system can protect her. She is unable to imagine alternatives or to make choices, and is paralyzed by helplessness, confusion, grief, terror, and the most powerful one, rage. She is trapped in a cultural and social system whose influence is negative and confusing and something she must fight against if she is to discover clear options.

It is also important for her therapist to recognize her/his own attitudes about women as victims. Some questions to ask one's self are:

- Do I believe women "ask for" or "deserve" the violence they experience?
- Do I believe that the courts or police should stay out of family matters?
- Do I believe that a woman's place is in the home and that she is subject to her husband?
- Do I believe that it is impossible for me to become the victim of battering or rape?
- Do I believe that I am incapable of verbal and physical abuse or violence?

If the answer to any of these questions is "yes," then it is recommended that the therapist not work with victims of violence, especially battered women or rape and incest victims. Therapists who embrace the above beliefs will only feed the victim's feelings of self-blame, helplessness, and hopelessness.

It is further essential that the therapist recognize that she or he can provide information, education, and alternatives, but that the power to change lies with the individual. It seems that most therapists clearly recognize this until it comes to treating battered women. What is happening and how to change it are so clear to the counselor that s/he may intrude upon the decision-making process and push the woman beyond her capacity to take risks and make changes. She is no longer in control of her treatment; the therapist has taken on an aspect of her conflict in his/her effort to "rescue" the woman and "protect" her from further harm. Unless *she sees* the options and *chooses* to change them, no change will occur. She will run back to the "safety" of her old patterns. If her husband is violent and abusive and has been for ten years, the counselor may urge her to leave: "He isn't going to change." If she is not ready to leave, she is likely to return to her partner and leave the therapy. It has become an either/or situation for her. Once again, she feels she has no options when the message from the therapist is so clearly that "good mental health" is achieved only by leaving the relationship.

PHILOSOPHY OF TREATMENT

Every individual has the right to live without violence in his or her life. Individuals can have more control in their lives by learning how not to blame others for their helplessness and how to make healthy choices for themselves. Strength is gained from learning how to take care of themselves, how to love and respect themselves. Power comes from learning how to respect others and the choices they make, and by realizing that one has no power to control or change another.

Clarity and skill in this area are essential in helping victims of family violence heal and reduce their potential for revictimization. Battered women and their children accept a great deal of responsibility for their own victimization (as do most victims), but effective use of therapeutic skills helps them to change that belief system.

For change to occur, the victim must be committed to change and be able to *see, feel,* and *totally experience* change. These victims are often out of touch with their own body and feelings. It is essential that an integration of body, mind and emotions occur. This is healing. The more a person is victimized, the more estranged and disconnected are these parts of her/himself. A victimized person needs a safe environment in which to explore feelings and allow this integration to take place.

The Treatment Plan

The major components in the treatment of battered women are: intake/evaluation, crisis intervention, advocacy, referral, therapy, education, coordination of treatment, and termination.

At the very least, the goals of therapy are to:

- Ensure the safety of the victim and her children;
- Increase their understanding of the problem;
- Increase their awareness of options and resources;
- Reduce their isolation;
- Assist them in seeing and making healthy choices for themselves;
- Facilitate integration and healing; and
- Help them develop a sense of their own power.

If a person is "in crisis," it is virtually impossible to conduct an intake/evaluation.

Consequently, it may take six or seven sessions to complete a procedure that would ordinarily take two or three sessions. Intake/evaluation includes medical and family history, a history of alcohol and drug use and abuse, mental health history, examination of the client's support network, a check for symptoms of post-traumatic stress disorder, and a detailed history of victimization. It is crucial to ask the questions directly, and not assume that the client will detail all the violence she may have experienced. Further disclosure of violence (both current and historic) is likely to come later as trust is gained. Once the intake is completed, the client and her therapist can define a treatment plan.

Crisis Intervention

Throughout her treatment, the battered woman will experience crises. Her therapist can help her anticipate these periodic crises and learn skills to manage them. Unless the batterer is involved in a new relationship, he will continue to harass and terrorize her in the hopes of "getting her back." Sometimes he will continue to terrorize her even when he is in a new relationship. These contacts may precipitate a crisis for her. Her life has been so crisis-oriented that even the smallest obstacle in her plan may throw her into crisis. Being realistic with her is essential. Letting her know that it is and will be difficult to change or leave will help prepare her for the inevitable struggles ahead. She will also be aided by learning conflict resolution and problem-solving techniques and their applications. Teaching her how to manage future crises on her own will aid her in regaining control and will reduce her tendency to "feel like a victim."

As does the rape victim, the battered woman attempts to deny or minimize her victimization. This can compromise her safety. It is important to help her identify herself as a battered woman. Encouraging her to take action to protect herself, and understanding her hesitancy to do so, are part of the role of the therapist, as is having an ability to listen without attempting to rescue. During these crisis periods, the battered woman has a high level of motivation in her treatment. She may be confused and frightened, but she will also be able to work out solutions with good facilitation.

Advocacy

As was mentioned earlier, the system does not provide support for the battered woman. It is a constant battleground with numerous "Catch 22's" thwarting her attempts at independence and freedom from violence. For instance, she may want to find a job and will request child care (provided by social services) so she can work outside of her home. But social services may require that she had secured a job in order to receive child care assistance. With no one to watch her children, how can she find a job?

Since the criminal justice system is overwhelming to experts, imagine how the battered woman feels facing it! She often does not know her rights and responsibilities. Flooded with feelings of fear and inadequacy, her learned helplessness is in full swing. She may feel trapped and be unable to recognize her options. The therapist must have the essential information or be able to help her access it. He or she can offer himself/herself as an expert to provide testimony in civil or criminal matters. S/he can also be a spokesperson for the battered woman when the system refuses to listen or respond to her.

Referral

An excellent referral network is essential for the therapist who works with battered women. Referrals can include a whole spectrum of services. One of the most essential resources is the battered women's shelter. If the woman is not feeling safe or if she believes her children are at risk, she will not stay in treatment, leaving herself stranded in a dangerous relationship. Of necessity, she will resort to old patterns of coping and surviving.

Obviously, the ideal situation is one in which she and her children can remain in the home after the batterer leaves. Those situations, however, are rare. More often, the woman and children must leave to find safety. In those cases, shelter housing is *essential.*

If she has physical injuries or if she is complaining of pain, a referral to a sensitive and aware medical doctor will be needed. She will need someone who is at least aware of family violence and sympathetic to the victim's needs. It is important to aid her in documenting physical injuries in case that documentation is needed for civil or criminal litigation.

The next important referral is a good attorney. He or she should be familiar with the issues and the dynamics of family violence. The attorney must be wise to the batterer's attempts to manipulate the system and be able to explain to the court why the man appears calm while she seems "wild-eyed," "crazy" and "emotional." The husband may attempt to obtain custody of the children; not because he wants them, but as yet another ploy to "get her back." Batterers frequently threaten to (or actually do) kidnap children to gain control of their mother. For example: one batterer had tried everything to get his wife back. She refused to return. One day he got a wig, rented a car, and followed her from work to the shelter. A few days later, she and several of the women from the shelter decided to take the children to the zoo. They had just gotten the children and strollers out of the car when two carloads of men jumped out, pushed the woman over, grabbed the child from her arms and drove away. She realized it was her husband and his friends and called the police. Incidentally, during the arrest, the batterer punched the police officer with one hand while holding his child in the other. The judge ruled that none of this information could be brought out in the custody case as it was deemed "irrelevant."

In addition to shelter, medical, and legal referrals, battered women and their children will need further resources. These may include vocational rehabilitation, resources for work or school, and treatment for the children. The children have witnessed the violence and trauma and their parents have become role models. Boys tend to be more aggressive and controlling while girls tend toward passivity and helplessness. It is our responsibility as therapists to interrupt this cycle of violence whenever possible. The children of these relationships deserve to resolve the ill effects in their own lives and discover alternatives to violence.

Resources for the batterer are essential as well. Finding or developing such resources is another important element of his partner's treatment. If the husband or partner is in treatment, his therapist is one with whom regular contact is essential. The battered woman needs to know what she can expect and what to do if battering or harassment continues or begins again. The more information she has, the more equipped she is to take care of herself and to maintain control in her life.

The local shelter will be a major source of referral information. Medical, legal, and mental health professionals are not necessarily enlightened on the issues of family violence, so it is important to select them carefully.

Major Components of Treatment

Many refuse to acknowledge that the battered woman and her children actually need therapy. This may be a function of denying that the violence occurred or produced trauma. For the battered woman, the stigmas associated with therapy are alarming. Such treatment is seen as appropriate for those who are "sick," "crazy" or have something "wrong" with them. She fears that if she seeks treatment, it will be used against her in civil or criminal court cases. The fact of the matter is that therapy has several positive uses. First and foremost, the victims are apt to require help to heal and recover. In addition, a good therapist who understands family violence may serve as an expert witness to the court, and thus help judge and jurors understand the issues.

Intake/evaluation, crisis intervention, advocacy, referral, and coordination are all components of the treatment plan. Next, the client must work with her counselor to choose a mode of therapy for the first phases of healing. Couples and/or family therapy may be appropriate later in treatment and will be discussed later.

We recommend group therapy as the primary mode of treatment and individual sessions to supplement it. Individual sessions are often called for if the woman is feeling overwhelmed and out of control. Managing the initial crisis may feel safer for her to undertake privately, with her therapist. She may also be reticent at first to discuss her situation in the presence of peers; issues of trust and confidentiality are important and need to be discussed in group. The therapist can help her identify ways to feel trusting and can explore strategies for her work in group. Both planning and setting goals enhance her feeling of control over her therapy.

Many battered women come to therapy feeling numb and isolated. Group therapy is effective for them because of the ways in which denial is confronted. Acceptance of one's anger and guilt is impeded by denial: she's not angry, she's numb. But she will be outraged about another's victimization. Eventually, she will claim the anger as her own.

Guilt is similarly easier to resolve in groups: she doesn't blame others for their victimization and she'll eventually give up blaming herself. Shared concerns for confidentiality inspire trust in other group members. Common experiences with abusive partners will strengthen the bond. A feeling of safety is established in the group and a consequent calmness and stability grows. Disclosure comes more easily.

In addition, there are several practical reasons to recommend group therapy:

- It reduces isolation and establishes the beginning of a support network;
- It becomes a forum to share problems and solutions for day-to-day struggles;
- It provides a safe setting to "practice" assertiveness and other new styles of communication;
- It provides support for confronting societal conditioning, myths, and labels; and
- It provides an impetus to work toward societal change.

While groups are difficult to start, once a number of women make the investment and come together, therapists and clients alike will be amazed at the power of the process. Often group members exchange phone numbers and provide each other support, child care, and encouragement between group sessions. It is not our intent to discuss group process here, but we do urge therapists to consider developing groups for victims. These are most successful when they are groups of peers who will readily identify with one another.

An important adjunct to therapy is an educational component. There are five essential educational issues: battering dynamics; communication skills; parenting skills; assertiveness training; and sexuality. Each component requires a set of sessions designed to provide information and promote exploration of the issues and their relationship to battering.

Four sessions are recommended for education regarding battering dynamics. These sessions introduce the cycle of violence, discussions of why men batter, and characteristics of abusive men; physical and psychological forms of abuse; how control interferes in relationships; sex roles in society, and how these promote violence.

Communication skills will require at least six sessions. This includes discussions and group exercises to explore communication patterns with parents, partners, and children; learning to talk about frightening issues; experimenting with honesty in communication, and exploring how the woman herself learned her communication patterns during her childhood.

Parenting skills need a minimum of four to six sessions. These can include: the effects of one's own models of parenting—discussion of those models and the discipline and rewards experienced; the effects of those experiences upon one's own use of discipline and reward; the effects upon one's parenting style; and the effect of battering upon children.

Assertiveness training usually takes six to ten sessions depending on the needs of the group. This includes teaching techniques for changing one's own behavior, role plays, exercises, practicing assertiveness in safe situations, expressing anger, clarifying values, discussing women and power, and defining passive, aggressive, and assertive behavior.

Sexuality classes focus on discussions of sex roles and their relationship to battering; the effect of battering upon sexuality; caring for and understanding your body (including masturbation); learning clear messages about touch; and using fantasy to promote feelings of safety about sexuality. Six to eight sessions are a good beginning.

We have found two other adjuncts to therapy to be powerful additions to the treatment plan. First, wilderness therapy provides a challenging outdoor experience that assists the individual or family in integrating the victimization. Second, self-defense for women teaches new skills and techniques to reduce the chances of being victimized in the future. Many cities have excellent programs for self-defense. It is important that the classes be taught by women so that students have a role model with whom they can identify.

THERAPEUTIC ISSUES

Various therapeutic issues arise as therapy progresses.

Initially, the woman will deny and minimize the violence. When the counselor begins to confront and dispel mythical beliefs, the client may respond in shock and disbelief: "He can't do that to me?" The counselor may also hear self-blame: "He told me I made him do it. I believe him." The client needs to be educated slowly and gradually about the dynamics of her situation.

Blame is not a useful tool for helping people feel strong. If self-directed, it only perpetuates the violence, only the victim is now beating herself. If directed at the batterer, it reinforces her helplessness and inability to change the situation.

As she begins to talk to the group about violence and to identify herself as a battered woman, she may experience a cathartic crisis. She may recognize the violence, but set a goal to change herself to avoid beatings. As she tests the theory, she will be confronted with crises. Group support, education, and crisis intervention will help reduce the need for such testing.

Group therapy helps the woman let go of guilt and self-blame. She realized that she had no control over him and that he chose the violence. She may now be receptive to education regarding assertiveness and communication. She needs to begin building her self-esteem and confidence. She begins reestablishing trust in herself and her judgement. She will learn to use the group and her therapist to understand her role in the abusive relationship.

As she begins to heal, to take better care of herself, to take responsibility for herself, to become less dependent on him, he may feel more threatened and out of control. He may thereby become more dangerous to her. Helping her assess his level of danger will increase her safety and awareness. Her therapist will need to help her identify changes in his behavior and assess those changes. Whenever the therapist or the client is in doubt about the level of danger, both should assume the worst and take all necessary precautions.

Therapy continues, and the client may become angry. As with the sexual assault victim, the anger stage is an easy place to become "stuck." She will need help directing her anger. She will direct some toward the batterer for not changing, and some toward society for the socialization she and her partner experienced. She will need help expressing her anger in healthy ways, without blaming. Beating pillows, hitting a punching bag, and yelling are acceptable ways to express that rage. The therapist can emphasize the importance of not hurting oneself or anyone else as anger is expressed, and can teach her how to express her anger in a non-abusive way.

In many cases, a woman may recognize that her partner is not going to change and the relationship is over. She may be deeply saddened by the losses: the relationship, her partner, and her dreams. The therapist can give her "permission" to cry. They are very deep and very painful. For a time, she may vacillate between this overwhelming sadness and her rage.

The process continues, and integrating the experience becomes the next task. One can anticipate that a woman who has been victimized for years will take years to heal. Encourage her and let her know that other women and their children have become stronger and healthier following recovery from such violence. She can learn to trust herself. Many women are able to trust a man again and to have a healthy, loving, violence-free relationship.

COUPLES THERAPY

We have strong concerns regarding couples therapy for battered women and the batterer. Since this is a symbiotic relationship, we urge therapists to wait until both individuals can identify their own issues and see themselves as separate from each other. This may take anywhere from one to four years, or even longer. Time is not the issue, individual readiness is. A second concern is that, in a relationship where partners have separated, he may use his desire for treatment as a way to "get her back." We have found that once she returns, his commitment to therapy wanes or ends.

FAMILY THERAPY

Family therapy is appropriate when the woman and man have agreed in an *individual* session with the therapist that this is what each one wants. Family therapy, when appropriate, should facilitate repair of the relationship, and include practicing safe methods of communication. Family therapy is initiated late in treatment after boundary issues are resolved. Family work should proceed slowly.

Therapists should first meet with parents and children individually. Information gathered from initial visits with children will enable the therapist to assess the children's safety in the home. Obviously, if the children report they do not feel safe, open, honest communication cannot occur. Considerable time may be required to establish feelings of safety so family therapy can occur.

If the couple has decided to end the relationship, sessions should be planned with father and children, and mother and children. Custody issues will most likely need to be addressed. A child's desire to live with a particular parent does not make that living situation the best for that child. Children may request to live with their father out of fear. They may see him as omnipotent, and male children may identify with his power. The children need a safe place to discuss their fears, to share openly and honestly. Therapists must ensure they have that place. Evaluations of all parties will probably be needed, but we recommend that the treating therapist not provide these evaluations.

The therapist must consider the entire environment of the family; this includes gathering pertinent information about the background and culture of the family. Some cultures believe a man has the right to beat his wife. Patterns of violence and abuse may be harder to change in cultures that espouse this belief. In cultures with a strong sense of family, it is unlikely that the woman will leave her home. If she does leave, feelings of guilt will be paramount. Regardless of the culture, the therapist must respect beliefs and behaviors that affect the therapeutic process. Listen to the client and begin where she is now.

TERMINATION OF THERAPY

One of the most important parts of a treatment plan for victimized women is termination, letting go. For the individual who has had to lose a relationship, let go of parents, dreams, or hopes for the future, this can be a particularly painful time. Now she is going to lose the ones who have opened the way to new solutions in her life—her therapist and therapy group. She has changed many styles of interaction and developed new ways of seeing others and herself. You, as therapist, have had an important role in that process. She will probably become angry with you during this phase of separation and feel that it is you who are leaving (abandoning) her. Acknowledge her anger, relate it to other losses she has survived. Realize together that this "goodbye" brings up other painful partings.

This is also an occasion in the therapy process to look back and reflect upon the period in therapy and the changes it has brought. Acknowledge together the changes, tools acquired, and skills she's gained. Acknowledge also the work remaining. Help her anticipate what may come up for her in the future and how she will meet her needs without you and without the group. Your acknowledgement of your role is important, too.

CONCLUSION

Family violence is a difficult and painful issue with which to work. However, when positive change occurs, the therapist will feel a great sense of reward from watching people heal and recover their sense of self and personal power. Seeing systems change and become more responsive to the victims gives a sense of satisfaction and accomplishment.

Personal power, commitment, sensitivity, awareness, and a strong desire to effect change are the tools a therapist needs to work with victims of family violence.

BIBLIOGRAPHY

Bloom, L.Z., Coburn, K.; Pearlman, J. (1975). *The assertive woman.* New York: Delacorte Press.

Diagram Group (1977). *Woman's body, an owner's manual.* Paddington Press, Ltd.

Fields, M.D., Lehman E. (1977). *A handbook for beaten women.* New York: Brooklyn Legal Services Corporation.

Gelles, Richard J. (1974). *The violent home.* New York: Publications, Inc.

Martin, Del (1977). *Battered wives.* New York: Simon and Schuster, Inc.

Paris, C.; Casey, B. (1976). *Project you: A manual of rational assertiveness training.* Denver: Institute of Living Skills Education.

Phelps, S.; Austin, N. (1975). *The assertive woman.* San Luis Obispo, CA: Impact Publishers, Inc.

Pizzey, Erin (1974). *Scream quietly or the neighbors will hear.* England: Penguin Books Ltd.

Rush, Anne Kent (1973). *Getting clear, body work for women.* New York: Pan American Copyright Conventions.

Smith, M.J. (1975). *When I say no, I feel guilty.* New York: Dial Press.

Walker, Lenore (1979). *The battered woman.* New York: Harper and Row, 1979.

Warrior, Betsy (1976). *Wifebeating.* Massachusetts: New England Free Press.

CHAPTER NINETEEN

PEACETIME COMBAT: TREATING AND PREVENTING DELAYED STRESS REACTIONS IN POLICE OFFICERS

Candis Williams

INTRODUCTION

Over the past five years, I have counseled hundreds of disillusioned Vietnam veterans and their families around issues of post-traumatic stress disorder (PTSD); recently, I began working with police officers. While there are remarkable similarities between the types of stresses on and the responses of the two groups, there is also one crucial difference: for cops, the "war" never ends—they are out there 24 hours a day, 7 days a week to "protect and serve," to fight the criminal—our peacetime enemy. The police officer is expected to be combat-ready at all times while remaining "normal" and socially adaptive away from the job. The psychological toll for many is great, unexpected, and not well understood. Their families and friends have been adversely affected and emotionally wounded, as well.

Very little research has been conducted on PTSD with police officers (Reiser, 1973). Even coping strategies have thus far been a neglected area in police stress investigation. Nonetheless, enlightened police agencies now recognize that there are psychological hazards connected with the job. We are beginning to realize that psychological disturbances in officers are attributable to job-related hazards rather than pre-existing personality traits at the time of hire (Meredith, 1984).

Historically, police psychologists have been primarily involved in psychological assessment—selection and screening of officer candidates—and "fitness for duty" evaluations. Many of us have entertained the myth that those who become police officers have specific types of personalities. There is absolutely no research data to support this. In fact, even our best selection criteria are not predictive of occupational suitability for more than two years after an officer joins the force.

Most mental health professionals now accept that a group of natural symptoms will surface when people experience traumatic events or persistent and unrelieved stress. The severity of PTSD symptoms is linked directly to the length and intensity of the traumatic experience. However, some in the military, government, industry and police administrations continue to discount the significant effects of traumatic stress. There are those in law enforcement who chide the psychological specialist by saying that there was no such thing as stress before the term was introduced, and that it is thereby a self-fulfilling prophecy. But the increasing evidence cannot be ignored: even the skeptics cannot deny the physiological symptoms and psychological problems that are apparent in the law enforcement profession.

Vietnam veterans and police officers exhibit symptoms of PTSD that may be attributable either to acute traumatic stress or to a chronically high stress level. Invariably, there are behavioral or personality changes with time (Niederhoffer, 1967). Self-disclosure decreases (Parker & Roth, 1973), and a general authoritarianism, resulting in distancing, alienation, anger, denial, and depression set in, damaging the individual and his or her relationships.

Most people who become police officers show fairly normal psychological profiles early in their careers. It is several years down the line that they take on characteristic attitudes and behaviors or so-called "police personality traits." If, over time, the behavior and attitudes of people in a certain profession become more similar, this phenomenon can only be described as learned behavior: the result of environmental factors and conditioning. We should stop searching for "model officers" and "model soldiers." There are none. Instead, we should be concentrating on environmental conditions; on how to provide normal people with the information, skills, and support to operate in an abnormal environment.

The focus of this chapter is peacetime combat veterans—police officers. The parallels between Vietnam veterans and police officers are noted. I will address how a law enforcement environment contributes to high negative (general) stress levels and examine "critical incidents" (acute traumatic stress). Treatment considerations are briefly reviewed.

Importantly, the theoretical approach and prevention model used by the Denver Police Department is described. We can alleviate acute post-traumatic symptoms. Instead of being reactive, we can take action in advance. We can do much with police officers to avoid the delayed stress so evidenced by war veterans, and we can thus lessen the injury to significant others and to our communities as well.

Finally, questions and implications for the future are noted. As we confront the legal and moral issues that are surfacing, we will develop a better understanding of the dynamics of stress responses so that we can better meet the needs of all victims of trauma.

STRESSES IN THE POLICE PROFESSION

Police work involves three major functions: (1) law enforcement, which includes crime prevention and arrests of law violators, (2) maintenance of order—that is, minimizing public disturbances, and (3) public service or human service provision, including victim assistance. Each function carries its own level of chronic stress, to which we must add those inescapable instances of acute stress—a drug bust, a shooting incident, a high-speed chase. It is difficult to draw a line between the effects of chronic high stress and those of acute stress; their effects are often synergistic. However, we should note that only about 6 percent of calls for police officers bring them into highly stressful situations.

The majority of the police officer's time is spent in routine performance of duty. Officers must try to "talk down" potential suicides, deal with mutilated homicide victims, and transport battered youngsters and psychotic adults to local facilities. Sometimes, these dramatic shifts in approach and style must be made within the course of one working shift. Officers also engage in what we consider to be their most common function—confronting criminals who have no compunctions about killing.

Emotional stress results when officers must face their inability to ease human suffering, or guarantee that justice will be done, or question and examine their loyalty and honesty with fellow officers. Jacobi (1975) argues that the most frequent common denominator of perceived stress is "performance anxiety" manifested in fears of doing something wrong, of being criticized or investigated, or of being tried and possibly suspended or dismissed. This anxiety is intensified in situations where officers feel they must rigidly adhere to defined roles and rules in spite of an impulse to assume other roles, to ignore the sanctioned role, or to function more effectively in a way that may defy prescribed procedures.

Less intense but chronically stressful aspects of the job include variable shift schedules and weekend duty. The officer has little control of the situation and only limited ability to plan for a personal life. Even the most basic aspects of living—eating and sleeping—can be drastically affected. Such chronic or prolonged stress can lead to compulsive overwork, exhaustion, and/or absenteeism.

Of the general stressors in police life, the pressures and nature of the organization itself are most frequently cited as contributing to other job pressures. Meeting the expectations of the department may be the most difficult task the officer faces. Different supervisors often expect different levels of performance, which creates morale problems. Whenever there is a command change, a new staff study, or revised directives come down, the officers must adjust or comply, a frustrating and aggravating routine. Certainly there is a dramatic effect on the young officer who is raising a family. Realignment of shifts and personnel can seem trivial to an administrator who has worked 9-5, Monday through Friday, for a long time and forgotten how disruptive shift work can be.

This is one reason that we stress the need for thorough first-line supervisory training: it is crucial to diluting negative pressures. Organizational practices and goals can effectively reduce stress; consistent goals and objectives within the department are a must and should be known to all personnel.

Some well-meaning police agencies, in a search for excellence and greater professionalism, become extremely introspective and self-critical. The line officer consequently feels more apprehension about supervisor responses than about criminal elements (Daviss, 1982). Front-line officers are finding it more and more difficult to deal with the complexities of their jobs. Difficulties are compounded by the conflicting expectations established by the dual roles of law enforcer and human service provider. Stress is even more pronounced in special units where supervisors are particularly anxious to maintain control and accountability.

Stress reactions, such as depression, have more to do with the managerial environment and supervisory conditions than with the officer's personality. In fact, we in Denver, in looking at the environment in which police officers work, operate on the assumption that law enforcement remains a predominantly negative environment. From a social-learning standpoint, it follows that there will be unhealthy individuals and an unhealthy organization by virtue of environmental influence and conditioning unless proactive interventions are applied. (For an illustration of our notion of how such a proactive, open system would look, see Appendices 1 and 2.)

Experiences in the police academy and later field training contribute significantly to an officer's adaptive or maladaptive behavior (Reiser & Geiger, 1984). New, inexperienced police officers tend to exaggerate their abilities and emphasize physical strength and ruggedness. Training and peer response reinforce this behavior. Young officers have a need to believe that they are invulnerable and able to handle any kind of danger. Ironically, these macho attitudes and behaviors can serve a survival function and protect an inexperienced officer in a physically dangerous and psychologically threatening environment. But they may exact a heavy price in suppressed feelings, cynicism, and emotional distancing.

Disenchantment

Administrative pressures, lack of public appreciation, and an increasing sense of alientation from the community contribute to the officer's growing disenchantment with police work. It is estimated that the greatest dissatisfaction takes place between the third and eighth year on the job (White, Olson, and Knowles, 1980). The only way for a police officer to "get out" is to quit and change professions, but because there is tremendous peer support on the job, many officers are reluctant to attempt to make it in an "alien world." Like the war veteran, the police officer is seen by society as different from others. Early in their careers, most police officers view themselves as well-trained, highly skilled professionals dedicated to public service. In the course of their careers, they feel they are feared, disliked, and unappreciated by the law-abiding public they are protecting and serving.

Disability retirement may be viewed as the only "acceptable" way out, and since the work is inherently dangerous, the opportunity to take additional risk or get the "million dollar wound" can be a great temptation. Frustration with the system may sometimes be a subconscious motivator to push the limits of personal safety. (Meredith, 1984)

Niederhoffer's (1967) research shows a positive correlation between the length of time an officer is on the force and the degree of cynicism he or she develops; officers also develop attitudes that are authoritarian and depersonalized. These attitudes have deleterious effects on personal lives and relationships. They also restrict the officer's perception of acceptable ways of handling police work; officers may adopt an authoritarian posture in situations when a better response would be flexibility and humanitarianism.

Guilt is another companion of police officers who consider themselves to be conscientious, moral people with high standards and expectations of themselves. They can be their own worst critics and guilt feelings can interfere with their sense of competence and positive self-identity. Paranoid reactions also seem to be common. Girodo (1985) believes that these are fostered by a lack of information and social isolation. Suspiciousness and paranoia are exacerbated by other team members who themselves are suspicious, distrustful, and paranoid; once such a paranoid process has set in, reason and logic are ineffective.

SUMMARY

Police officers certainly evidence a higher incidence of health and psychological problems than do those in most other occupations. The profession ranks among the highest in disability claims that often lead to retirement, hospital admissions, and stress-related, premature deaths (Blackmore, 1978; Kroes & Hurrell, 1975). Schaefer (1985) argues that lack of control is a major cause of stress: police officers are called upon daily to make split-second, life-or-death decisions. In many cases, there is no good resolution, so there must be some stress-reducing habits built in that will make it easier to deal with these difficult, irresolvable situations. Schaefer argues that the better one's physical health is at the onset of stressful events, the better able one is to resist the kinds of detrimental physical and psychological responses that are described in the next section.[1]

VIETNAM SOLDIERS AND POLICE OFFICERS: PSYCHOLOGICAL SIMILARITIES

There are many parallels between the experience and the environment of the Vietnam soldier and today's police officers. Both groups share the goal of fighting an enemy. Both face hazardous duty that necessitates rigorous training in self-defense, assault, and confrontation. The danger factor requires constant alertness, and the enemy is often hard to identify. Relations even with non-enemies are frequently negative or adversarial. Essentially, both of these groups put their lives on the line without a great deal of appreciation from those they serve. Let us look briefly at some of the other similarities.

Very often there is a "we-them" attitude that makes police officers (and veterans) feel "different" from others in the community. The police group identity becomes increasingly important as public rejection and aversive situations add up; other cops understand and that bolsters self-esteem and confidence. A strong peer culture has both positive and negative consequences: according to Stratton (1984), "Policemen's macho images, their need for non-emotional responses and their penchant for seeking out the most life-threatening and violent assignments can lead to an inability to express feelings of inadequacy or pain. If affected by trauma, they must continue to keep up a brave front so that it appears as if they were unaffected by the incident." The support system thus becomes an emotional liability.

Survival sometimes requires that they maintain a certain distance; this suspiciousness and distrust are job-adaptive behaviors, but they alienate and isolate veterans and officers in their personal lives. Paranoia is often an outgrowth of an otherwise useful suspiciousness: both groups are reluctant to sit with their backs to the door or other open area.

Law enforcement agencies have a quasi-military command structure whose rigid hierarchy reinforces impersonality and severely limits autonomy. The strict and unquestioned discipline that works well for rapid mobilization and response to threat conflicts with the softer, more humane posture that is needed for the officers' role as "human service provider."

Certainly, many police officers choose their occupations because they have altruistic beliefs and because their primary mission is to help people; many soldiers enlisted out of patriotic motives. Many end up being cynical and disillusioned because of their initial idealism and the consequent rude awakening that results from confronting the reality of the street or the politics of war.

Both in war and in law enforcement, a great degree of emotional distancing is necessary to get the job done and to survive. Also, the particular nature of the job means that the soldier or officer deal with only a small segment of the population—and not a segment that is going to provide warm interpersonal experiences. However, off the job, this tactic produces an individual who seems cold, aloof, and unable to achieve intimacy with family or friends.

Police, particularly, socialize mostly with their own to avoid the ill-will they often experience in the outside world. Unfortunately, this sense of rejection is carried over to their families. Divorce and family break-ups are significantly higher for police and veterans: 38 percent of Vietnam soldiers who were married were divorced within 6 months of their return to this country (Stratton, 1984). Police marriages are known to break up more in the early years. Serial marriages and extramarital relationships are a "norm" in many police circles.

Frequently, there has been an unspoken rule that veterans and/or police officers will not talk about their war or street experiences. They believe that others, including wives or partners, cannot understand. Sometimes this is true: their stories may horrify the uninitiated. Whether the veteran or police officer chooses to withhold or to protect by this lack of sharing is sometimes immaterial: the end result is that significant others feel left out and rejected, and have very little understanding or appreciation for their family members' professional lives. The "no talking" rule keeps veterans and officers emotionally isolated and perpetuates a tendency to see themselves as different or special.

Chapman (1986) describes this self-imposed exile as a "terminal case of uniqueness." Horowitz and Solomon (1980) have suggested a way there can still be sharing with significant others that would not be shocking: they urge that the veteran or officer talk about feelings rather than the details of the traumatic event(s); however, as we have seen, this is easier said than done for those who have made a practice of suppressing feelings. Suicide rates for veterans and for police are much above the national norm.

All too often, the "solution" to this emotional pain and high stress is substance abuse. Vietnam veterans had easy access to illegal drugs overseas. Some have not broken their addictions, although the drug of choice for both groups is alcohol. Whatever the substance abused, it interferes with already difficult and tenuous functioning for many; and it usually exacerbates impulses toward anger and violence. These tendencies bubble just beneath the surface and have often been used to relieve tension and restore the sense of control that is lost to depression or hyperalertness.

In a war zone—at home or abroad—combatants are in a constant state of vigilance. Alternating periods of boredom and potentially dangerous situations keep the body in constant flux and cause shifts in adrenalin and blood sugar levels. These weaken bodily defenses and increase the likelihood of various stress-related physical diseases, including high blood pressure, heart attacks, diabetes, ulcers, chronic fatigue, skin problems, headaches, panic attacks (hyperventilation), gastric disturbance, sexual dysfunction and myriad other disorders. Physical disabilities and ailments are evidenced in much greater numbers than in the rest of the population. Stressful psychological factors are chronic and cumulative. Consequent emotional exhaustion further weakens immunological systems and a deteriorating mind-body interaction can ensue.

Traumatic incidents potentiate horrible nightmares that are so vivid that individuals will scream, sob uncontrollably, and/or "aggress" against a sleeping partner mistaken for the enemy. (Women report being hit or strangled by spouses who were reacting in their sleep.) The dread and fears associated with falling asleep and dreaming can reinforce self-medication—alcohol abuse—in an attempt to "black-out" or obliterate shocking and fearful recurring nightmares. Sleep disturbance becomes a major secondary stressor. Resulting behavioral concomitants such as irritability, poor job performance, reduced sex drive, fatigue and lethargy are well-documented.

Cops or veterans who have a need to have weapons readily available are exhibiting a need to feel protected by being constantly "prepared." However, this defensive preparedness, emotionally and physically, can become an obsession and a liability. Exaggerated startle reactions and obsession with weapons are not uncommon to either veterans or police. Startle response may be a result of chronic readiness states learned from duty, e.g., individuals may overreact to someone coming up from behind them. The sounds of gunfire, firecrackers, helicopters, as well as various smells can send a veteran diving for cover, and police officers may be hyperalert to danger-related stimuli.

It is not uncommon to find a large proportion of "action junkies" or "sensation seekers" (Wilson, 1980)—people who are essentially addicted to adrenalin highs (thrills, excitement, emotional, physical, and death-defying challenges)—among both veteran and police groups. These individuals are bored with anything less than constant excitement and/or stress, even in their intimate relationships, where they seek the "high" of romance and move on when the relationship settles in to something less exciting.

Similarily, there are also a number of "saviors" or "pro-social humanitarians" (Wilson, 1980)—former soldiers and cops who have changed careers to become counselors because they take solace for themselves from giving to and helping others. For some, this seems to atone for guilt and fill an altruistic need to spare others some of the pain they may have felt; at the same time, it helps them resolve their own pain. This is a positive coping response except when it is carried to an extreme and becomes sacrificial.

The parallels between military combat experience and policing are obviously considerable, which may help us to interchange both theory and preventive efforts when we attempt to ameliorate the effects of stress in each group.

POST-TRAUMATIC STRESS DISORDER IN POLICE OFFICERS

We used the terms "war neurosis" and "combat fatigue," and their law enforcement analogs, "post-shootings" and "critical incidents," long before the concept of post-traumatic stress disorder was introduced. All of the symptoms and behaviors that are described by these terms are subsumed within the diagnostic category of PTSD. There are unfortunately some misconceptions about this constellation of symptoms that should be dispelled:

- A person experiencing PTSD is not mentally ill. He or she is responding to specific experiences and needs help in identifying and resolving the issues raised by these experiences.
- Frequently, a person may be experiencing PTSD but may be completely unaware of it. PTSD is not an excuse for unacceptable behavior, although it may be the basis for that behavior.
- As with alcoholism or drug abuse, the spouse or family of the person involved experiences their own symptoms that often are similar to the veteran's or the police officer's.

According to Tom Williams (1985), Director of the Post-Trauma Treatment Center in Denver and a national specialist on PTSD in Vietnam veterans, "Problems are worse if somebody is killed during the trauma, or if the trauma was man-made, rather than a natural disaster. Often the problems can go untreated because the sufferer feels ashamed about seeking help. They fear they are losing their minds." Williams believes that these denial responses are not unusual because we frequently tell the victim to "Just forget it, you'll be okay." In so doing, we convey an attitude that the person is weak or a crybaby, thus causing him or her to try even harder to suppress the pain.

A post-traumatic stress response is not necessarily tied to any personality deficiencies, particular weaknesses, or poor coping abilities. The post-trauma stress syndrome is normal, a normal reaction to an abnormal situation. When something occurs that is beyond the normal range of human experience, then the response to that event is also going to be out of the ordinary.

Both combat veterans and police officers who have killed in the line of duty are prone to PTSD. It can ruin their careers and their lives. According to some estimates, 70 percent of officers involved in a killing leave the force within 7 years of the incident. As Williams says, "There's no one to guide the officer through periods of self-doubt, depression, anger and guilt. If unresolved, the trauma can ruin the officer's life." In the police training academy, individuals learn how to kill people when they must, but not how to care for themselves afterwards; similarly, we taught our wartime soldiers to enter into combat, but not to deal with the after effects of that experience.

Acute Post-Traumatic Stress

It is sometimes difficult, if not impossible, to distinguish between the effects of traumatic, cumulative, protracted, and periodic or episodic stress. Clearly there are interactive effects, especially within a profession where the danger level and stress potential remain fairly high. More general stressors for individuals in law enforcement were described earlier. This section considers specific examples of acute stress situations and responses; it looks particularly at situations where weapons are used.

Dr. Jack Seitzinger (personal communication), Director of the St. Louis Police Academy and also a psychologist, works with police officers who have been forced to kill in the line of duty. He finds that 6 out of 10 police officers are traumatized and 2 of those 6 have severe reactions to taking a life in the course of their jobs. Severely traumatized officers who have been involved in police related killings or other similarly critical incidents can experience nightmares, flashbacks, and symptoms of severe depression (weeping, physical withdrawal and isolation, loss of appetite, lethargy). Emotional responses such as intense sorrow and confusion are not uncommon.

It is important to note that shootings are certainly not the only events that can cause PTSD—high speed chases, fights, undercover narcotics and vice work, bomb squad work, injuries and accidents also take their psychological toll. When these events occur, the officer may have no choice but to discard the typical macho shield that has kept his feelings under wraps, and thus the usual defenses are not available. Typically reported reactions immediately following or during the traumatic event include time distortion, emotional numbing, and feelings of isolation. Anxiety, nervousness or edginess and rapid mood changes, as well as rapid defense postures, are resulting "coping" behaviors. Typical symptoms of depression occur, along with low motivation, disappointment and disillusionment with the job. Physiological effects include sleeplessness, loss of sex drive (which may also appear some time after the initial stressor), weight loss, and reductions in productivity.

Those who face combat situations have learned to protect themselves by suppressing feelings. But, in the emotional aftermath, it is unlikely that they can prevent nightmares and flashbacks. Gruesome scenes are vividly recollected. The mutilated bodies of girls and women can be particularly horrifying and incidents relating to children invariably cause intense emotional pain. Such experiences are not forgotten. They color an individual's behavior toward loved ones; family members often suffer. Extreme responses range from avoidance behavior to intense intimacy and overprotectiveness. Many officers replay the traumatic scene over and over again, telling themselves that the outcome might have been different if only they had done thus and so. It's an occupational hazard and it does not seem to matter whether the officer's behavior was above reproach or questionable. Long after the event, nightmares, insomnia, psychological/physiological symptoms, guilt, and low self-esteem may still be present; if endless self-doubt continues, it exacerbates PTSD symptoms. Still, some find it difficult to end this negative cognitive process. Because of guilt feelings or secondary gain, they may actually choose to cling to the negatives.

Secondary Effects

The aftermath of the particular event is also highly stressful. Responses from others have a powerful influence. Typically, an officer is isolated and taken off his or her duties immediately following a shooting or other serious incident. He or she may feel a "separateness" because of having shot someone—an experience that many officers will never have. The investigation as to the "righteousness" or legitimacy of the shooting or other action becomes an additional pressure. Beyond the effects of questioning oneself and dealing with peer and administration responses, other factors increase anxiety: a fear of lawsuits, trial boards and other sanctions can lead to errors in judgment or questionable decision-making during and following critical incidents. Forty-seven percent of sixty officers in a survey experienced fears related to legal entanglements or job security. About fourteen percent were concerned with the department's reaction to them (Stratton, 1984). Media attention, including frequent distortions and a resulting lack of privacy for the officer and his or her family, causes even greater disequilibrium.

In recent years, Federal officials have reviewed the prosecutor's findings to make sure the civil rights of the civilian victims have not been violated, and that no cover-up has occurred. Rarely does anyone ask about the police officer or consider him or her to be a victim of circumstance as well. The longer the review and judicial process, the greater the pressure on the officer's family and intimate relationships. Withdrawal reactions may protect the officer from additional stress, but are not helpful when transferred to personal relationships. Feelings of alienation usually accompany a withdrawal reaction and these can evolve to anger and resentment against peers who have offered opinions on how the officer should have behaved. Internal investigations are often felt as a persecutory attack. Such perceptions and attitudes feed into existing guilt feelings and self-criticism. The result is bitterness toward the department.

Delayed Effects

Reactions to a traumatic event may be delayed. Like Vietnam veterans, officers may seem to be handling a trauma well initially; assistance seems unnecessary (see Shovar, this volume). They return to work and function normally. Then, a month, a year, or even several years later, they begin to develop difficulties, psychosomatic illnesses, fatigue, sleeplessness, or other symptoms for no apparent reason. Although this delayed reaction is usually precipitated by new stressors on an already fully loaded system (Kroes and Hurrell, 1975), it may be triggered by something innocuous. A Vietnam veteran who is now a member of a police SWAT team relates that even in routine police activities, certain weather conditions conjure vivid memories of combat situations faced in Vietnam.

Common Coping Responses

Joseph Wambaugh, in his novel, The Choirboys (1975), talks about the need for police officers to "let down" after a traumatic event. Inasmuch as alcohol supports a macho image and allows the individual to self-medicate—to relax and unwind—it is a regular part of many police officers' lives. "Choir practice" is the rest of the world's "happy hour": officers meet at the end of their shift to socialize. In some ways, this may be considered a crude form of "group therapy" in which individuals can talk about their experiences, often in a humorous way. Unfortunately, it may take several drinks to become "okay," to be able to talk about one's feelings with the safest person—another police officer.

Other "coping" behaviors include overeating, gambling, and the use of tobacco and tranquilizers. High rates of amphetamine and barbiturate use have been reported, but alcohol abuse seems to be the most common and the most difficult to control inasmuch as choir practice is strongly reinforced (Blackmore, 1978; Kroes and Hurrell, 1975). As a consequence, it is increasingly frowned upon by both administrative personnel and family members. Substitute support measures are needed: people who work in chronically high stress environments lose their resiliancy to cope with the occasional traumatic events that occur.

Talking about painful experiences helps avoid stress-related illness and disease. Even though emotional responses are normal and desirable, law enforcement is an occupation that typically reinforces the opposite behavior. Job survival requires that police be objective, emotionally uninvolved, and taciturn. Given such complexities and contradictions, how can we handle treatment issues and therapeutic interventions?

PSYCHOLOGICAL SURVIVAL TACTICS FOR POLICE OFFICERS

Stress is essential to living, and most often it is a positive stimulus. Even crisis situations may have positive outcomes. The Chinese character for crisis symbolizes both danger and opportunity. The danger is that there will be a maladaptive psychological and social adjustment following a disruptive experience. But the opportunity exists for growth and expansion of one's coping skills and view of the world.

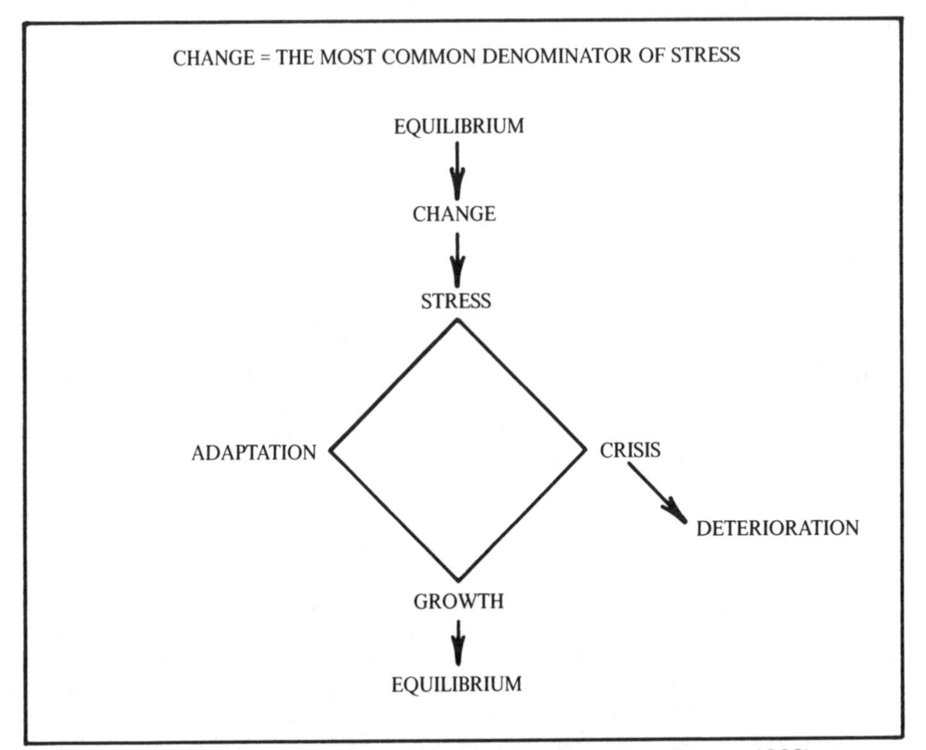

Figure 1. Balance theory of stress and adaptation (Reese, 1982).

Uncontrolled stress has destructive physical and psychological consequences. Hence, our common use of the term "management" of stress, which clearly implies that we have control over events in our lives. Indeed, when we have some control, we manage stress reasonably well.

But there are many circumstances in which we have little control, and these circumstances arise frequently in the line of police work. This is why it is so important to understand what "normal responses" to uncontrollable or abnormal circumstances may be; these repsonses provide us with defenses against acute and debilitating reactions when direct control is not possible. The realization and acceptance of "no control" also facilitates our return to a satisfactory emotional balance.If coping mechanisms are inadequate to meet the situation, upheaval occurs and a painful period of disorganization and disequilibrium follows.

The reintegration process following a traumatic experience usually begins immediately and continues for four to six weeks after the event. The individual may return to the same level or a higher or lower levei of psychological functioning depending on how he or she has been able to cope. What most affects adjustment after a trauma is: (1) immediacy of treatment, (2) the effectiveness of treatment, and (3) the ability of the people who provide the treatment.

Violanti and Marshall (1983) believe that the potential for the alleviation of acute distress and the prevention of delayed stress (PTSD) are correlated to a police officer's years of service. He sees a significant negative relationship between chronic distress and years of service. He divides these years of service into four stages, and notes that stress and tension levels seem to ebb and flow with each stage. The four career stages described are: (1) the alarm stage (first six years); (2) disenchantment stage (6-13 years); (3) personalization stage (14-20 years); (4) introspection stage (20 years and more). Stress and tension levels increase significantly during the alarm and disenchantment stages and seem to decrease more during the personalization and introspection stages.

Normal Coping Responses: Helpful or Not?

Outsiders to the law enforcement culture frequently deplore police officers' seemingly indifferent or irresponsible behavior, but they do not understand how important it is for self-preservation. Violanti and Marshall (1983) consider that cynicism and deviance are both attempts to lessen stress by psychologically and behaviorally adjusting to the strain of work demands. As a coping strategy, deviance is an expression of a police officer's will and individuality when job restraints and strong peer pressure typically limit autonomous functioning and control.

Disassociation and suppression of emotions are often beneficial; they are certainly advantageous for the police officer in the line of duty (see Reiser and Geiger, 1984), especially in the face of very painful and/or shocking situations. As the internal emotional demands for disassociation and authoritarianism increase, relative cynicism also is heightened. "Gallows humor" is common to those in dangerous occupations; it reflects a need to distance oneself from the emotional intensity of some experiences.

The disparity between occupationally demanded and usually desirable human emotions creates a difficult dilemma: the choices between occupational necessity and personal considerations. The police culture firmly insists on strength and competence in all areas of the job, and many extend this expectation to their off-duty lives as well as their families.

Perhaps one of the most difficult aspects in providing treatment to the law enforcement population is that these clients may be so concerned that they will be seen as mentally ill that they refuse assistance. As will be discussed in the next section, we have found that beginning our prevention and treatment program at the level of physical health is a very effective way of invovling officers in taking better care of their emotional selves.

Acute Post-Traumatic Stress: Positive Resolution

Resolving post-shooting trauma is similar to resolving the loss of a loved one. It involves moving in stages through a grief process: (1) initial shock—denial and anger at oneself and at the victim for forcing the officer to shoot; (2) a bargaining process in which basic values are sorted out and self-doubt emerges; withdrawal may be evidenced here; (3) depression, also an isolating time, and (4) it is to be hoped, eventual acceptance of the experience.

Every police department should be able to assist officers in working through this process, and their response should be immediate and effective. Emotional debriefing should remain confidential between the officer seeking assistance and those assisting. Occasionally, departments and officers have regarded a consultation with a psychologist after a traumatic incident as an evaluation or a fitness assessment, but this should not be the purpose of such a session (administrative decisions should not rest on the conclusions drawn from an emotional debriefing). The officer should be offered help in coping with a significant emotional event, not because his or her emotional fitness is being questioned.

Interventions must be uniquely suited to the person and the circumstances. Some general intervention techniques are appropriate for most people experiencing post-trauma. These include providing PTSD information and educational materials as well as an appreciation of the grief process so that people more readily accept their emotional reactions. Systematic desensitization to the horrifying parts of an event may be indicated. Cognitive restructuring around the officer's perception of the event is a way of positively reframing events so the recovery process is facilitated.

The officer will regain confidence by developing support networks, learning problem solving, interpersonal and adaptive coping skills, stress management techniques, and conflict resolution methods. Accepting or integrating the traumatic experience into one's history and sense of self is a final objective.

Police supervisors and psychologists should be sensitive to and aware of common post-traumatic reactions and that these cannot be commanded out of existence by denial or adopting the "cop is super-human" philosophy. The officer involved in a highly stressful incident will be in crisis, a state of emotional instability that can improve or deteriorate depending on the nature of the intervention (Reese, 1982). The officer should not be treated either as weak or suspect, but like another victim who needs sensitive handling, care, and support. Additional trauma can be minimized when those involved keep post-event interviews short, adopt a helpful rather than adversarial attitude, communicate an awareness that victimization is traumatic for everyone, and provide programs designed specifically to assist traumatized officers.

This sensitivity is demonstrated when departments provide psychological services (counseling, therapy and referral), give light duty assignments that allow a gradual re-entry into the mainstream, offer or require officers involved in life threatening situations to have a session with a psychologist, and provide remediation programs such as biofeedback and stress management training. These types of interventions demonstrate to the officer/victim that management and peers do care, and that the unpleasant thoughts and feelings they are experiencing are not abnormal reactions. Such treatment will also facilitate the integration of the traumatic event, allowing it to become a part of the past rather than an ordeal that is constantly relived in the present. The philosophy that underlies such actions encourages faster and more complete recovery from PTSD. It ultimately benefits the officers, the department, and the communities that they serve (Schwartz and Schwartz, 1975).

DENVER'S CRITICAL INCIDENT PROGRAM

The Critical Incident Program, like the Fitness Program, has been accepted by most in the police department—an unusual situation, since a characteristic response to innovations is skepticism or active sabotage. Initially, the "post-shooting information" and critical incident policy had many upper administrative people complaining that we were simply molly-coddling the troops. After a year, both programs are generally well accepted and the skepticism has decreased significantly.

The general objective of the Critical Incident Program is to prevent delayed PTSD and to alleviate acute distress. All personnel in the department are expected to attend a Critical Incident Workshop. The term "critical incident" was selected because it clearly conveys the idea that officers need not have been invovled in a shooting in order to receive help—that they can seek us out for any incident that has been difficult for them.

In the several years that post-trauma information has been conveyed, there has been a significant turnaround in attitudes and behavior. The officer victim is much less likely to be emotionally abused during the investigatory phase. Peers are likely to be considerate and solicitous rather than withdrawing and/or "congratulatory."

The critical incident response team provides two major services within the Denver Police Department. The first is a response or support function. The second is an information function. When a critical incident occurs, our public information officer contacts the team coordinator (an officer) who either responds himself or contacts other team members. They go immediately to headquarters and are available for involved officers. A team member also may call or visit family members and is generally available for the officer and his or her family. The team member will follow-up a day or two later as seems appropriate to assist the officer and family.

An officer's social support system may be the most significant variable for healthy adjustment (Reiser & Geiger, 1984). The social network includes relatives, marital partner, fellow officers, friends, professional organizations and social and church groups. Significant others provide affection and caring, a sense of belonging, and feelings of recognition and self-worth. The officer who does not have adequate external social support is more at risk for developing stress-related disorders. Research indicates that stress overload is easier or less pronounced for persons with good marital relationships characterized by open communication, sharing, and an atmosphere of equality (Haynes, 1978). The combat veterans who have a "supportive [intimate] relationship" seem to be better adjusted than those who lack a significant other (Legacies, 1981).

Prospects for positive adjustment are thus tied to the presence or lack of support within the marital dyad, and that can be vital. Salvadore Minuchin (1974), a family therapist, notes that family systems can be double-edged swords. They can assist in alleviating symptoms or they can intensify them. Figley & Sprenkle (1978) conclude that PTSD symptoms can be imbedded within an already existing family pathology. Jay Haley (1978) suggests that family events such as birth, marriage, beginning school, etc., can also trigger PTSD symptoms. Normal developmental changes within the family and in individuals can and do create later stress for all family members. It follows that positive readjustment may sometimes require involvement of the family in the therapeutic process, or at least their exposure to basic information around PTSD and the effects of police work. Officers who make the most positive adjustments to their professions and to acute and chronic stress situations are most likely to be those in healthy marital and family environments.

Hightshoe and Hightshoe (1978) have designed three-week training groups for officers and their spouses. These groups discuss common problems and concerns. Group leaders teach couples basic communication skills. These are practiced during the sessions. One therapy group for officers and spouses resulted in the identification of shift work as a major cause for family difficulties. That department responded to group feedback by reorganizing shift assignments.

Debriefing

It is department policy for an officer involved in an incident to be contacted by Psychological Services within 48 hours and be scheduled for a debriefing appointment with the psychologist. The suggestion that the officer cannot handle the situation is removed because the visit is mandatory.

I advise officers that they have no obligation to speak to me or to describe the incident or their feelings, but that I want to provide them with information so they may better understand and handle possible reactions to the situation. Usually the officer is very willing

Figure 2. Denver's Critical Incident Program

CRITICAL INCIDENT TEAM

PSYCHOLOGIST
COORDINATOR/OFFICERS

MONTHLY MEETINGS FOR:
PERSONAL SUPPORT
COORDINATION OF SERVICE
PROGRAM PLANNING

INTERVENTIONS

1. **Recruit Training** (officers)
   - Two-day format with didactic presentation by Critical Incident Team faculty similar to Post-Trauma Workshop
2. **Critical Incident Response** (officers)
   - Officer responds to Headquarters
   - Available to officer and family immediately
   - Short-term follow-up
3. **Mandatory Debriefing** (psychologist)
   - Psychological Services contacts officer within 48 hours for appointment
   - Post-traumatic stress disorder information provided
   - Voluntary discussion of incident, feelings; reactions of peers, family, administration, media
   - Examination of individual response support system, coping abilities and short-term expectations
   - Group session may be arranged for principles and/or family members
4. **Critical Incident Workshop*** (team)
   - **Day 1:**
   - Introduction to Post-Traumatic Stress Disorder and Preventive Measures
   - Critical Incidents and the Nature of Law Enforcement
   - Traumatic Experience and the Shock Phase
   - Small group for personal sharing facilitated by team member
   - **Day 2:**
   - Critical Incident After-effects
   - The Impact Phase, Resolution and Integration
   - Stress Management and Coping Techniques
   - Small group discussion on positive coping
   - Relaxation, resources

*Critical Incident Workshops are being held for family members and couples

ISSUES

As a result of critical incident involvement, 65% of police officers experience moderate to severe problems.

Severity of reaction may be cumulative & depends on the individual person, current life situation, prior history, & support systems.

Most shootings by officers occur during their first few years.

Delayed reaction—80% leave the force within 7 years.

BENEFITS

Officers helping officers

Someone cares (administration and other officers)

It's OK to be human (avoid later emotional numbing)

Reduces possibility of negative coping and psychological difficulties later (post-traumatic stress disorder)

Provides for family support and positive involvement

Can better resume duties and life

Sensitizes community to problems that police officers face

to talk. In addition to exploring feelings and reactions, I evaluate the officer's support systems, assess general coping abilities, life style, as well as his or her expectations for what will happen in the near future. The psychologist appointment is usually a single session. The officer is invited to return any time and to include their family, friends or peers. Several handouts are provided for officers to read and to share with their family members. These include a description of PTSD symptomatology, a personal account of one officer's experience, and suggestions on general coping and stress management.

During a recent episode when an officer was shot and critically wounded, I facilitated a therapeutic group discussion that included the officer's girlfriend, his sister, the detective on the case and the detective's wife, the backup officer and her husband (also an officer), and the team coordinator. This allowed them an opportunity to exchange feelings and provided an immediate support network that they could continue. Hearing different perspectives and receiving reassurance about their behavior contributed to a very intense and therapeutic session for those involved.

Although officers are willing to talk during the initial session, I have found that they are subsequently reluctant to discuss the guilt, doubts, fear and other emotions that have been elicited by their experience, thus never really conquering the anger/anxiety and depression cycle and increasing the probability for post-traumatic stress symptoms later, perhaps many years later.

Critical Incident Workshops

The third intervention, after the peer response and debriefing session, is a two-day Critical Incident Workshop that uses an instructional unit on PTSD. Other members of the team give personal accounts of relevant issues; e.g., how other officers treated them, the response of the administration or the media, and how they evaluated their own behavior. This then sets the stage for affected officers to share their own experiences in small group sessions I monitor but that are facilitated by Critical Incident Team members.

The response to the workshops has been very positive. Officers are assisting other officers rather than being lectured by "outside" specialists. These are crucial issues; (1) the program belongs to the officers and it is experiential; (2) it provides one of the few forums in law enforcement work where the environment is conducive to police officers' being human—displaying emotions, expressing and sharing feelings; (3) significant others are included in the therapeutic process. The Team has sponsored a Critical Incident Workshop for families and couples. Modifications in the workshop formula are in process now so that chronic and cumulative stress as well as positive coping strategies will receive much greater emphasis.

DENVER'S TOTAL FITNESS PROGRAM

Perhaps the most acceptable and most powerful stress management tool we can make available to police officers is a comprehensive physical fitness program. Fitness is seen as a primary mitigating behavior that reduces physiological outcomes of stress. Many departments have fitness programs available for police during working hours and some have incentives for good physical conditioning, e.g., semi-annual fitness tests with possible bonus or vacation days for attaining certain levels of good health.

A department with healthy officers benefits in several ways: there are fewer early medical retirements, abesenteeism is reduced, health care costs and turnover go down, and productivity and morale improve. Job performance is directly and significantly affected by fitness levels. Readiness in an emergency, trainability, survivability, fatigue tolerance, accident prevention, stress management, increased response repertoire and endurance are important benefits.

Physical fitness is a core stress management tool. It is possibly the best way for psychologists and mental health specialists to appeal to a law enforcement population without generating skepticism or hostility. As a stress management technique, it emphasizes health and personal responsibility—a proactive stance. Moreover, legal/ethical considerations become more pressing as court decisions increasingly underscore liability that law enforcement agencies could face if they have "unfit" officers. We are moving away from physical ability/agility tests that discriminate and have questionable validity and toward a more global notion of good health as an indicator of job performance. These health considerations are crucial for a profession that characteristically shows earlier mortality (58 years for men), relatively high cardiovascular and hypokinetic disease, poor coronary risk, high percentage of body fat, alcoholism, disproportionate suicides, etc.

Development of the Program

For more details on how the program was developed—from idea to implementation—interested readers should write to me. Briefly, however, the program evolved from a departmental request to organize a fitness program. Its design and organization closely involved some 40 officers representing a cross section of ranks and departments, and that reflected the racial and ethnic make-up of the department and included some of the women on the force. This group met with me monthly for one year to hammer out our needs and direction. We distributed a fitness survey and received 800 responses to the 1300 questionaires that were sent out. Interestingly, 78 percent of the officers considered their own level of fitness to be medium or low, and 75 percent were supportive of mandatory, age-adjusted physical fitness standards for the entire department.

The department contracted with the Cooper Aerobics Institute of Dallas, Texas to develop and implement a plan. Forty fitness trainers were trained for one week, and four staff training officers visited Dallas for consultation in preparing the three day in-service program. Finally, two police officers from the Training Academy were appointed to coordinate the program.

An in-service training in physical fitness and nutrition is now in operation for the entire department. With twenty officers receiving training each week, it will take at least one year for the initial training. A Fitness Trainer is assigned to each officer who will periodically retest him or her (every 6 months) for fitness and assist in developing individual fitness prescriptions. At this time, in-service training and fitness testing and prescriptions are mandatory, but follow-through or "working out" is voluntary. In several years, when the program is well-established, mandatory fitness standards may be instituted.

We are measuring fitness according to fairly well-accepted guidelines in the health field:

Flexibility (sit and reach)
Cardiovascular (mile or 12-minute run)
Dynamic strength (situps)
Absolute strength (arm and leg bench press)
Lean body mass (percentage of fat to muscle tissue).

Fitness training and testing are preceded by a thorough medical screening including a stress or step test, HDL cholesterol ratio, glucose, etc. A questionnaire on health habits and family history is also part of the total assessment. Each officer receives a thorough explanation of his or her health status and how to improve it.

Research efforts are directed to examining the impact of the program on health, and job, and life satisfaction. Economic benefits to the Department are important as well. The test battery includes the Maslow Burnout Inventory, psychological well-being, and stress scales. Additionally, we are evaluating such variables as locus of control, self-esteem, and Type A/B behavior. The University of Colorado is assisting our research efforts at no cost to the department.

To enhance the possibility of lasting benefits to the officer, we are also planning to include the family system. We will present special sessions where family members get an overview of benefits, fitness information, and resources to support their own programs.

The long-term plan is to develop a "Total" Fitness Program by offering classes in specific areas such as weight control, nutrition, relaxation techniques, substance use and abuse, smoking cessation, interpersonal skills, etc. Community specialists will be recruited to provide this training and police families will be encouraged to attend evening and weekend seminars. (See Appendix 3 for graphic representation of the history and future of this program.) Other ways of combating physical stress reactions include biofeedback training so that muscle tension levels are lowered before and after exposure to stressful situations and cognitive self-control techniques. The latter may include behavioral rehearsal or preparation for provocation on the job by role-playing situations and practice in conflict resolution methods and negotiating skills.

Given the close relationships and camaraderie among police officers, many have asked to be trained in counseling techniques so that they can assist each other. Furthermore, police officers, like Vietnam veterans, are typically skeptical of mental health professionals and may be reluctant to seek their services. Organizational as well as self-image factors are influential. Many in the helping professions are not truly knowledgeable about the unique environmental pressures that can lead to an officer's or a veteran's frustration, anxiety and denial. A peer support and referral network can assist officer victims and reduces the stigma tied to having to see a "professional shrink." In Denver, members of the Critical Incident Team respond to those in traumatic incidents and Peer Support Program members provide guidance for officers with chronic or cumulative stress problems. Peer counseling skills training consists of neuro-linguistic program training in listening, responding, confronting, and planning for action skills. Studies show improvement after training on the Karcuff Empathy Scale (Depue, 1979; Ferstenberg, 1975).

Lectures and workshops on traumatic and chronic stress management, communications, conflict management and related topics can be given to police academy classes and to groups of regular officers to educate them about the ways in which psychological information and self-control techniques may be beneficial.

Schaefer (1985) asserts that stress management is essentially a personal skill; to be used by an individual: "...coping cannot be done by someone else; it must be internalized as a part of each individuals personal makeup." We have little or no control over negative events we are exposed to, but we do have control of ourselves, he reminds. Most events are actually neutral. We give them meaning and can make them positive or negative. Much of the stress that members of law enforcement and that sub-culture experience is self-induced. Distress can be a product of an entire life-style. It may be personal and/or organizational in nature. It is not the outcome of an occasional crisis. Schaefer encourages the habit of beginning each day with a positive attitude. Whenever that positive charge is lost, one should immediately make a conscious effort to reverse the thought pattern. Accentuating the positive is one of the best and healthiest coping techniques available to police officers.

Last, we need to seek alternative methods which encourage the venting of emotions in a positive and constructive manner. Simple catharsis or talking about a situation over and over without some change in attitude will be fruitless. So-called "venting" needs to be accompanied by cognitive restructuring (a positive reinterpretation or "reframing") such that events will be accepted. They can be retained and integrated into one's history and experience, and daily activities can be resumed. Understanding and awareness of one's emotions can prevent lapsing into depression.

There are countless programs and recommendations for general stress management. Schaefer, a law enforcement person, also has a good psychological grounding. Following is his version of positive coping strategies.

Unstress Remedy List

1. Eat three meals a day, including breakfast.
2. Avoid sugar, salt, animal fats and processed white flour.
3. Pursue a regular program of physical activity and/or other leisure pursuits.
4. Nurture and maintain friendships.
5. Get enough sleep and rest.
6. Practice abdominal breathing and relaxation.
7. Schedule time and activities alone and with others in order to maintain a well-rounded life style of living and working.
8. Do not smoke.
9. Limit alcohol and caffeine intake.
10. Identify and accept emotional needs.
11. Pace yourself to allow for an even flow of demands.
12. Recognize the early behavior or physical signs of stress and take action against the stressor.
13. Allocate your time and energy to allow for periods of rest and stimulation.
14. Take appropriate supplement if needed for proper nutrition.

Schaefer (1985)

CONCLUSION

Clearly, mental health professionals and persons in law enforcement are negligent if they do not provide psychological assistance to their personnel. Throwing cookbook stress management programs and other similar panaceas at officers or retaining psychologists for the most severely disabled is not sufficient. Times have changed. Law enforcement must respond accordingly. Agencies must take the initiative—be proactive, provide prevention programs, as well as clinical services. They should also act to make aversive organizational structures and policies more responsive and sensitive to the needs of individual police officers.

Meredith concludes that we must recognize the effects of the organization and the environment when we attempt to institute therapeutic change efforts: "There is a direct connection between stress and brutality, but often too much emphasis is placed on stress management. That emphasis individualizes a problem that is ecological—cultural, organizational and individual in nature—and puts the whole load on the individual officer."

If we are to have some benefits from our experience with war and its many tragedies, let it be that we find ways to prevent delayed stress reactions, alleviate individual traumantic responses, and reduce acute PTSD. By so doing, we can assist in the rehabilitation of victims of many kinds of trauma. This attention will not only benefit the individual, but will assist those who are close to the victim and who are also adversely affected.

NOTES

1. But Schaefer also points out that an over-emphasis on health, exercise, diet, and spiritual or emotional needs can be equally as debilitating. The running, health, or religious fanatic does not cope well with stress by concentrating exclusively on only one coping technique, because even greater personal imbalance results.

APPENDIX 1

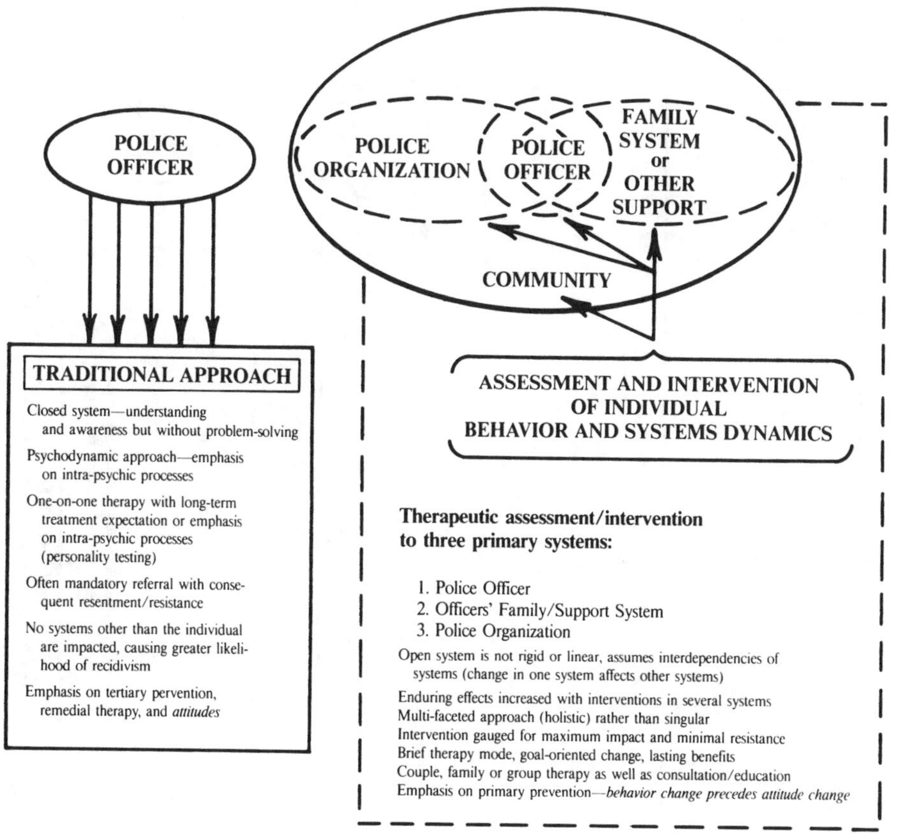
OPEN SYSTEMS FRAMEWORK FOR LAW ENFORCEMENT
POLICE OFFICER
POLICE ORGANIZATION
POLICE OFFICER
FAMILY SYSTEM or OTHER SUPPORT
COMMUNITY
TRADITIONAL APPROACH
Closed system—understanding and awareness but without problem-solving
Psychodynamic approach—emphasis on intra-psychic processes
One-on-one therapy with long-term treatment expectation or emphasis on intra-psychic processes (personality testing)
Often mandatory referral with consequent resentment/resistance
No systems other than the individual are impacted, causing greater likelihood of recidivism
Emphasis on tertiary pervention, remedial therapy, and attitudes
ASSESSMENT AND INTERVENTION OF INDIVIDUAL BEHAVIOR AND SYSTEMS DYNAMICS
Therapeutic assessment/intervention to three primary systems:
1. Police Officer
2. Officers' Family/Support System
3. Police Organization
Open system is not rigid or linear, assumes interdependencies of systems (change in one system affects other systems)
Enduring effects increased with interventions in several systems
Multi-faceted approach (holistic) rather than singular
Intervention gauged for maximum impact and minimal resistance
Brief therapy mode, goal-oriented change, lasting benefits
Couple, family or group therapy as well as consultation/education
Emphasis on primary prevention—behavior change precedes attitude change

APPENDIX 2

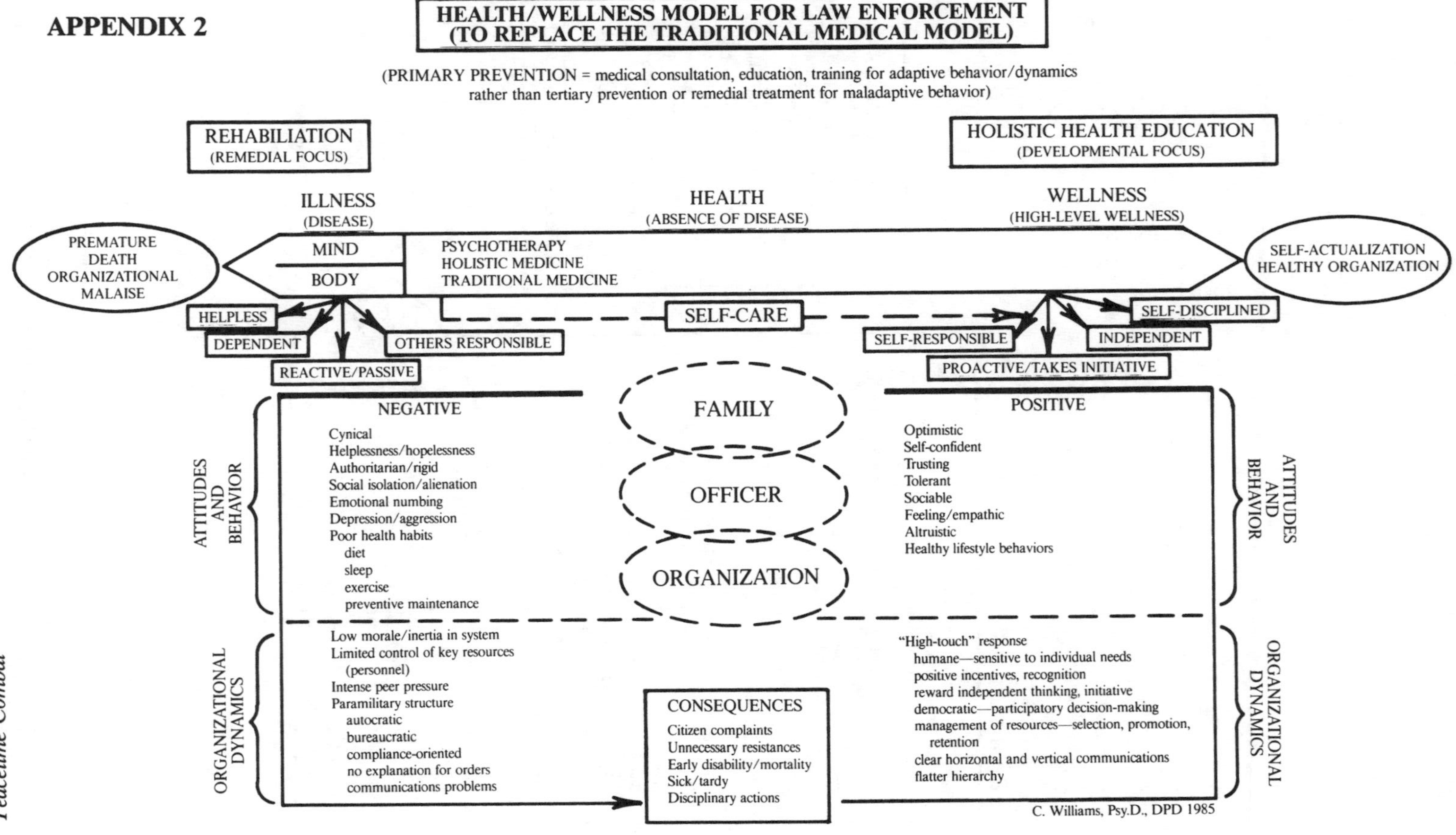
HEALTH/WELLNESS MODEL FOR LAW ENFORCEMENT
(TO REPLACE THE TRADITIONAL MEDICAL MODEL)
(PRIMARY PREVENTION = medical consultation, education, training for adaptive behavior/dynamics rather than tertiary prevention or remedial treatment for maladaptive behavior)
REHABILIATION
(REMEDIAL FOCUS)
HOLISTIC HEALTH EDUCATION
(DEVELOPMENTAL FOCUS)
ILLNESS
(DISEASE)
HEALTH
(ABSENCE OF DISEASE)
WELLNESS
(HIGH-LEVEL WELLNESS)
PREMATURE
DEATH
ORGANIZATIONAL
MALAISE
MIND
BODY
PSYCHOTHERAPY
HOLISTIC MEDICINE
TRADITIONAL MEDICINE
SELF-ACTUALIZATION
HEALTHY ORGANIZATION
HELPLESS
DEPENDENT
REACTIVE/PASSIVE
OTHERS RESPONSIBLE
SELF-CARE
SELF-RESPONSIBLE
PROACTIVE/TAKES INITIATIVE
INDEPENDENT
SELF-DISCIPLINED
ATTITUDES
AND
BEHAVIOR
NEGATIVE
Cynical
Helplessness/hopelessness
Authoritarian/rigid
Social isolation/alienation
Emotional numbing
Depression/aggression
Poor health habits
diet
sleep
exercise
preventive maintenance
FAMILY
OFFICER
ORGANIZATION
POSITIVE
Optimistic
Self-confident
Trusting
Tolerant
Sociable
Feeling/empathic
Altruistic
Healthy lifestyle behaviors
ATTITUDES
AND
BEHAVIOR
ORGANIZATIONAL
DYNAMICS
Low morale/inertia in system
Limited control of key resources
(personnel)
Intense peer pressure
Paramilitary structure
autocratic
bureaucratic
compliance-oriented
no explanation for orders
communications problems
CONSEQUENCES
Citizen complaints
Unnecessary resistances
Early disability/mortality
Sick/tardy
Disciplinary actions
"High-touch" response
humane—sensitive to individual needs
positive incentives, recognition
reward independent thinking, initiative
democratic—participatory decision-making
management of resources—selection, promotion,
retention
clear horizontal and vertical communications
flatter hierarchy
ORGANIZATIONAL
DYNAMICS
C. Williams, Psy.D., DPD 1985

APPENDIX 3

SYSTEMS INTERVENTIONS IN LAW ENFORCEMENT

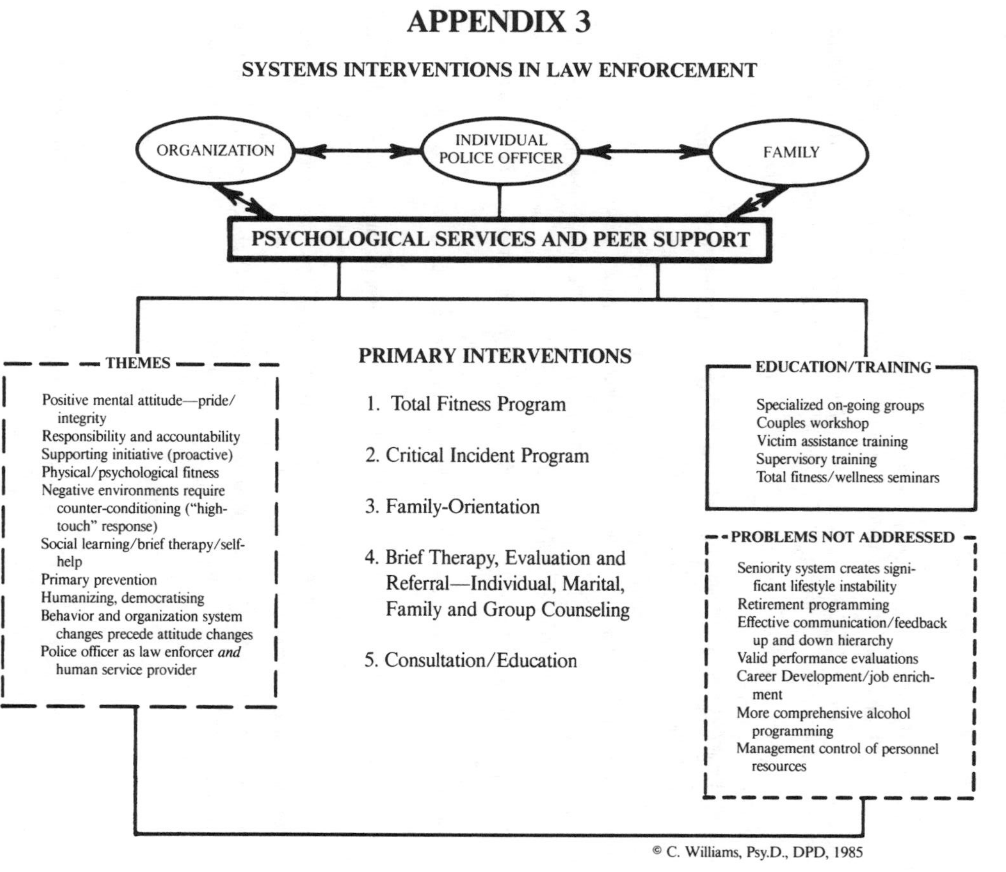

REFERENCES

Blackmore, J. (1978, March). Are police allowed to have problems of their own? *Police Magazine,* pp. 47-55.

Chapman, Harry (1986). In conversation with the author.

Daviss, B. (1982, May). Burnout. *Police Magazine*, pp. 9-18.

Depue, R. (1979, February). Turning inward: The police officer counselor. *Law Enforcement Bulletin*, pp. 8-12.

Donahue, M.J. (1977). *Peer counseling for police officers—A program for skill development and personal growth.* Ph.D. Dissertation, Boston University. Ann Arbor, MI: University Microfilms.

Egendorf, A., Rothbart, G. Sloan, L., et al. (1981). *Legacies of vietnam: Comparative adjustment of veterans and their peers.* Washington, D.C.: U.S. Government Printing Office.

Figley, C.R. (1978). *Stress disorders among vietnam veterans: Theory, reasearch and treatment.* New York: Bruner/Mazel.

Figley, C.R. & Sprenkle, D. (1978). Delayed stress response syndrome: Family therapy implications. *Journal of Marriage and Family Counseling, 6*:53-59.

Furstenberg, Mark H. (1975, May). *Dealing with police stress.* Paper presented at symposium on "Job Stress and the Police Officer: Identifying Stress Reduction Techniques." Cincinnati, OH.

Girodo, M. (1985). Psychological factors in undercover narcotics agents. Presentation at World Conference on Police Psychology, FBI Academy.

Haley, Jay. (1984). *Problem-solving therapy: New strategies for effective family therapy.* New York: Har-Row.

Haynes, William D. (1978). *Stress related disorders in policemen.* San Francisco: R&E Research Associates.

Hightshoe, N. & Hightshoe, R. (1978, April). St. Louis county department of police—Police family program. *The Police Chief,*

Horowitz, M.J. & Solomon, G.F. (1980). Ap = Predictor of delayed stress response in Vietnam veterans. *Institute of Social Issues, 31*(4), 67-80.

Jacobi, Jerome H. (1975, May). *Reducing police stress: A psychiatrist's point of view.* Paper presented at symposium on "Job Stress and the Police Officer: Identifying Stress Reduction Techniques." Cincinnati, OH.

Kroes, W. & Hurrell, J., Jr. (Eds.) (1975). Job stress and the police officer—Identifying stress reduction techniques. Proceedings of the symposium in Cincinnati, O. Washington, D.C.: U.S. Government Printing Office.

Maslach, C. and Jackson, S.E. (1979). Burned out cops and their families. *Psychology Today, 12*(12):59-62.

Meredith, N. (1984, May). Attacking the roots of police violence. *Psychology Today*, pp. 20-26.

Minuchin, S. (1967). *Families and family therapy.* Cambridge, MA: Harvard University Press.

Neiderhoffer, A. (1967). *Behind the shield: The police in urban society.* New York: Anchor Books.

Parker, L. & Roth, M. (1973, September). The relationship between self-disclosure, personality and a dimension of job performance of policemen. *Journal of Police Science and Administration.*

Reese, James T. (1982). Life in the high-speed lane: Managing police burnout. *Police Chief*, 49(6).

Reiser, Martin & Geiger, Steven P. (1984). Police officer as victim. *Professional Psychology: Research and Practice.* American Psychological Association, 15(3), pp. *315-323.*

Schaefer, Robert B. (1985, March). Maintaining control: A step toward personal growth. *F.B.I. Law Enforcement Bulletin.*

Schwartz, Jeffrey A. and Cynthia B. (1975, May). *The personal problems of police officers: A plea for action.* Paper presented at symposium on "Job Stress and the Police Officer: Identifying Stress Reduction Techniques." Cincinnati, OH.

Seitzinger, Jack G. Personal communication.

Stratton, John G. (1984). *Police passages.* Manhattan Beach, CA: Glennon.

Violanti, John M. & Marshall, James R. (1983). The police stress process. *Journal of Police Science and Administration,* 2(4).

Wambaugh, J. (1975). *The choirboys.* New York: Delacorte Press.

White, J., Olson O. & Knowles, L. (1980, Fall). Police stress and years of service. *Journal of California Law Enforcement.*

Williams, Tom (1985, August 15). Trauma victims learn to live again. *Rocky Mountain News,* Denver, CO.

Wilson, J.P. (1980). Conflict, stress and growth: The effects of the Vietnam war on psychological development among Vietnam veterans. In C.R. Figley & S. Leventman (Eds.) *Strangers at home: Vietnam veterans since the war.* New York: Praeger.

BIBLIOGRAPHY

Alkus, Stephen & Padesky, Christine. (1983). Special problems of police officers: Stress-related issues and interventions. *The Counseling Psychologist, 11*:2, 55-64.

Denver police department physical fitness program task force report. (1985). Unpublished.

Ellison, K.W. & Genz, John L. (1983). *Stress and the police officer.* Springfield, IL: CC Thomas.

Kolb, L.C. (1983, March). Healing the wounds of Vietnam. *Hospital Community Psychiatry.*

Williams, Candis (1985). Health of the police organization: The Denver chief of police and the psychologist. Presented at the American Psychological Association Conference, Los Angeles.

CHAPTER TWENTY

COMMUNITY DISASTERS AND POST-TRAUMATIC STRESS DISORDER: A DEBRIEFING MODEL FOR RESPONSE

Cynthia A. Griffin

The public has become increasingly aware of the diagnostic category known as post-traumatic stress disorder, or PTSD (American Psychiatric Association [APA], 1980 and see also Appendix A to this volume). Due to the media attention to Vietnam veterans (Morganthau, 1981; "The War Came Home," 1981), the general public and mental health professionals have gained greater awareness of the problems that can occur following exposure to extreme stress. Since 1979, a total of 188 federally funded outreach agencies, known as Veteran Centers, have been established to meet the needs of veterans affected by the trauma of Vietnam. In many instances, the staff of these Vet Centers have become local "experts" in the treatment of PTSD.

While Vet Center staff are often recognized in the community for their expertise in working with stress disorders, they usually limit their services to Vietnam-era veterans and their families. Thus, they are not generally regarded as a crisis intervention resource for the community at large. Similarly, crisis hotlines and drop-in centers are typically geared toward the management of individual and family concerns, rather than large-scale emergencies.

Nonetheless, large-scale disasters do occur, and such events require immediate and well-coordinated services. Few agencies have systematic plans to meet the massive psychological needs when whole communities are affected by disaster. A review of the literature indicates that such services, when offered, are ultimately provided by a variety of agencies, using a variety of approaches. Services are also directed toward different target groups. They might be offered to the victims themselves (Horowitz, 1976, 1980; Lindemann, 1944; Lindy, Green, Grace, Titchner, 1983), to family members (Kligman & Eli; 1981, Tuckman, 1973), to other relevant community members (such as teachers, in the case of crises involving schoolchildren [Kligman & Eli, 1981; Tuckman, 1973], or to rescue workers and disaster crews [Dunning & Silva, 1980; Jones, 1985]).

In reporting on treatment of disaster-induced trauma experienced by three groups of rescue workers, Dunning and Silva (1980) describe a variety of intervention approaches. Following the collision of two airplanes in San Diego in 1978, police officers were offered individual interviews with clinical psychologists. After the evacuation of the Jonestown, Guyana, suicide victims, military personnel involved in the operation were referred to a base chaplain. And finally, following the crash of an American Airlines DC 10 in Chicago on May 25, 1979, police officers involved in the rescue work were offered a voluntary debriefing program. Officers attended discussion groups led by professional therapists. Debriefing sessions for all crisis teams are suggested by other authors. Jones (1985) says that such sessions may help defuse future emotional effects on rescue workers, and he suggests that support be offered in group discussions led by mental health professionals.

Other authors focus on the needs of victims, rather than rescue workers. Several writers distinguish between victims of natural and man-made disasters (Beigel & Berren, 1985; Frederick, 1980), and feel that presenting symptoms (and thus clinical issues) may vary accordingly. Other authors (Lindy, 1985) are less concerned with this distinction, and focus instead on the problem of gaining clinical access to victims. According to Lindy, "from the survivor's vantage point, professionals interested in treating or studying PTSD threaten to disturb a fragile equilibrium. Fear of affect over-load makes the survivor wary...." (Lindy, 1985, p. 154). Because victims may go through a denial phase in response to a stressful event (Horowitz, 1976), clinical access may be difficult to gain.

For those who do seek help, intervention approaches vary. In some cases, victims may need special, individualized treatment, as described by Horowitz (1976, 1980) and others (Lindemann, 1944; Lindy et al., 1983). Children and adults have different ways of expressing needs and will probably require different treatment approaches (Terr, 1981). Among adult disaster victims, crisis intervention is generally viewed as the accepted initial treatment approach (Wilkinson & Vera, 1985). However, victims may be seen individually or in groups, using more or less aggressive outreach techniques (Wilkinson & Vera, 1985). Services may be offered by mental health professionals (Lindemann, 1944; Lindy et al., 1983) paraprofessionals (Klingman & Eli, 1981; Richard, 1974), or volunteers. Depending on the situation, intervention can be presented as anything from psychotherapy to "human service counseling" (Heffron, 1977). Even the term "victim" may be viewed to include (or exclude) a variety of individuals; for example, Wilkinson (1983) points out that victims and observers both displayed stress symptoms at the time of the Hyatt Regency skywalk collapse, and both were offered counseling services.

In reviewing the spectrum of treatment approaches used in crisis situations, one could suggest that a systematic, planned approach would be of value to a community in crisis. When disaster occurs, it requires prompt, well-integrated, and innovative community services. One such model of intervention is presented here.

THE RENO AIRLINE CRASH

At approximately 1 a.m. on the morning of January 21, 1985, an airline crash near downtown Reno, Nevada left 68 people dead and 3 others injured. Immediately following the crash, city and county firefighters were called in to assist with the disaster, first by firefighting and later by delivering support services (e.g., photography of the crash scene). Similarly, members of the sheriff's department "hasty" team were called in to locate and retrieve bodies. Some of the rescue team members worked continuously for up to 17 hours, until colleagues insisted on providing relief. When questioned later, one team member reported feeling "immersed" in his duties; others stated that they had been oblivious to hunger and exhaustion.

Other individuals were involved in responding to the disaster. Ambulance drivers provided transportation to hospitals for three survivors; rescue crews filtered through debris, placed bodies in body bags, and loaded them into refrigerated trucks. Media staff from Nevada and California came to report on the event, and several families of victims flew into Reno from Minnesota to learn more about the circumstances of the tragedy and to recover the bodies. Airport authorities met with the families of victims and offered assistance; airline companies provided them with transportation and lodging.

In addition, community members made contact with the local crisis hotline; five such calls were documented by hotline volunteers. Callers expressed such concerns as grief, fear for their own future safety on airplanes, and intrusive recurring thoughts of the event.

Almost immediately following the crash, social service agencies began offering assistance. First to become involved was the social services department of the local medical center.

Within an hour of the disaster, their staff began contacting family members of the injured survivors and working directly with one of the victims. A private psychiatric hospital established a special telephone hotline for crash-related concerns.

Within 48 hours of the crash, a coordinated community response was planned and initiated. Dr. John Chappel, professor of psychiatry at the University of Nevada School of Medicine, contacted various agencies to organize an open debriefing session for those affected by the disaster. Among the agencies contacted were the crisis hotline, the Vet Center, the Veterans Administration Medical Center, the social services department of the county medical center, and the psychiatry faculty from the medical school.

Psychologists and social workers from several of these agencies met informally to plan for the debriefing session and decided to invite the public via the media. The debriefing session took place within 72 hours of the disaster. Roughly 30 people attended. They were residents living near the scene of the crash, airport authority firefighters, ambulance drivers, and community members.

One reporter, who asked to come for personal (rather than professional) reasons was allowed to attend. (This reporter's participation was allowed only because she said she needed to address personal issues related to her work at the crash scene. All other press members were excluded because of the speakers' wishes to protect participants' confidentiality).

The meeting began with introductions of speakers and an overview of the agenda. Participants were told that the speakers had come to provide information about common emotional reactions to severe trauma and to address any concerns participants expressed. Before the session began, speakers requested that participants' statements be held in confidence.

Following introductions, the speakers discussed a few reactions that can occur with delayed stress, such as temporary sleep disturbance and episodic, intrusive recollections of the event (APA, 1980). Panelists tried to focus on the concerns that brought participants to the meeting, rather than delineating (and thus suggesting) an exhaustive list of specific symptoms they might encounter. Speakers emphasized that everyone reacts to stress in a different way, and that the speakers were not predicting or presuming that all participants would experience a stress reaction or would react in a given manner. They also said that a stress response was a *normal* reaction to an event of this magnitude, and should not be viewed as abnormal unless symptoms persisted or became debilitating.

The speakers explained coping strategies and, following the therapeutic model described by Williams (1980), emphasized the importance of expressing emotions and talking about feelings with trusted friends. They discouraged the use of "self-medication" with drugs, such as alcohol, as a coping technique. It was hoped the debriefing session would provide a sense of community for those attending.

Next, participants talked about individual issues, with the emphasis on processing feelings. They spoke of sleep disturbance, anxiety, and anger toward the press covering the event. One woman who lived near the crash site reported survival guilt (see T. Williams, this volume) and expressed a compelling urge to contact one of the crash survivors. Others expressed feelings of isolation. One participant, for example, said repeatedly, "Unless you were actually there, you just can't know what it was like." Several people reported avoiding the crash site, even though it was directly en route to their homes. Participants were encouraged not to avoid the crash site, but to be patient and gradually confront their fear and anxiety.

Following a ten-minute break, small, informal groups formed to allow for further catharsis. Speakers joined the various small groups to facilitate discussion. Before the meeting ended, representatives of several agencies offered follow-up services, a resource list was presented, and free, short-term counseling and referrals were offered by several speakers.The psychiatrist in attendance offered consultations with staff members of other agencies.

Within a week of the crash, debriefing sessions were held for the 38 members of the sheriff's department "hasty" team and about 45 city fire department workers. The sessions were held because several men within the departments reported stress reactions. According to one agency chief, some of the men were experiencing sleeping problems, nightmares, and intrusive recollections of their work at the crash site, as well as anxiety and other symptoms of stress. At the debriefing, one of the men reported episodes of vague, unexplained rage toward "no one in particular." Another reported feeling very guilty because he was using "gruesome, sick jokes" to cope with his stress. Several others expressed discomfort with their perceived inability to "handle this whole thing better," and they felt that, as professionals, they "ought to be able to take it."

As in the community-wide session, these debriefing sessions focused first on educating the men about common reactions to severe traumatic events, and later focused on coping techniques. Finally, there was a group discussion. When it began, the men were reluctant to express their concerns. To encourage participation, group leaders initiated discussion by asking such questoins as, "Which of you was the first (and second, and third) to arrive on the scene? What was your role there? What did you feel at the time? What happened next?" From this point on, the discussion became quite active, and the agenda was established largely by the men.

After a break, the group was divided into smaller discussion sections. Participants were not required to join a particular small group, and many of them gathered spontaneously into their own natural working groups, e.g., men who worked together in one engine company joined together. These small groups proved to be quite useful, because the levels of self-disclosure were greater in them than in the large, open session. Discussions centered around feelings of helplessness (regarding rescue workers' inability to "save lives"), and reluctance to share emotions with wives (for fear of "worrying them").

After small group discussions, the large group was reunited for a brief wrap-up segment. The men were given follow-up resource information, and speakers once again encouraged their audience to continue the support/catharsis process with colleagues on the job.

In addition to the work done by mental health professionals, additional ways of responding to the tragedy were offered by other organizations. On January 25, 1985, four days after the crash, a community-wide memorial service was conducted at a prominent local church. The service was initially planned by the Salvation Army staff. The clergy members who conducted it hoped it would help both community members and crisis teams to work through their grief and bereavement. The service was divided into subsections, directed toward families of victims and crisis workers. Three hundred programs were printed for the service, but more than 700 people attended—firefighters, police, rescue workers, medical staff, and families of the crash victims, as well as hundreds of local residents.

A local reporter also helped with the debriefing process. About three weeks after the crash, two of her articles appeared in the Sunday edition of the local newspaper. One of them, entitled "Aftermath of Disaster," (Macias, 1985a) explained some of the symptoms of PTSD as they were felt by rescue workers and other community members. A second article, "Counseling Sessions Help Workers Relieve Stress," (Macias, 1985b) emphasized the value of debriefing sessions for rescue workers. Regrettably, neither article gave much resource information, but they were valuable in educating readers to the signs of PTSD, and probably reduced the sense of isolation the symptomatic felt.

DISCUSSION

With large-scale disasters, as with individual crisis, several of the basic principles of crisis intervention apply. Immediate assessment, as described by Resnik and Ruben (1975), is especially relevant (see Shovar, this volume). Services must be offered quickly, and they must reach the ones who need the services most. The individual or agency coordinating service delivery must be astute in identifying the groups most likely to need debriefing services, and the agencies that should provide the service. Rescue workers—firefighters, police, and rescue teams—are an obvious target population as victims of stress. Also likely to feel the after-effects of disaster are neighbors, medical and paramedical personnel, ambulance crews, and relatives. Victims themselves benefit from immediate, short-term crisis intervention services, followed by other available forms of assistance as well.

The Reno debriefing sessions attempted to integrate the services of multiple agencies. These included the staff of the crisis hotline, whose volunteers provide free, front-line counseling to the community at large; the VA Medical Center, whose mental health staff are experts in the treatment of PTSD; the Vet Center staff, also experts in treating PTSD; the local medical center, whose social workers deal regularly with members of the police and fire departments, as well as with crime and fire victims and their families; and the medical school faculty, whose psychiatrists provided back-up expertise. Reno's PTSD response approach suggests the value of using the widest network of resources and assistance available in the local community, as well as national groups such as the Red Cross, if necessary.

A needs assessment, though informal, was conducted initially. The assessment was done by telephoning the key agency officials involved in providing and requesting help. These officials included police and fire chiefs, who were aware of the stress levels of their own employees, as well as administrators of the agencies listed above. Collectively, these agencies helped to assess the need for debriefing sessions. They also provided valuable input about the specialized needs of particular groups.

Following the needs assessment, brief informal meetings were held with representatives of participating agencies. These proved valuable for developing a service plan, dividing up responsibilities, and compiling a list of available resources.

Debriefing sessions were designed with the aim of educating the participants about the symptoms of PTSD, suggesting coping strategies, and allowing the catharsis and processing of feelings. Large groups were eventually broken down into smaller ones to facilitate personal sharing. In the fire department debriefing session, the smaller groups formed on the basis of a naturally occurring common denominator, e.g., working groups. Follow-up resource information was provided particpants in the group.

In summary, the Reno debriefing sessions followed a model of education, catharsis, and follow-up resource information. In other communities, or other situations, different methods might have been used. Nonetheless, it is the opinion of this author that crisis intervention services of some sort are indicated at the time of community disaster, even when a community is small and resources are limited. It is not necessarily important *who* initiates the response effort, but rather, that the effort be made, and that agencies work cooperatively, rather than competitively, delivering the best possible services to the community.

REFERENCES

American Psychiatric Association. (1980). *Diagnostic and statistical manual of mental disorders* (3rd ed.). Washington, DC: American Psychiatric Press Inc.

Beigel, A., & Berren, M. (1985). Human-induced disasters. *Psychiatric Annals*, *15*(3), 143-150.

Dunning, C., & Silva, M. (1980). Disaster-induced trauma in rescue workers. *Victimology*, *5*(2-4), 287-297.

Frederick C. (1980). Effects of natural vs. human-induced violence upon victims. *Evaluation and Change* (Special Issue), pp. 71-75.

Heffron, E. F. (1977). Project outreach: Crisis intervention following natural disasters. *Journal of Community Psychology*, *5*, 103-111.

Horowitz, M. J. (1976). *Stress response syndromes*. New York: Aronson.

Horowitz, M. J., & Kaltreider, N. (1980). Brief treatment of post-traumatic stress disorders. *New Directions for Mental Health Services*, *6*, 67-79.

Jones, D. R. (1985). Secondary disaster victims: The emotional effects of recovering and identifying human remains. *American Journal of Psychiatry*, *142*(3), 303-307.

Klingman, A., & Eli, Z. B. (1981). A school community in disaster: Primary and secondary prevention in situational crisis. *Professional Psychology*, *12*, 523-533.

Lindemann, E. (1944). Symptomatology and management of acute grief. *American Journal of Psychiatry*, *101*, 141-148.

Lindy, J. (1985). The trauma membrane and other clinical concepts derived from psychotherapeutic work with survivors of natural disasters. *Psychiatric Annals*, *15*(3), 153-160.

Lindy, J. D., Green, B. L., Grace, M., and Titchener, J. (1983). Psychotherapy with survivors of the Beverly Hills Supper Club fire. *American Journal of Psychotherapy*, *37*, 593-610.

Macias, S. (1985a, February 10). Aftermath of disaster. *Reno Gazette-Journal*, pp. 1E, 3E.

Macias, S. (1985b, February 10). Counseling sessions help workers relieve stress. *Reno Gazette-Journal*, pp. 1E, 3E.

Morganthau, T. (1981, March 30). The troubled Vietnam vet. *Newsweek*, pp. 24-25.

Resnik, H. L. P., & Ruben, H. L. (1975). *Emergency psychiatric care*. Bowie, MD: Charles Press.

Richard, W. C. (1974). Crisis intervention services following natural disasters: The Pennsylvania recovery project. *Journal of Community Psychology*, *2*, 211-219.

Terr, L. (1981). Forbidden games: Post-traumatic child's play. *Journal of the American Academy of Child Psychiatry*, 741-759.

Tuckman, A. J. (1973). Disaster and mental health intervention. *Community Mental Health Journal*, *9*(2), 151-157.

The war came home. (1981, April 6). *Time Magazine*, p. 17.

Wilkinson, C. B. (1983). Aftermath of a disaster: The collapse of the Hyatt Regency Hotel skywalks. *American Journal of Psychiatry*, *140*, 1134-1139.

Wilkinson, C. B., & Vera, E. (1985). The management and treatment of disaster victims. *Psychiatric Annals*, *15*(3), 174-184.

Williams, T. (Ed.). (1980). *Post-traumatic stress disorders of the Vietnam veteran*. Cincinnati, OH: Disabled American Veterans.

APPENDIX A

SEPTEMBER 12, 1986, PROPOSED REVISION OF CRITERIA FOR PTSD FOR *DSM-III, REVISED*

The following is quoted directly from a memorandum from Bob Spitzer to the American Psychiatric Association's Advisory Committee on Post-traumatic Stress Disorder. The reader is advised that these criteria are proposed at this writing but have not been officially adopted by the American Psychiatric Association.—Ed.

309.89 Post-traumatic Stress Disorder.

A. The individual has experienced an event that is outside the range of usual human experience and that would be markedly distressing to almost anyone, e.g., serious threat to one's life or physical integrity; serious threat or harm to one's children, spouse, or other close relatives and friends; sudden destruction of one's home or community; or seeing another person who is being (or has recently been) seriously injured or killed as the result of an accident or physical violence.

B. The distressing event is persistently reexperienced in at least one of the following ways:

   (1) recurrent and instrusive distressing recollections of the event (which may be associated with guilty thoughts about behavior before or during the event)

   (2) recurrent distressing dreams of the event

   (3) sudden acting or feeling as if the event were recurring (includes a sense of reliving the experience, illusions, hallucinations, and dissociative [flashback] episodes, even those that occur upon awakening or when intoxicated) (in young children, repetitive play in which themes or aspects of the distressing event are expressed)

   (4) intense psychological distress at exposure to events that symbolize or resemble an aspect of the event, including anniversaries of the event.

C. Persistent avoidance of stimuli associated with the distressing event or numbing of general responsiveness (not present before the event), as indicated by at least three of the following:

   (1) deliberate efforts to avoid thoughts or feelings associated with the event

   (2) deliberate efforts to avoid activities or situations that arouse recollections of the event

   (3) inability to recall an important aspect of the event (psychological amnesia)

   (4) markedly diminished interest in significant activities (in young children, loss of recently acquired developmental skills such as toilet training or language skills)

   (5) feeling of detachment or estrangement from others

   (6) restricted range of affect, e.g., unable to have loving feelings

   (7) sense of a foreshortened future, e.g., child does not expect to have a career, marriage, or children, or a long life.

D. Persistent symptoms of increased arousal (not present before the event) as indicated by at least two of the following:

(1) difficulty falling or staying asleep

(2) irritability or outbursts of anger

(3) difficulty concentrating

(4) hypervigilance

(5) exaggerated startle response

(6) physiologic reactivity at exposure to events that symbolize or resemble an aspect of the event [sic] (e.g., a woman who was raped in an elevator breaks out in a sweat when entering any elevator).

F. Duration of the disturbance of at least one month.

Specify delayed onset if the onset of symptoms was at least six months after the distressing event.

THE AUTHORS

Carolyn A. Agosta, MSA, ACSW, and **Mary Loring McHugh** are co-founders and co-directors of Ending Violence Effectively (EVE) in Denver. As victims of sexual assaults themselves, they use their experience to help others. Both are members of the National Coalition Against Sexual Assault, the state and national Organizations for Victim Assistance, and the Denver Victim Services Center. They work nationwide training professionals and nonprofessionals in prevention techniques and educating communities about the impact of victimization.

Captain Jim Goodwin holds a Doctor of Psychology from the University of Denver's School of Professional Psychology and is a psychologist on active duty with the Army under orders to Fairbanks, Alaska. He was with the Marine Corps in Vietnam.

Cynthia A. Griffin, ACSW, is currently working on a Ph.D. in counseling psychology at the University of Utah. She is clinical instructor in psychiatry and behavioral sciences at the University of Nevada's School of Medicine and Director of the Vet Center in Reno.

Pat Hickman holds a Masters of Social Work from the Graduate School of Social Work at the University of Denver. She is now in private practice in Denver.

Melvin R. Jacob is a Lutheran chaplain at the VA Medical Center in Augusta, Georgia, and assistant clinical professor at the Medical College of Georgia's department of psychiatry and health behavior. He was instrumental in the development of the PTSD rehabilitation unit at the medical center. A Chaplain (Major) in the U.S. Army Reserve, Jacob is a popular speaker on the subject of the pastoral response to the Vietnam veteran.

Mike Jelinek holds a Doctor of Psychology from the University of Denver's School of Professional Psychology. He served with the U.S. Army Special Forces in Vietnam and is now in private practice in Denver.

Ron Langer holds a Masters in Social Work from the University of Denver and is on the staff of the Veteran's Administration Medical Center in Denver where he continues to do both individual and group therapy with ex-POWs.

Gary May, MSSW, ACSW, is in private practice in Evansville, Indiana. He has bilateral above-the-knee amputations as a result of wounds during his tour with the Marines in Vietnam.

James Newman is the Clinical Director of the Post-trauma Treatment Center in Aurora, Colorado. Dr. Newman in a graduate of the United States Military Academy and a veteran of the Vietnam war.

Steve Oboler received his Doctor of Medicine from the Stanford School of Medicine and is now the District Coordinator of the Veteran's Administration Ex-POW Program in Denver.

Bob Rheault founded the Vietnam Veterans Outward Bound program in 1983, twelve years after he began working with Outward Bound. He was Commander of Special Forces during his second tour with the Army in Vietnam. He is a graduate of West Point and earned a Masters Degree in International Affairs at George Washington University. He lives in Owl's Head, Maine.

Rose Sandecki served as a nurse in Vietnam and is now the team leader at the Vet Center in Concord, California. She is a graduate of California State University at Hayward, where she received a Master of Sciences in Nursing. She is also the Chairperson of the VA working group on Women Veterans.

G. Phil Shovar, CRNA, MA, is a former Navy Hospital Corpsman. He is an honor graduate of St. Francis School of Nursing, Columbus, Ohio, a Vietnam veteran, graduate of the United States Army School of Anesthesia for Army Nurse Corps Officers, and holds his Bachelor's degree in nursing and psychology and Master of Arts in clinical psychology from Antioch University, Yellow Springs, Ohio. He is currently associated with the Post-Trauma Treatment Center, in Aurora, Colorado, where he works as a therapist.

Candis Williams holds a Doctor of Psychology from the University of Denver's School of Professional Psychology. She was the Denver Police Psychologist for many years and is now an outplacement psychologist with Drake Beam Morin, a private international consulting firm.

Tom Williams is director of the Post-Trauma Treatment Center in Aurora, Colorado, and a police psychologist. He holds a Doctor of Psychology degree from the University of Denver's School of Professional Psychology, where he is a clinical associate, and is a graduate of the Naval Academy in Annapolis. As a Marine Corps Officer, he served two tours of duty in Vietnam.

John F. Yost, a graduate of Creighton Medical School, is the Medical Director of the Post-Trauma Treatment Center in Aurora, Colorado. He was the psychiatric consultant to the U.S. Army Special Forces in Vietnam.

Patti Lowery, technical editor for this book, has a BA in psychology from George Washington University and has done graduate work in the field at both Georgetown and Loyola. She is a free-lance editor in Alexandria, Virginia.